TEST ITEM FILE

MICHAEL HAMPTON
UNIVERSITY OF CENTRAL FLORIDA

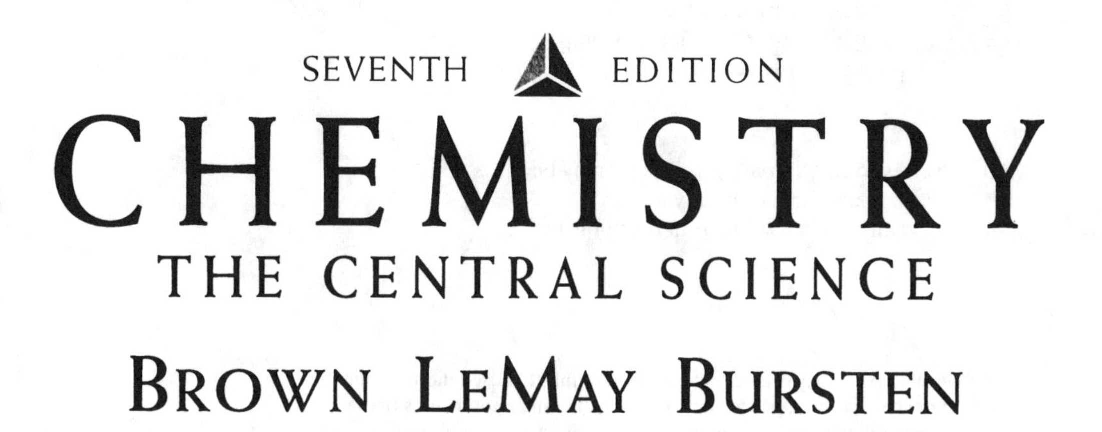

PRENTICE HALL Upper Saddle River, NJ 07458

Acquisitions Editor: ***Mary P. Hornby***
Cover Designer: ***Paul Gourhan***
Special Projects Manager: ***Barbara A. Murray***
Production Editor: ***Kimberly Dellas***
Supplements Manager: ***Paul Gourhan***
Production Coordinator/Buyer: ***Benjamin D. Smith***

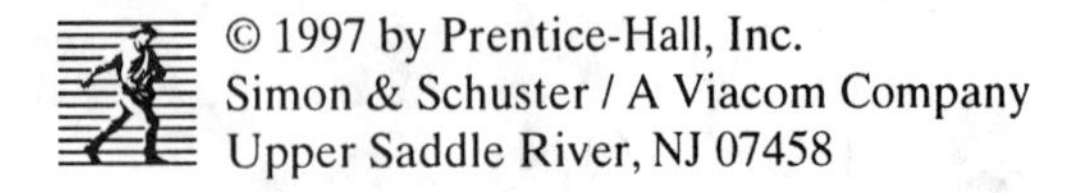

Simon & Schuster / A Viacom Company
Upper Saddle River, NJ 07458

Warning: This book may provide references and links to descriptions on the Internet of chemical uses, properties, and reactions, and photographs or diagrams of experiments that are potentially dangerous and harmful, and Prentice Hall makes no representations or warranties as to whether the information in the text or accessible via the Web Site(s) is accurate, complete or current. DO NOT attempt to perform these experiments relying solely on the information presented in this text or the Web Site that it references. No experiment or chemical usage should be undertaken without proper supervision, equipment, and safety precautions.

Printed in the United States of America

10 9 8 7 6 5 4

ISBN 0-13-578303-8

Prentice-Hall International (UK) Limited, *London*
Prentice-Hall of Australia Pty. Limited, *Sydney*
Prentice-Hall Canada, Inc., *Toronto*
Prentice-Hall Hispanoamericana, S.A., *Mexico*
Prentice-Hall of India Private Limited, *New Delhi*
Prentice-Hall of Japan, Inc., *Tokyo*
Simon & Schuster Asia Pte. Ltd., *Singapore*
Editora Prentice-Hall do Brasil, Ltda., *Rio de Janeiro*

Contents

Prentice Hall: Instructor Support for Test Item Files

This hard copy test item file is just one part of Prentice Hall's comprehensive testing support service, which also includes:

1. **Prentice Hall Custom Test:** This powerful computerized testing package is designed to operate on the DOS, WINDOWS and MACINTOSH platforms. It offers full mouse support, complete question editing capabilities, random test generation, graphics, and printing capabilities.

Prentice Hall Custom Test has a unique two-track design --*Easytest* for the novice computer user, and *Fulltest* for those who wish to write their own questions and create their own graphics.

The built-in algorithmic module enables the instructor to create thousands of questions and answers from a single question template.

In addition to traditional printing capabilities, Prentice Hall Custom Test also offers the On-Line Testing System -- the most efficient, time-saving examination aid on the market. With just a few keystrokes, the instructor can administer, correct, record, and return computerized exams over a variety of networks.

Prentice Hall Custom Test is designed to assist educators in the recording and processing of results from student exams and assignments. Much more than a computerized gradebook, it combines a powerful database with analytical capabilities so the instructor can generate a full set of statistics. There is no grading system more complete or easier to use.

The Prentice Hall Custom Test is free. To order a specific Prentice Hall Custom Test title, you may contact your local rep or call our Faculty Support Services Department at 1-800-526-0485. Please identify the main text author and title.

Toll-free **technical support** is offered to all userser at **1-800-550-1701.**

2. For those instructors without access to a computer, we offer the popular **Prentice Hall Telephone Testing Service:** It's simple, fast and efficient. Simply pick the questions you'd like on your test from this bank, and call the Simon & Schuster Testing Service at 1-800-550-1701; outside the US and Canada, call 612-550-1705.

Identify the main text and test questions you'd like, as well as any special instructions. We will create the test (or multiple versions if you wish) and send you a master copy for duplication within 48 hours. Free to adopters for life of text use.

Chapter 1: Introduction

MULTIPLE CHOICE

1. Which one of the following is not matter?
   a) pizza
   b) light
   c) dust
   d) elemental phosphorus
   e) dimethyl sulfoxide

   Answer: b Page: 1

2. Matter in which physical state has no specific shape but does have a specific volume?
   a) gas
   b) solid
   c) liquid

   Answer: a Page: 5

3. A sample of matter, found in Australia, was identified as X and was found to consist of 98% silicon and 2% aluminum. Another sample of matter, also identified as X, was found in Texas and was determined to consist of 90% silicon and 10% aluminum. X is a(n)
   a) pure substance
   b) element
   c) mixture

   Answer: c Page: 6

4. Which one of the following is a physical process?
   a) the rusting of iron
   b) the condensation of water vapor
   c) the baking of a potato
   d) the formation of polyethylene from ethylene
   e) the explosion of nitroglycerine

   Answer: b Page: 11

5. Which one of the following is not a physical property of water?
   a) it boils at 100°C at a pressure of 1 atmosphere
   b) it freezes at 0°C
   c) it is clear and colorless
   d) it is non-toxic to humans
   e) it reacts rapidly with potassium metal to form potassium hydroxide

   Answer: e Page: 11

6. The initial or tentative explanation of an observation is called a(n)
   a) law
   b) theory
   c) hypothesis
   d) experiment

   Answer: c Page: 13

7. Which one of the following has been the most extensively tested?
   a) law
   b) hypothesis
   c) theory

   Answer: a Page: 13

8. Solids are characterized as having __________ shape which means they are __________.
   a) definite, compressible
   b) definite, incompressible
   c) indefinite, compressible
   d) indefinite, incompressible

   Answer: b Page: 5

9. Gases and liquids share the property of
   a) compressibility
   b) definite volume
   c) constant composition
   d) indefinite shape

   Answer: d Page: 5

10. Which is a chemical process?
    a) melting of lead
    b) dissolving sugar in water
    c) tarnishing of silver
    d) crushing of stone

    Answer: c Page: 11

11. The law of constant composition applies to
    a) solutions
    b) heterogeneous mixtures
    c) compounds
    d) homogeneous mixtures

    Answer: c Page: 10

12. A combination of sand, salt, and water is an example of a
    a) homogeneous mixture
    b) heterogeneous mixture
    c) compound
    d) pure substance

    Answer: b Page: 7

13. Consider a mixture of sand in salt water. This mixture could be separated into its three components (sand, salt, and water) by first ____________ the mixture and then ____________ the remaining mixture.
    a) distilling, distilling
    b) distilling, filtering
    c) filtering, distilling
    d) filtering, filtering

    Answer: c Page: 8

14. Which one of the following has the element name and symbol correctly matched?
    a) P, potassium
    b) C, copper
    c) Mg, manganese
    d) Ag, silver

    Answer: d Page: 10

15. Which one of the following elements has a symbol that is not derived from its foreign name?
    a) tin
    b) aluminum
    c) mercury
    d) copper
    e) lead

    Answer: b Page: 10

16. A health food store was advertising vitamin C in tablet form, each containing 100 mg of pure vitamin C. The only difference between the advertised brands of vitamin C was the source of the vitamin. Vitamin C from which source is the healthiest choice?
    a) rose hips
    b) broccoli
    c) laboratory synthesis
    d) oranges
    e) all the above

    Answer: e Page: 10

17. Passing an electric current through a certain substance produces oxygen and sulfur. This substance <u>cannot</u> be a(n)
    a) compound
    b) mixture
    c) element
    d) pure substance

    Answer: c Page: 9

18. Which one of the following is a pure substance?
    a) concrete
    b) wood
    c) salt water
    d) boron

    Answer: d Page: 6

19. Which one of the following is often easily separated into its components by simple techniques such as filtering or decanting?
    a) heterogeneous mixture
    b) compounds
    c) homogeneous mixture
    d) elements

    Answer: a Page: 8

FILL-IN-THE-BLANK

20. The symbol for the element potassium is _____.

    Answer: K Page: 10

21. Sn is the symbol for the element _____.

    Answer: Tin Page: 10

MULTIPLE CHOICE

22. The symbol for the element sodium is
    a) S
    b) W
    c) So
    d) Na

    Answer: d Page: 10

23. The SI unit for mass is
    a) kilogram
    b) gram
    c) pound
    d) troy ounce
    e) none of these

    Answer: a Page: 14

24. Which one of the following is the smallest mass?
    a) 25 kg
    b) 2.5×10^{-2} Mg
    c) 2.5×10^{15} pg
    d) 2.5×10^{9} fg
    e) 2.5×10^{10} ng

    Answer: d Page: 15

25. Which one of the following is the highest temperature?
    a) 38°C
    b) 96°F
    c) 302 K
    d) none the above

    Answer: a Page: 16

26. On which temperature scale is one degree the smallest?
    a) Kelvin
    b) Centigrade
    c) Fahrenheit

    Answer: c Page: 16

27. Which one of the following is true about the liter?
    a) it is the SI base unit for volume
    b) it is equivalent to a cubic decimeter
    c) it is slightly smaller than a quart
    d) it contains 10^{6} cubic centimeters

    Answer: b Page: 17

28. Which one of the following objects is the most dense?
    a) an object with a volume of 2.5 L and a mass of 12.5 kg
    b) an object with a volume of 139 mL and a mass of 93 g
    c) an object with a volume of 0.00212 m^3 and a mass of 4.22×10^{4} mg
    d) an object with a volume of 3.91×10^{-24} nm^3 and a mass of 7.93×10^{-1} ng
    e) an object with a volume of 13 dm^3 and a mass of 1.29×10^{3} μg

    Answer: d Page: 18

29. Express the temperature, 422.35 K, in degrees centigrade and in degrees Fahrenheit.
    a) 792.23°C, 519.08°F
    b) 149.20°C, 300.56°F
    c) 695.50°C, 354.39°F
    d) 50.89°C, 324.04°F
    e) 22.78°C, 98.60°F

    Answer:
    b

    Page: 16

30. What is the volume of a 12.2 g piece of metal with a density of 9.43 g/cm^3?
    a) 12.2 cm^3
    b) 1.29 cm^3
    c) 0.773 cm^3
    d) 115 cm^3
    e) none of these

    Answer: b Page: 18

31. Which of the following is not an intensive property?
    a) density
    b) temperature
    c) physical state
    d) heat content

    Answer: d Page: 11

32. An object will sink in a liquid if the density of the object is greater than that of the liquid. What volume must an object have if its mass is 9.83 g for it to sink in liquid mercury (density = 13.6 g/cm^3)?
    a) <0.723 cm^3
    b) <1.38 cm^3
    c) <134 cm^3
    d) <7.48 cm^3
    e) none of these

    Answer: a Page: 18

33. Which one of the following is an intensive property?
    a) mass
    b) temperature
    c) heat content
    d) volume

    Answer: b Page: 11

34. Which one of the following is an extensive property?
    a) density
    b) mass
    c) boiling point
    d) freezing point

    Answer: b Page: 11

35. Which type of property can be used to identify a substance?
    a) intensive
    b) extensive

    Answer: a Page: 11

36. A common English set of units for expressing velocity is miles/hour. What is the set of basic SI units for velocity?
    a) km/hr
    b) km/s
    c) m/hr
    d) m/s

    Answer: d Page: 14

37. The units of force in the English measurement system are $\frac{lb \cdot ft}{s^2}$. What are the basic SI units of force?
    a) $\frac{g \cdot cm}{s^2}$
    b) $\frac{kg \cdot m}{hr^2}$
    c) $\frac{kg \cdot m}{s^2}$
    d) $\frac{g \cdot m}{s^2}$

    Answer: c Page: 14

38. Momentum is defined as the product of mass and velocity. What are the basic SI units for momentum if the units in the English system of measurement are $\frac{lb \cdot ft}{s}$?
    a) $\frac{kg \cdot m}{s}$
    b) $\frac{kg \cdot m}{hr}$
    c) $\frac{g \cdot m}{s}$
    d) $\frac{g \cdot km}{s}$

    Answer: a Page: 14

39. What fraction of a meter is a nanometer?
    a) 10^{-2}
    b) 10^{-12}
    c) 10^{-6}
    d) 10^{-3}
    e) 10^{-9}

    Answer: e Page: 15

40. The basic SI unit of temperature is
    a) K
    b) °C
    c) °F
    d) t

    Answer: a Page: 14

41. Convert 400 K to °F.
    a) 261
    b) 286
    c) 88
    d) 103

    Answer: a Page: 16

42. Which one of the following is not an exact number?
    a) 3 ft/yd
    b) 2.54 cm/in
    c) 1000 μg/mg
    d) 0.946 L/qt
    e) 60 min/hr

    Answer: d Page: 21

43. A temperature of 63°F is _____ K.
    a) 17
    b) 276
    c) 290
    d) 29

    Answer: c Page: 16

44\. A laboratory analyzed a standard known to contain 135 ppm lead. The following results were obtained. Which one of the following is true concerning this data set?

Trial	ppm Lead
1	169
2	114
3	142
4	115

a) the data set is both precise and accurate
b) the data set is neither precise nor accurate
c) the data set is accurate but not precise
d) the data set is precise but not accurate

Answer: c Page: 22

45\. In which one of the following numbers are <u>all</u> of the zeros significant?
a) 100.090090
b) 143.29
c) 0.05843
d) 0.1000
e) 00.0030020

Answer: a Page: 22

46\. Which one of the following numbers contains 6 significant figures?
a) 0.003702
b) 1.003702
c) 4.2010
d) 1000.00
e) none of these

Answer: d Page: 22

47\. $\frac{(0.002843)(12.80184)}{0.00032} =$
a) 113.73635
b) 113.736
c) 113.74
d) 113.7
e) 110

Answer: e Page: 24

48\. 12.00 - 0.83747 + 0.001 =
a) 11.16353
b) 11.16
c) 11.1635
d) 11

Answer: b Page: 24

49. The volume of a regular cylinder, a function of its radius (r) and its height (h), is given by the formula $V = \pi r^2 h$. Using the value 3.1416 for the constant π, the volume, in cm^3, of a cylinder of radius 2.34 cm and height 19.91 cm expressed to the correct number of significant figures in cm^3 is
a) 342.49471 cm^3
b) 342.495 cm^3
c) 342.49 cm^3
d) 343 cm^3
e) 342 cm^3

Answer: e Page: 24

50. Round the number 0.007225 to three significant figures.
a) 0.007
b) 0.00722
c) 0.0072
d) 0.00723

Answer: b Page: 24

51. In which one of the following is the number correctly rounded to 3 significant figures?
a) 3.2550 → 3.25
b) 0.01832 → 0.018
c) 100 → 100
d) 10.25001 → 10.3
e) 1.325 → 1.33

Answer: d Page: 24

52. How many significant figures should there be in the answer to the following problem?

$$\frac{(29.2 - 20.0)(1.79 \times 10^5)}{1.39}$$

a) 1
b) 2
c) 3
d) 4

Answer: b Page: 24

53. Round the number 0.07535 to two significant figures.
a) 0.08
b) 0.076
c) 0.0754
d) 0.075

Answer: d Page: 24

54. How many significant figures should there be in the answer to the following problem?

$$\frac{(10.07 + 7.395)}{2.5}$$

a) 1
b) 2
c) 3
d) 4

Answer: b Page: 24

55. How many significant figures should be retained in the result of the following calculation?

$$\frac{(11.13 - 2.6) \text{ X } 10^{4}}{(103.05 + 16.9) \text{ X } 10^{-6}}$$

a) 1
b) 2
c) 3
d) 4

Answer: b Page: 24

56. Which one of the following is the greatest mass?
a) 4.22×10^{8} Mg
b) 6.83×10^{-5} Mg
c) 9.73×10^{9} pg
d) 7.73×10^{-2} mg

Answer: a Page: 25

57. The output of a plant is 4335 pounds of ball bearings per week (5 days). If each ball bearing weighs 0.0113 g, how many ball bearings does the plant make in a single day?
a) 3.84×10^{5}
b) 7.67×10^{4}
c) 867
d) 3.48×10^{7}
e) 2.91×10^{6}

Answer: d Page: 25

58. A flow reactor has an output of 8709 L/min. What is the output of this reactor in gallons per hour?
a) 1.381×10^{5} gal/hr
b) 5.524×10^{5} gal/hr
c) 9206 gal/hr
d) 2302 gal/hr

Answer: a Page: 25

59. The density of mercury is 13.6 g/cm^3. What is the density of mercury in the units kg/m^3?
a) 1.36×10^{-2} kg/m^3
b) 1.36×10^{4} kg/m^3
c) 1.36×10^{8} kg/m^3
d) 1.36×10^{-5} kg/m^3

Answer: a Page: 25

60. An English cubit is 18 in. What is the volume of a cubic English cubit of water in liters?
a) 96 L
b) 46 L
c) 5.83×10^{3} L
d) none of these

Answer: a Page: 25

61. How many times more expensive is buying a carbonated beverage in 12-oz cans at forty cents each relative to buying it in three-liter bottles at $1.49 each? Use the facts that 1.000 L = 1.057 qt and one quart contains thirty-two ounces.
a) 1.33
b) 2.27
c) 2.54
d) 2.89
e) 3.72

Answer: b Page: 25

62. 20.0 cubic yards is how many cubic meters?
a) 6.02 m^3
b) 2.37 m^3
c) 15.3 m^3
d) 0.425 m^3
e) 98.6 m^3

Answer: c Page: 25

63. Which of the following is the same as 0.001 cm?
a) 0.01 mm
b) 0.01 dm
c) 0.01 m
d) 100 mm

Answer: a Page: 25

64. A dg is ______ cg.
    a) 100
    b) 10
    c) 0.1
    d) 0.01

    Answer: b Page: 25

65. The barometric pressure in the eye of a hurricane sometimes dips as low as 27.2 inches of mercury. How many millimeters of mercury is this?
    a) 1.1 mm
    b) 6.9 mm
    c) 691 mm
    d) 107 mm

    Answer: c Page: 25

66. One mg/cm^2 equals ______ kg/m^2.
    a) 10^{-4}
    b) 10^{2}
    c) 10^{-6}
    d) 10^{-2}

    Answer: d Page: 25

67. One angstrom, symbolized Å, is 10^{-10} m. 1 cm^3 = ______ $Å^3$.
    a) 10^{24}
    b) 10^{-24}
    c) 10^{30}
    d) 10^{-30}
    e) 10^{-9}

    Answer: a Page: 25

SHORT ANSWER

68. Set up, but do not solve. Conversion 2.12×10^{-8} cm/min to fathoms per fortnight given that a fortnight is 14 days and a fathom is 6 feet.

    Answer:

$$\left[\frac{2.12 \times 10^{-8}\ \text{cm}}{1\ \text{min}}\right]\left[\frac{1\ \text{in}}{2.54\ \text{cm}}\right]\left[\frac{1\ \text{ft}}{12\ \text{in}}\right]\left[\frac{1\ \text{fathom}}{6\ \text{ft}}\right]\left[\frac{60\ \text{min}}{1\ \text{hr}}\right]\left[\frac{24\ \text{hr}}{1\ \text{day}}\right]\left[\frac{14\ \text{days}}{1\ \text{fortnight}}\right]$$

    Page: 25

MULTIPLE CHOICE

69. 3 km is the same as __________ m.
a) 3000
b) 300
c) 0.003
d) 0.03

Answer: a Page: 25

70. There are __________ ng in a pg.
a) 0.001
b) 1000
c) 0.01
d) 100

Answer: a Page: 25

71. An acceleration of 320 ft/min^2 is ______ m/s^2.
a) 3.51×10^7
b) 5.85×10^5
c) 1.63
d) 0.0271

Answer: d Page: 25

72. One edge of a cube is measured and found to be 13 cm. What is the volume of the cube in m^3?
a) 2.2×10^{-3} m^3
b) 2.2×10^{-6} m^3
c) 2.2 m^3
d) 2.2×10^3 m^3

Answer: a Page: 25

73. There are exactly 32 ounces in a quart. How many in^3 are in 1.0 ounce?
a) 12 in^3
b) 4.8×10^2 in^3
c) 1.8×10^3 in^3
d) 1.8 in^3

Answer: d Page: 25

74. Lead has a density of 11.4 g/cm^3. What is the mass (in grams) of a lead ball with a radius of 0.50 mm?
($V_{sphere} = 4\pi r^3/3$)
a) 6.0 g
b) 4.6×10^{-2} g
c) 4.6×10^{-5} g
d) 6.0×10^{-3} g

Answer: d Page: 25

75. Zinc has a density of 446 lb/ft^3. What is the density of zinc in g/cm^3?
   a) 7.14 g/cm^3
   b) 0.0323 g/cm^3
   c) 6.64×10^3 g/cm^3
   d) 3.65 g/cm^3

   Answer: a Page: 25

76. Alcohol has a density of 0.78 g/mL. How many grams of alcohol would it take to fill a 2 fluid ounce shot glass?
   a) 59 g
   b) 368 g
   c) 46 g
   d) 122 g

   Answer: c Page: 25

77. The density of magnesium is 1.74 g/cm^3. What is the mass of a magnesium block that measures 2.5 cm X 3.5 cm X 1.5 cm?
   a) 48 g
   b) 23 g
   c) 12 g
   d) 7.5 g

   Answer: b Page: 25

Chapter 2: Atoms, Molecules, and Ions

MULTIPLE CHOICE

1. Which one of the following is not one of the postulates of Dalton's atomic theory?
   a) all matter is composed of tiny, indivisible particles called atoms
   b) all atoms of a given element are identical to each other and different from those of other elements
   c) during a chemical reaction, atoms are changed into atoms of different types
   d) compounds are formed when atoms of different elements combine

   Answer: c Page: 37

2. Water, no matter where it is found, consists of hydrogen and oxygen combined in a 1:8 ratio by mass. This is a statement of
   a) the law of multiple proportions
   b) the law of constant composition
   c) the law of conservation of mass
   d) the law of conservation of energy
   e) none of these

   Answer: b Page: 38

3. Methane and ethane are both made up of carbon and hydrogen. In methane, there are 12.0 g of carbon for every 4.00 g of hydrogen, a ratio of 3:1 by mass. In ethane, there are 24.0 g of carbon for every 6.00 g of hydrogen, a ratio of 4:1 by mass. This is a statement of the law of
   a) constant composition
   b) multiple proportions
   c) conservation of matter
   d) conservation of mass
   e) octaves

   Answer: b Page: 38

4. The basic chemical building block is considered the
   a) cation
   b) anion
   c) atom
   d) molecule
   e) neutron

   Answer: c Page: 38

5. Which one of the following is not true concerning cathode rays?
   a) they originate from the negative electrode
   b) they travel in straight lines in the absence of electric or magnetic fields
   c) they impart a negative charge to metals exposed to them
   d) they are made up of electrons
   e) the characteristics of cathode rays depend on the material from which they are emitted

   Answer: e Page: 39

6. The charge on an electron was determined in the
   a) cathode ray tube, by J. J. Thompson
   b) Rutherford gold foil experiment
   c) Millikan oil drop experiment
   d) Dalton atomic theory

   Answer: c Page: 40

7. ______ rays are a stream of fast moving electrons.
   a) alpha
   b) beta
   c) gamma
   d) none of these

   Answer: b Page: 41

8. The gold foil experiment performed in Rutherford's lab
   a) confirmed the plum-pudding model of the atom
   b) lead to the discovery of the atomic nucleus
   c) was the basis for Thompson's model of the atom
   d) utilized the deflection of beta particles by gold foil

   Answer: b Page: 41

9. Which statement below correctly describes the responses of the three radiation types to an electric field?
   a) both beta and gamma are bent in the same direction, while alpha shows no response
   b) both alpha and gamma are bent in the same direction, while beta shows no response
   c) both alpha and beta are bent in the same direction, while gamma shows no response
   d) alpha and beta are bent in opposite directions, while gamma shows no response
   e) only alpha is bent, while beta and gamma show no response

   Answer: d Page: 41

10. _____ and _____ reside in the atomic nucleus.
   a) protons, electrons
   b) electrons, neutrons
   c) protons, neutrons
   d) none of these

   Answer: c Page: 43

11. Which one of the following forces is so small that it has no chemical significance?
   a) weak nuclear force
   b) strong nuclear force
   c) electromagnetic forces
   d) gravitational forces

   Answer: d Page: 43

12. Which one of the following is false concerning Coulomb's law?
   a) it gives the magnitude of the magnetic force between two particles
   b) it indicates that the attractive force between two particles increases as the charges increase
   c) it indicates that the attractive force between two charged particles decreases as the distance between their centers increases
   d) it is given mathematically as, $F = kQ_1Q_2/d^2$
   e) using this law, one obtains a negative value for force if the two particles under consideration are attracted to each other

   Answer: a Page: 43

13. Gravitational forces act between objects in proportion to their
   a) volumes
   b) masses
   c) charges
   d) polarizability

   Answer: b Page: 43

14. Which basic force is most influential in chemical reactions?
   a) electric
   b) strong nuclear
   c) gravity
   d) weak nuclear

   Answer: a Page: 43

15. 200 pm is the same as ______ Å.
   a) 2000
   b) 20
   c) 200
   d) 2
   e) 2×10^{-12}

   Answer: d Page: 44

16. The smallest and lightest subatomic particle is the
   a) neutron
   b) proton
   c) electron
   d) nucleus
   e) isotope

   Answer: c Page: 44

17. All atoms of a given element have the same
   a) mass
   b) number of protons
   c) number of neutrons
   d) number of electrons

   Answer: b Page: 45

18. Which one of the following is a pair of isotopes of the same element?
   a) ${}^{116}_{92}X^{2+}$, ${}^{119}_{92}X$
   b) ${}^{116}_{92}X^{2+}$, ${}^{122}_{89}X^{2+}$
   c) ${}^{96}_{45}X$, ${}^{116}_{92}X$
   d) ${}^{233}_{99}X^{2+}$, ${}^{116}_{92}X^{4+}$
   e) ${}^{22}_{11}X$, ${}^{79}_{38}X^{2+}$

   Answer: a Page: 45

19. How many electrons, protons, and neutrons are contained in an atom ${}^{116}_{92}X$?
   a) 116 electrons, 116 protons, 92 neutrons
   b) 92 electrons, 92 protons, 116 neutrons
   c) 24 electrons, 42 protons, 92 neutrons
   d) 92 electrons, 92 protons, 24 neutrons

   Answer: d Page: 45

20. How many electrons, protons, and neutrons are in an atom of $^{77}_{35}X^{3-}$?
    a) 38 electrons, 35 protons, 42 neutrons
    b) 77 electrons, 32 protons, 77 neutrons
    c) 32 electrons, 80 protons, 35 neutrons
    d) 77 electrons, 77 protons, 35 neutrons

    Answer: a Page: 45

21. In the Rutherford nuclear atom model
    a) the heavy subatomic particles, protons and neutrons, reside in the nucleus
    b) the three principal subatomic particles, protons, neutrons, and electrons, all have essentially the same mass
    c) the light subatomic particles, protons and neutrons, reside in the nucleus
    d) mass is spread essentially uniformly throughout the atom
    e) both the three principal subatomic particles, protons, neutrons, and electrons, all have essentially the same mass and mass is spread essentially uniformly throughout the atom

    Answer: a Page: 43

22. An atom of the most common isotope of gold, ^{197}Au, has
    a) 197 protons, 79 neutrons, and 118 electrons
    b) 118 protons, 79 neutrons, and 39 electrons
    c) 79 protons, 197 neutrons, and 197 electrons
    d) 79 protons, 118 neutrons, and 118 electrons
    e) 79 protons, 118 neutrons, and 79 electrons

    Answer: e Page: 45

23. Which species has 45 neutrons?
    a) $^{80}_{36}Kr$
    b) $^{80}_{35}Br$
    c) $^{78}_{34}Se$
    d) $^{34}_{17}Cl$

    Answer: b Page: 45

24. Which species has 36 electrons?
   a) $^{80}_{36}Kr$

   b) $^{80}_{35}Br$

   c) $^{78}_{34}Se$

   d) $^{34}_{17}Cl$

   Answer: a Page: 45

25. Isotopes are atoms that have the same number of ________ but differing number of ________.
   a) protons, electrons
   b) neutrons, protons
   c) protons, neutrons
   d) electrons, protons

   Answer: c Page: 45

26. In the modern periodic table the elements are arranged in
   a) alphabetical order
   b) order of increasing atomic number
   c) order of increasing metallic properties
   d) order of increasing neutron content

   Answer: b Page: 47

27. In the modern periodic table, the rows are called _____ and the columns are called _____.
   a) octaves, groups
   b) staffs, families
   c) periods, groups
   d) cogeners, families

   Answer: c Page: 47

28. Which group in the periodic table contains only nonmetals?
   a) 1A
   b) 6A
   c) 2B
   d) 2A
   e) 8A

   Answer: e Page: 48

29. Which one of the following is a nonmetal?
a) W
b) Sr
c) Os
d) Ir
e) Br

Answer: e Page: 48

30. All of the following except _____ are metalloids.
a) B
b) Al
c) Si
d) Ge
e) As

Answer: b Page: 48

31. The elements in groups 1A, 6A, and 7A are called, respectively
a) alkaline earth metals, halogens, chalcogens
b) alkali metals, chalcogens, halogens
c) alkali metals, halogens, noble gases
d) alkaline earth metals, transition metals, halogens

Answer: b Page: 48

32. Which one of the following should be the most similar to strontium in chemical and physical properties?
a) Li
b) At
c) Rb
d) Ba
e) Cs

Answer: d Page: 48

33. Which pair of elements below should be the most similar in chemical properties?
a) N and O
b) P and S
c) K and Ca
d) K and Mg
e) Sr and Ba

Answer: e Page: 48

34. Which pair of elements below should be the most similar in chemical properties?
 a) C and O
 b) B and As
 c) I and Br
 d) K and Kr
 e) Cs and He

 Answer: c Page: 48

35. An element in the upper right corner of the periodic table
 a) is either a metal or metalloid
 b) is definitely a metal
 c) is either a metalloid or a non-metal
 d) is definitely a non-metal
 e) is definitely a metalloid

 Answer: d Page: 48

36. An element in the lower left corner of the periodic table
 a) is either a metal or metalloid
 b) is definitely a metal
 c) is either a metalloid or a non-metal
 d) is definitely a non-metal
 e) is definitely a metalloid

 Answer: b Page: 48

37. The alkali metals are found in which group?
 a) w
 b) x
 c) y
 d) z

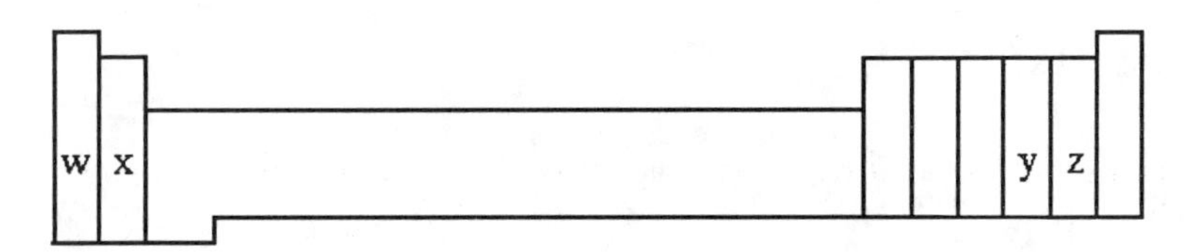

 Answer: a Page: 48

38. The most metallic elements would be found at the bottom of which group?
    a) w
    b) x
    c) y
    d) z

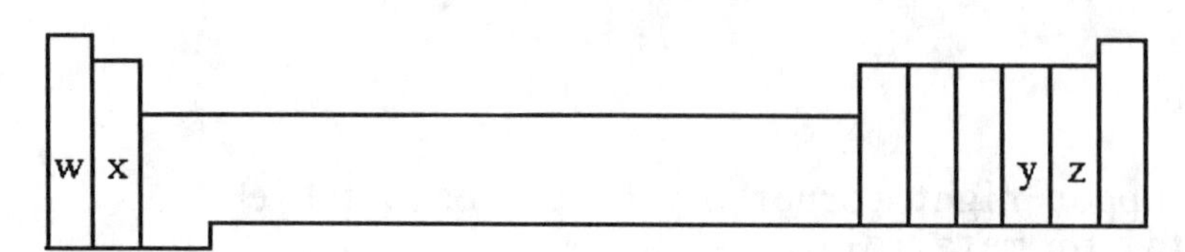

Answer: a Page: 48

39. Which group of the periodic table contains elements with chemical properties similar to silicon?
    a) w
    b) x
    c) y
    d) z

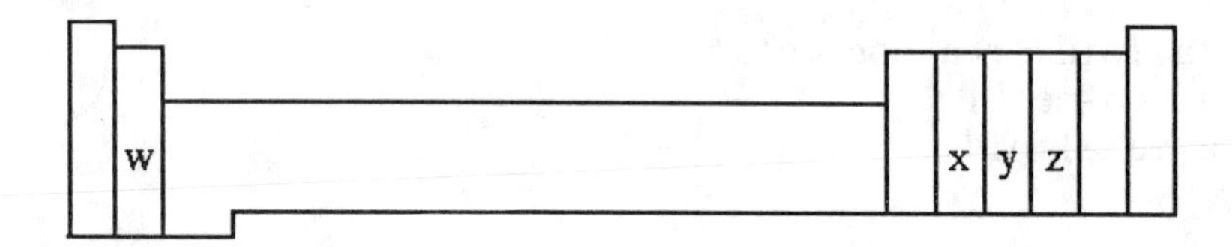

Answer: b Page: 48

40. The elements found in which group are found uncombined, as monatomic species in nature?
    a) noble gases
    b) chalcogens
    c) alkali metals
    d) alkaline earth metals
    e) halogens

Answer: a Page: 48

41. Which one of the following does not occur as diatomic molecules in elemental form?
    a) oxygen
    b) nitrogen
    c) sulfur
    d) hydrogen
    e) bromine

Answer: c Page: 49

42. Which one of the following molecular formulas is also an empirical formula?
   a) $C_6H_6O_2$
   b) C_2H_6SO
   c) H_2O_2
   d) $H_2P_4O_6$
   e) C_6H_6

   Answer: b Page: 50

43. When a metal and a nonmetal react, the ____ tends to lose electrons and the ____ tends to gain electrons.
   a) metal, metal
   b) nonmetal, nonmetal
   c) metal, nonmetal
   d) nonmetal, metal
   e) none of these, these elements share electrons

   Answer: c Page: 52

44. Which one of the following contains the greatest number of electrons?
   a) P^{3+}
   b) P
   c) P^{2-}
   d) P^{3-}
   e) P^{2+}

   Answer: d Page: 52

45. Which one of the following is most likely to lose electrons when forming an ion?
   a) F
   b) P
   c) Rh
   d) S
   e) N

   Answer: c Page: 52

46. Elements belonging to which group of the periodic table form ions with a 2+ charge?
   a) alkaline earth metals
   b) halogens
   c) chalcogens
   d) alkali metals

   Answer: a Page: 52

47. The empirical formula of a compound made up of molecules containing 12 carbon atoms, 14 hydrogen atoms, and 6 oxygen atoms is
a) $C_{12}H_{14}O_6$
b) CHO
c) CH_2O
d) $C_6H_7O_3$
e) C_2H_4O

Answer: d Page: 50

48. Of the choices below, which one is not an ionic compound?
a) PCl_5
b) $MoCl_6$
c) RbCl
d) $PbCl_2$

Answer: a Page: 49

49. What type of formulas can be written for ionic compounds?
a) structural
b) molecular
c) empirical

Answer: c Page: 54

50. What is the formula of the compound formed between strontium ions and nitrogen ions?
a) SrN
b) Sr_3N_2
c) Sr_2N_3
d) SrN_2
e) SrN_3

Answer: b Page: 54

51. $^{131}I^-$ has
a) 131 protons, 53 neutrons, and 54 electrons
b) 131 protons, 53 neutrons, and 52 electrons
c) 53 protons, 78 neutrons, and 54 electrons
d) 53 protons, 131 neutrons, and 52 electrons
e) 78 protons, 53 neutrons, and 72 electrons

Answer: c Page: 52

52. $^{90}Sr^{2+}$ has
a) 38 protons, 52 neutrons, and 36 electrons
b) 38 protons, 52 neutrons, and 38 electrons
c) 38 protons, 52 neutrons, and 40 electrons
d) 52 protons, 38 neutrons, and 50 electrons
e) 52 protons, 38 neutrons, and 54 electrons

Answer: a Page: 52

53. Which species has 54 electrons?
   a) $^{132}_{54}Xe^{+}$
   b) $^{128}_{52}Te^{2-}$
   c) $^{118}_{50}Sn^{2+}$
   d) $^{112}_{48}Cd$

   Answer: b Page: 52

54. Which species has 16 protons?
   a) ^{31}P
   b) $^{34}S^{2-}$
   c) ^{36}Cl
   d) $^{80}Br^{-}$

   Answer: b Page: 52

55. Use the following information to identify the atom or ion.

Mass Number	Protons	Neutrons	Electrons
32	16	16	18

   a) S^{2-}
   b) Ge^{2-}
   c) S
   d) S^{2+}

   Answer: a Page: 52

56. Use the following information to identify the atom or ion.

Mass Number	Protons	Neutrons	Electrons
16	8	8	10

   a) S^{2+}
   b) O
   c) O^{2-}
   d) O^{2+}

   Answer: c Page: 52

57. Which species has 16 neutrons?
   a) ^{31}P
   b) $^{34}S^{2-}$
   c) ^{36}Cl
   d) $^{80}Br^{-}$

   Answer: a Page: 52

58. Which species is an isotope of ^{39}Cl?
    a) ^{40}Ar
    b) $^{34}S^{2-}$
    c) $^{36}Cl^{-}$
    d) ^{80}Br

    Answer: c Page: 52

59. Which one of the following species has as many electrons as it has neutrons?
    a) ^{1}H
    b) $^{40}Ca^{2+}$
    c) ^{14}C
    d) $^{19}F^{-}$

    Answer: d Page: 52

60. Which particle has 48 electrons?
    a) $^{118}_{50}Sn^{+2}$
    b) $^{116}_{50}Sn^{+4}$
    c) $^{112}_{48}Cd^{+2}$
    d) $^{68}_{31}Ga$

    Answer: a Page: 52

61. Magnesium reacts with a certain element to form a compound with the general formula MgX. What would the most likely formula be for the compound formed between potassium and element X?
    a) K_2X
    b) KX_2
    c) K_2X_3
    d) K_2X_2

    Answer: a Page: 54

62. Which type of formula provides the most information about a compound?
    a) empirical
    b) molecular
    c) simplest
    d) structural

    Answer: d Page: 51

63. Which group of elements is most likely to form ions by losing one electron?
    a) w
    b) x
    c) y
    d) z

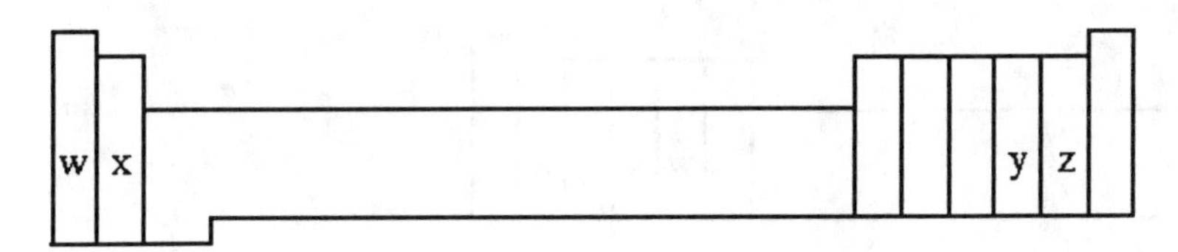

Answer: a Page: 54

64. Element X reacts with sodium to form an ionic compound with the formula Na_2X. Element X is a member of group
    a) w
    b) x
    c) y
    d) z

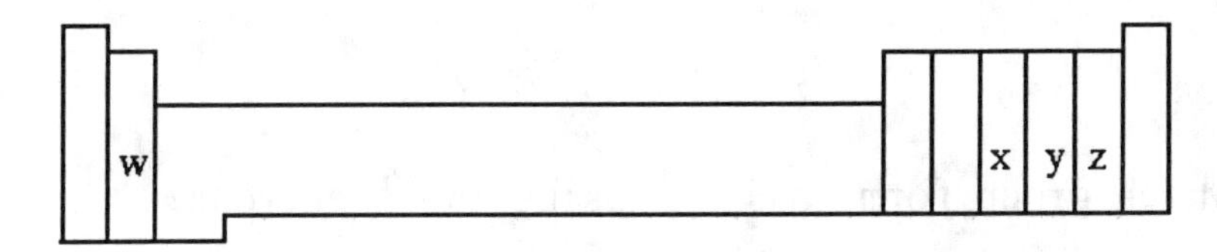

Answer: c Page: 54

65. Which group of elements is most likely to form ions by gaining two electrons?
    a) w
    b) x
    c) y
    d) z

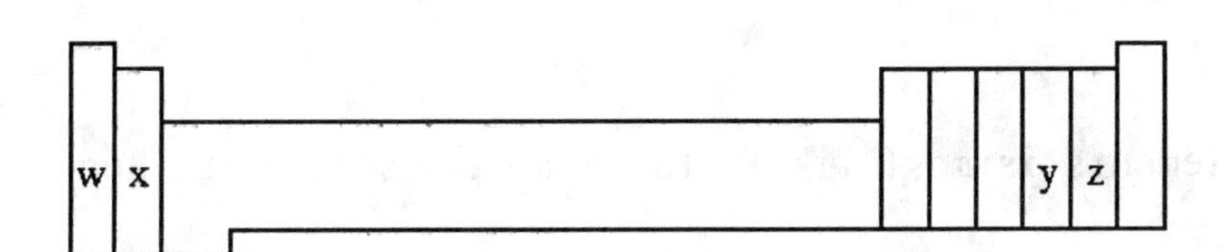

Answer: c Page: 54

66. Which group of elements is most likely to react with calcium to form ionic compounds with the general formula Ca_3X_2?
a) w
b) x
c) y
d) z

Answer: b Page: 54

67. A certain metallic element forms a compound with chlorine having the general formula XCl_2. The X ion in this compound has 28 electrons. What is element X?
a) Ni
b) Zn
c) Fe
d) V

Answer: b Page: 54

68. The elements of which group form ions by losing two electrons?
a) w
b) x
c) y
d) z

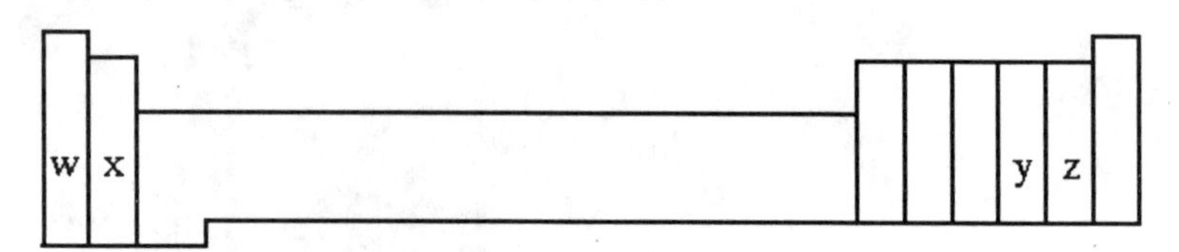

Answer: b Page: 54

69. Which group of elements is most likely to form oxides with the general formula XO?
a) w
b) x
c) y
d) z

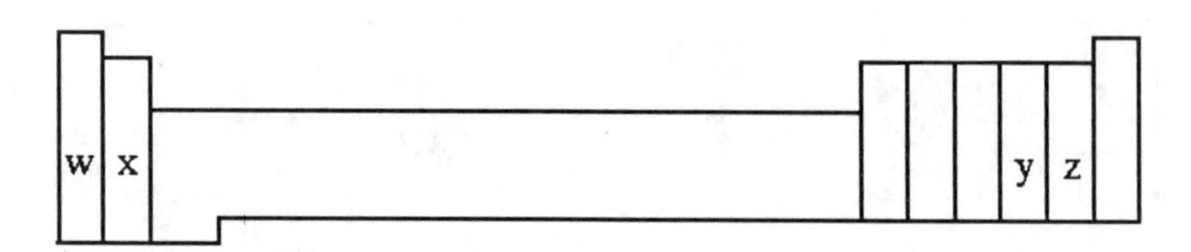

Answer: b Page: 54

70. Which group of elements is most likely to form ions with a 2- charge?
   a) w
   b) x
   c) y
   d) z

Answer: c Page: 54

71. Which group of elements will react with the alkali metals to form compounds with the general formula M_2X?
   a) w
   b) x
   c) y
   d) z

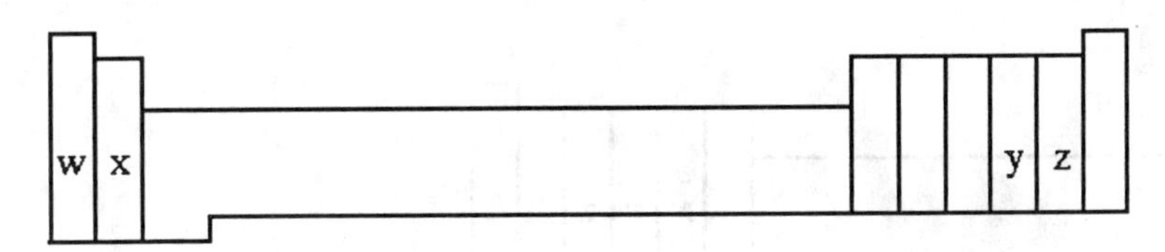

Answer: c Page: 54

72. Which group of elements is most likely to form ions with a 2+ charge?
   a) w
   b) x
   c) y
   d) z

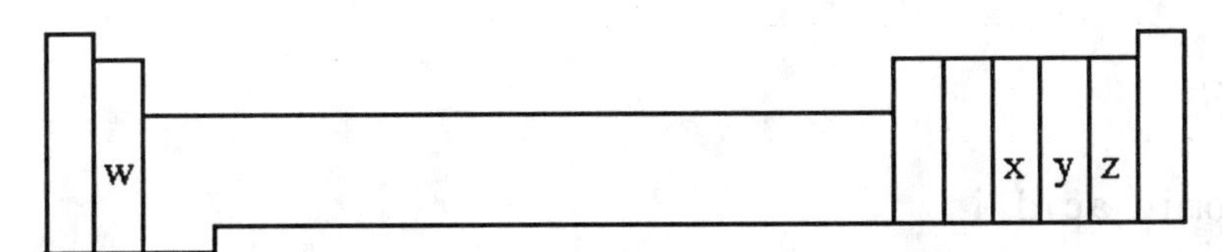

Answer: a Page: 54

73. Element Y reacts with oxygen to form an ionic compound with the formula YO. Element Y is a member of which group?
a) w
b) x
c) y
d) z

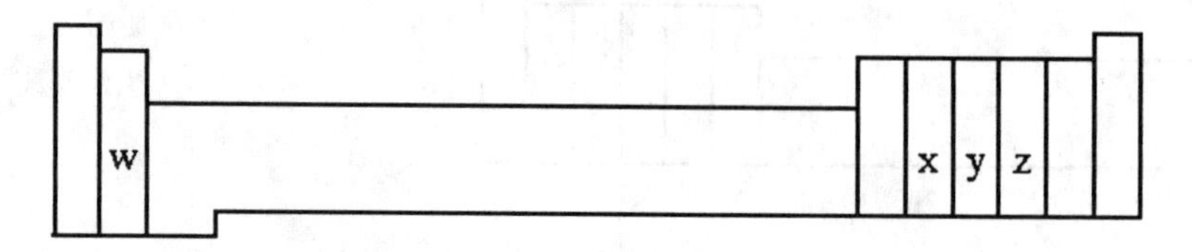

Answer: a Page: 54

74. A certain nonmetallic element forms a compound with aluminum having the general formula Al_2X_3. Element X is a member of which group?
a) w
b) x
c) y
d) z

Answer: d Page: 54

75. The correct name of the compound NaN_3, is
a) sodium nitride
b) sodium azide
c) sodium trinitride
d) sodium(IX) nitride

Answer: b Page: 60

76. The formula of bromic acid is
a) HBr
b) $HBrO_4$
c) HBrO
d) $HBrO_3$
e) $HBrO_2$

Answer: d Page: 60

77. The formula of plumbous sulfide is
   a) PbS
   b) $PbSO_4$
   c) $PbSO_3$
   d) $Pb(SO_4)_2$

   Answer: a Page: 60

78. The correct formula for molybdenum(IV) hypochlorite is
   a) $Mo(ClO_3)_4$
   b) $Mo(ClO)_4$
   c) $Mo(ClO_2)_4$
   d) $Mo(ClO_4)_4$

   Answer: b Page: 60

79. The correct name of the compound, PCl_3, is
   a) potassium chloride
   b) phosphorus trichloride
   c) phosphorous(111) chloride
   d) monophosphorous trichloride

   Answer: b Page: 63

80. The formula of the salt formed from Ca^{2+} and PO_4^{3-} is
   a) $CaPO_4$
   b) $Ca_2(PO_4)_3$
   c) Ca_2PO_4
   d) $Ca(PO_4)_2$
   e) $Ca_3(PO_4)_2$

   Answer: e Page: 55

81. Which one of the following is hydrochloric acid?
   a) $HCl(g)$
   b) $HClO_4(aq)$
   c) $HClO(aq)$
   d) $HCl(aq)$
   e) $HClO_2(aq)$

   Answer: d Page: 62

82. When is the *-ide* ending used in chemical nomenclature?
   a) for monatomic anion names
   b) for polyatomic cation names
   c) for the name of the first element in a molecular compound
   d) to indicate binary acids
   e) for the names of polyatomic anions containing only one oxygen atom

   Answer: a Page: 60

83. Bromic acid is
    a) HBr
    b) $HBrO$
    c) $HBrO_2$
    d) $HBrO_3$
    e) $HBrO_4$

    Answer: d Page: 62

84. The formula of aluminum ion in its compounds is
    a) Al^{2-}
    b) Al^{2+}
    c) Al^{-}
    d) Al^{3+}
    e) Al^{+}

    Answer: d Page: 54

85. The correct formula of iron(III) bromide is
    a) $FeBr_2$
    b) $FeBr_3$
    c) $FeBr$
    d) Fe_3Br_3
    e) Fe_3Br

    Answer: b Page: 60

86. Nitrate ion is
    a) NO_2^-
    b) NO_2^+
    c) NO_3^+
    d) NO_3^-
    e) NO_4^-

    Answer: d Page: 60

87. What is the charge on manganese in the salt MnF_3?
    a) 1+
    b) 1-
    c) 2+
    d) 2-
    e) 3+

    Answer: e Page: 56

88. For which of the following "ous" ions is charge not 2+?
    a) cuprous
    b) ferrous
    c) manganous
    d) nickelous
    e) cobaltous

    Answer: a Page: 57

89. For which of the following "ic" ions is charge 2+?
    a) chromic
    b) ferric
    c) cupric
    d) cobaltic
    e) all of the above

    Answer: c Page: 57

90. Aluminum reacts with a certain nonmetallic element to form a compound with the general formula AlX. Element X is a diatomic gas at room temperature. Element X must be
    a) O_2
    b) F_2
    c) Cl_2
    d) N_2

    Answer: d Page: 54

91. Element M reacts with fluorine to form an ionic compound with the general formula MF_3. The <u>M ion</u> has 18 electrons. Element M is
    a) P
    b) Sc
    c) Ar
    d) Ca

    Answer: b Page: 54

92. The formula for the ionic compound formed between magnesium and sulfur is
    a) MgS
    b) Mg_2S
    c) MgS_2
    d) Mg_2S_2

    Answer: a Page: 54

93. Which one of the following compounds is chromium(III) oxide?
 a) Cr_2O_3
 b) CrO_3
 c) Cr_3O_2
 d) Cr_3O

 Answer: a Page: 62

94. Which one of the following compounds is copper(I) chloride?
 a) CuCl
 b) $CuCl_2$
 c) Cu_2Cl
 d) Cu_2Cl_3

 Answer: a Page: 60

95. Ammonium carbonate is
 a) $(NH_4)_2CO_3$
 b) NH_4CO_2
 c) $(NH_3)_2CO_4$
 d) $(NH_3)_2CO_3$

 Answer: a Page: 60

96. Carbonate ion is
 a) CO_2^{2-}
 b) CO_3^{2-}
 c) CO_3^{3-}
 d) CO_2^{-}

 Answer: b Page: 60

97. Chromate ion is
 a) CrO_4^{2-}
 b) CrO_2^{3-}
 c) CrO^{-}
 d) CrO_3^{2-}

 Answer: a Page: 60

98. Which one of the following ions has a 3- charge?
   a) sulfate
   b) acetate
   c) permanganate
   d) phosphate

   Answer: d Page: 60

99. Which one of the following polyatomic ions has the same charge as the hydroxide ion?
   a) ammonium
   b) carbonate
   c) nitrate
   d) sulfate

   Answer: c Page: 60

100. Which element forms an ion with the same charge as the ammonium ion?
   a) potassium
   b) chlorine
   c) calcium
   d) oxygen

   Answer: a Page: 54

101. When a fluorine atom forms the fluoride ion, it has the same charge as the __________ ion.
   a) sulfite
   b) ammonium
   c) nitrite
   d) phosphate

   Answer: c Page: 60

102. Which one of the following is the correct name for $Mg(ClO_3)_2$?
   a) magnesium chlorate
   b) manganese chlorate
   c) magnesium chloroxide
   d) magnesium perchlorate

   Answer: a Page: 60

103. Which one of the following is the correct formula for ammonium sulfide?
   a) NH_4SO_3
   b) $(NH_4)_2SO_4$
   c) $(NH_4)_2S$
   d) NH_3S

   Answer: c Page: 62

104. The formula for the compound formed between aluminum ions and phosphate ions is
a) $Al_3(PO_4)_3$
b) $AlPO_4$
c) $Al(PO_4)_3$
d) $Al_2(PO_4)_3$

Answer: b Page: 60

105. When calcium reacts with sulfur the compound formed is
a) Ca_2S_2
b) Ca_3S_2
c) CaS
d) CaS_2

Answer: c Page: 54

106. The correct name for $CrCl_3$ is
a) chromium chlorine
b) chromium(III) chloride
c) monochromium trichloride
d) chromium(III) trichloride

Answer: b Page: 60

107. The correct name for N_2O_4 is
a) nitrogen oxide
b) nitrous oxide
c) nitrogen(III) oxide
d) dinitrogen tetroxide

Answer: d Page: 63

108. The formula for zinc phosphate is $Zn_3(PO_4)_2$. What is the formula for cadmium arsenate?
a) $Cd_4(ASO_2)_3$
b) $Cd_3(AsO_4)_2$
c) $Cd_3(AsO_3)_4$
d) $Cd_2(AsO_4)_3$

Answer: b Page: 60

109. The formula for aluminum hydroxide is
a) AlOH
b) Al_3OH
c) $Al_2(OH)_3$
d) $Al(OH)_3$

Answer: d Page: 60

110. What is the name given to $KBrO_4$?
   a) potassium perbromate
   b) potassium bromate
   c) potassium hypobromate
   d) potassium perbromite

   Answer: a Page: 60

111. The correct name for V_2O_3 is
   a) vanadium(III) oxide
   b) vanadium oxide
   c) vanadium(II) oxide
   d) vanadium(III) trioxide

   Answer: a Page: 60

112. The elements Mg, Cl, and O combine to form a compound called magnesium chlorate, $Mg(ClO_3)_2$. What is the formula for the compound formed between Ca, Br, and O?
   a) $CaBrO_2$
   b) $Ca(BrO_3)_2$
   c) $Ca(BrO_2)_3$
   d) Ca_2BrO_3

   Answer: b Page: 60

113. The formula for zinc phosphate is $Zn_3(PO_4)_2$. What is the formula for cadmium arsenite?
   a) $Cd_2(AsO_4)_3$
   b) $Cd_3(AsO_3)_2$
   c) $Cd_3(AsO_4)_2$
   d) $Cd_4(AsO_2)_3$

   Answer: b Page: 60

114. The correct name for NH_4CN is
   a) nitrogen hydrogen cyanate
   b) ammonium carbonitride
   c) ammonium cyanide
   d) ammonium hydrogen cyanate

   Answer: c Page: 60

115. The correct name for $(NH_4)_3PO_4$ is
   a) ammonium phosphate
   b) nitrogen hydrogen phosphate
   c) tetrammonium phosphate
   d) ammonia phosphide

   Answer: a Page: 62

116. The correct name for $Ni(CN)_2$ is
a) nickel(I) cyanide
b) nickel cyanate
c) nickel carbonate
d) nickel(II) cyanide

Answer: d Page: 62

117. Which one of the following substances is perchloric acid?
a) $HClO$
b) $HClO_3$
c) $HClO_4$
d) $HClO_2$

Answer: c Page: 63

118. The formula for hydroselenic acid is
a) H_2Se
b) HSe
c) H_2SeO_4
d) H_2SeO_3

Answer: a Page: 63

119. The formula for bromic acid is
a) $HBrO_4$
b) $HBrO_3$
c) $HBrO_2$
d) HBr

Answer: b Page: 63

120. The correct name for HIO_2 is
a) hypoiodic acid
b) hydroiodic acid
c) periodous acid
d) iodous acid

Answer: d Page: 63

121. What is the charge on the silver (Ag) ion in Ag_2CO_3?
a) 3-
b) 1+
c) 2+
d) 3+

Answer: b Page: 62

MULTIPLE CHOICE

1. When the reaction below is correctly balanced, the coefficients are
$NH_3 + O_2 \rightarrow NO_2 + H_2O$

a) 1,1,1,1
b) 4,7,4,6
c) 2,3,2,3
d) 1,3,1,2
e) none of these

Answer: b Page: 72

2. The coefficients required to correctly balance the reaction below are
$Al(NO_3)_3 + Na_2S \rightarrow Al_2S_3 + NaNO_3$

a) 2,3,1,6
b) 2,1,3,2
c) 1,1,1,1
d) 4,6,3,2
e) none of these

Answer: a Page: 72

3. What is the coefficient of H_2 when the following equation is correctly balanced?

$$K(s) + H_2O(l) \rightarrow KOH(aq) + H_2(g)$$

a) 1
b) 2
c) 3
d) 4

Answer: a Page: 72

4. What is the coefficient of Al when the following equation is correctly balanced?

$$Al + H_2O \rightarrow Al(OH)_3 + H_2$$

a) 1
b) 2
c) 3
d) 5

Answer: b Page: 72

5. What is the coefficient of H_2O when the following equation is correctly balanced?

$$Ca(s) + H_2O(l) \rightarrow Ca(OH)_2(aq) + H_2(g)$$

a) 1
b) 2
c) 3
d) 5

Answer: b Page: 72

6. What is the coefficient of Al_2O_3 when the following equation is correctly balanced?

$$Al_2O_3(s) + C(s) + Cl_2(g) \rightarrow AlCl_3(s) + CO(g)$$

a) 1
b) 2
c) 3
d) 4

Answer: a Page: 72

7. What is the coefficient of Fe_3O_4 when the following equation is correctly balanced?

$$Al + Fe_3O_4 \rightarrow Al_2O_3 + Fe$$

a) 2
b) 3
c) 4
d) 5

Answer: b Page: 72

8. What is the coefficient of H_2S when the following equation is correctly balanced?

$$FeCl_3 + H_2S \rightarrow Fe_2S_3 + HCl$$

a) 1
b) 2
c) 3
d) 5

Answer: c Page: 72

9. What is the coefficient of H_2O when the following equation is correctly balanced?

$$PCl_3 + H_2O \rightarrow H_3PO_3 + HCl$$

a) 1
b) 2
c) 3
d) 4

Answer: c Page: 72

10. What is the coefficient of HCl when the following equation is correctly balanced?

$$CaCO_3(s) + HCl(aq) \rightarrow CaCl_2(aq) + CO_2(g) + H_2O(l)$$

a) 1
b) 2
c) 3
d) 4

Answer: b Page: 72

11. What is the coefficient of $FeCl_3$ when the following equation is correctly balanced?

$$FeCl_3 + Na_2CO_3 \rightarrow Fe_2(CO_3)_3 + NaCl$$

a) 1
b) 2
c) 3
d) 5

Answer: b Page: 72

12. What is the coefficient of H_2S when the following equation is correctly balanced?

$$H_2S + Fe(OH)_3 \rightarrow Fe_2S_3 + H_2O$$

a) 2
b) 3
c) 4
d) 5

Answer: b Page: 72

13. What is the coefficient of HNO_3 when the following equation is correctly balanced?

$$HNO_3(l) + CaCO_3(s) \rightarrow Ca(NO_3)_2(s) + CO_2(g) + H_2O(l)$$

a) 1
b) 2
c) 3
d) 5

Answer: b Page: 72

14. What is the coefficient of H_3PO_4 when the following equation is correctly balanced?

$$H_3PO_4 + NaOH \rightarrow Na_3PO_4 + H_2O$$

a) 1
b) 2
c) 3
d) 4

Answer: a Page: 72

15. What is the coefficient of $C_3H_8O_3$ when the following equation is correctly balanced?

$$C_3H_8O_3 + O_2 \rightarrow CO_2 + H_2O$$

a) 1
b) 2
c) 3
d) 7

Answer: b Page: 74

16. What is the coefficient of O_2 when the following equation is correctly balanced?

$$C_2H_4O + O_2 \rightarrow CO_2 + H_2O$$

a) 2
b) 3
c) 4
d) 5

Answer: d Page: 74

17. What is the coefficient of H_2 when the following equation is correctly balanced?

$$CO(g) + H_2(g) \rightarrow H_2O(g) + CH_4(g)$$

a) 1
b) 2
c) 3
d) 4

Answer: c Page: 74

18. What is the coefficient of H_2SO_4 when the following equation is balanced?

$$H_2SO_4(aq) + NaOH(aq) \rightarrow Na_2SO_4 + H_2O$$

a) 1
b) 2
c) 3
d) 4

Answer: a Page: 72

19. What symbol is used to indicate heat in chemical equations?
a) $h\upsilon$
b) Δ
c) h
d) λ

Answer: b Page: 73

20. In a chemical equation, the fact that a substance is dissolved in water is indicated by
a) (*g*)
b) (*s*)
c) (*aq*)
d) (*l*)
e) Δ

Answer: c Page: 73

21. Predict the missing product in the following unbalanced equation, knowing that magnesium reacts with water to form the hydroxide and elemental hydrogen.

$$Ca + H_2O \rightarrow Ca(OH)_2 + \_\_\_\_\_\_\_\_$$

a) H_2O
b) H_2
c) CaH_2
d) CaOH

Answer: b Page: 74

ESSAY

22. Complete and balance the following reaction, knowing that elemental rubidium reacts with elemental sulfur to form $Rb_2S(s)$.

$$Na(s) + S(s) \rightarrow$$

Answer: $2Na_{(s)} + S_{(s)} \rightarrow Na_2S_{(s)}$ Page: 74

23. Write the balanced chemical equation occurring when elemental potassium is added to water, given that elemental sodium reacts with water to form sodium hydroxide and elemental hydrogen.

Answer: $2K + 2H_2O \rightarrow 2KOH + H_2$ Page: 74

MULTIPLE CHOICE

24. What is the coefficient of Ca when the following equation is completed and balanced? Magnesium reacts with water to form magnesium hydroxide and elemental hydrogen.

$$Ca(s) + H_2O(l) \rightarrow$$

a) 1
b) 2
c) 3
d) 4

Answer: a Page: 74

SHORT ANSWER

25. Write the balanced general equation for an alkali metal reacting with water. Use M to symbolize the alkali metal.

Answer: 2M + 2H2O → 2MOH + H2 Page: 74

MULTIPLE CHOICE

26. Of the following compounds, which one will form something other than carbon dioxide and water when combusted?
    a) C_2H_6
    b) CH_4
    c) $C_{32}H_{44}O_9$
    d) CH_3OCH_3
    e) C_5H_5N

    Answer: e Page: 75

27. When a hydrocarbon is combusted in air, what component of air reacts?
    a) oxygen
    b) nitrogen
    c) carbon dioxide
    d) water
    e) argon

    Answer: a Page: 75

28. What is the coefficient of O_2 when the following equation is <u>completed</u> and <u>balanced</u>?

    $$C_4H_8O_2 + O_2 \rightarrow$$

    a) 2
    b) 3
    c) 5
    d) 6

    Answer: c Page: 75

29. Of the reactions below, which one is a combination reaction?
    a) $C + O_2 \rightarrow CO_2$
    b) $2Mg + O_2 \rightarrow 2MgO$
    c) $2N_2 + 3H_2 \rightarrow 2NH_3$
    d) $CaO + H_2O \rightarrow Ca(OH)_2$
    e) $Cd(NO_3) + Na_2S \rightarrow CdS + 2NaNO_3$

    Answer: e Page: 76

30. Of the reactions below, which one is a decomposition reaction?
    a) $NH_4Cl \rightarrow NH_3 + HCl$
    b) $2Mg + O_2 \rightarrow 2MgO$
    c) $2N_2 + 3H_2 \rightarrow 2NH_3$
    d) $Zn + Cu(NO_3)_2 \rightarrow Cu + Zn(NO_3)_2$
    e) $Cd(NO_3)_2 + Na_2S \rightarrow CdS + 2NaNO_3$

    Answer: a Page: 76

ESSAY

31. Complete and balance the following combination reaction.

$$Li + F_2 \rightarrow$$

Answer: $2Li + F_2 \rightarrow 2 LiF$ Page: 76

MULTIPLE CHOICE

32. Which one of the following substances would be the product of this combination reaction?

$$Al(s) + I_2(s) \rightarrow$$

a) AlI_2
b) AlI
c) AlI_3
d) Al_2I_3

Answer: c Page: 76

33. Predict the missing product in the following unbalanced combination reaction.

$$Al_2 + N \rightarrow \_\_\_\_\_\_\_\_$$

a) AlN
b) Al_3N
c) AlN_2
d) Al_3N_2

Answer: a Page: 76

34. Which one of the following is not true concerning automotive air bags?
a) they are inflated as a result of a decomposition reaction
b) they are loaded with sodium azide initially
c) the gas used for inflating them is oxygen
d) the two products of the decomposition reaction are sodium and nitrogen

Answer: c Page: 76

SHORT ANSWER

35. Write the balanced chemical equation for the reaction that occurs when magnesium burns in oxygen.

Answer: $2Mg + O_2 \rightarrow 2MgO$ Page: 76

36. Many metal carbonates decompose when heated. Write the balanced chemical equation for the decomposition of sodium carbonate.

    Answer: $Na_2CO_3 \rightarrow Na_2O + CO_2$ Page: 76

MULTIPLE CHOICE

37. Lime, also known as quicklime, has the formula
    a) $La(NO_3)_3$
    b) CaO
    c) $CaCO_3$
    d) $LiCl$
    e) $NaCl$

    Answer: b Page: 76

38. Currently the atomic mass unit is based on what element?
    a) hydrogen
    b) oxygen
    c) sodium
    d) carbon

    Answer: d Page: 78

39. The atomic masses in the periodic table are not exact numbers. For example, carbon is listed as 12.01115 instead of 12.00000. Why?
    a) our technology does not allow for exact measurement of such a small quantity
    b) atoms gain and lose electrons easily and that changes their masses significantly
    c) atomic masses listed in the periodic table are weighted averages of isotopic masses
    d) atomic masses are measured in real samples that are always contaminated with other elements

    Answer: c Page: 78

40. From the information below, calculate the weighted average atomic mass of the element X.

Isotope	Percent Relative Abundance	Exact Mass(u)
^{221}X	74.22	220.9
^{220}X	12.78	220.0
^{218}X	13.00	218.1

    a) 219.7 amu
    b) 220.4 amu
    c) 22042 amu
    d) 218.5 amu

    Answer: b Page: 78

41. The element Z has two isotopes: ^{102}Z has an exact mass of 102.44 and ^{98}Z has an exact mass of 97.99. If the weighted average atomic mass of Z is 100.32, which isotope has the greatest relative abundance?
a) ^{102}Z
b) ^{98}Z
c) they are both the same relative abundance

Answer: a Page: 78

42. Element X has three naturally occurring isotopes. The mass of each isotope and its % abundance is: 37.919 (5.07%), 39.017 (15.35%), and 42.111 (79.58%). What is the average atomic mass of element X?
a) 41.42 amu
b) 39.68 amu
c) 39.07 amu
d) 38.64 amu

Answer: a Page: 78

43. A certain element has three isotopes. The isotopic masses and abundances are: 159.37 (30.60%), 162.79 (15.79%), and 163.92 (53.61%). What is the average atomic weight of the element?
a) 161.75 amu
b) 162.03 amu
c) 162.35 amu
d) 163.15 amu

Answer: c Page: 78

44. Assume that element X has three naturally occurring isotopes. The mass and abundance of each isotope is: 52.62 (19.61%), 56.29 (53.91%), and 58.31 (26.48%). What is the average atomic weight of element X?
a) 33.33 amu
b) 55.74 amu
c) 56.11 amu
d) 57.23 amu

Answer: c Page: 78

45. What is the average atomic weight of an element if the two known isotopes of the element have the following characteristics?

Isotope	Mass (amu)	% Abundance
Isotope 1	31.163	35.16
Isotope 2	34.296	64.84

a) 30.197 amu
b) 33.194 amu
c) 34.016 amu
d) 35.221 amu

Answer: b Page: 78

46. The average atomic weight of copper is 63.5. Copper has two naturally occurring isotopes. One of the isotopes has an atomic weight of 62.9 and an abundance of 69.1%. The other isotope has an abundance of 30.9%. What is the atomic weight of this isotope?
a) 63.2 amu
b) 63.8 amu
c) 64.1 amu
d) 64.8 amu

Answer: d Page: 78

47. The table shown below lists the naturally occurring isotopes of element X. Use this data to calculate the average atomic weight of element X.

Mass of Isotope	Isotipic Abundance
15.33 amu	28.6%
17.26 amu	13.3%
18.11 amu	58.1%

a) 17.20 amu
b) 16.90 amu
c) 17.65 amu
d) 17.11 amu

Answer: a Page: 78

48. Of the following substances, which one does not exist in the form of molecules?
a) PCl_5
b) $SOCl_2$
c) KF
d) AsH_3

Answer: c Page: 79

49. The molecular weight in amu of nitrobenzene, $C_6H_5NO_2$, is
a) 107.11 amu
b) 43.03 amu
c) 109.10 amu
d) 123.11 amu
e) 3.06 amu

Answer: d Page: 79

50. The formula weight in amu of potassium dichromate, $K_2Cr_2O_7$, is
a) 107.09 amu
b) 255.08 amu
c) 242.18 amu
d) 294.18 amu
e) 333.08 amu

Answer: d Page: 79

51. The formula weight in amu of potassium phosphate is
    a) 173.17 amu
    b) 251.37 amu
    c) 212.27 amu
    d) 196.27 amu
    e) 86.07 amu

    Answer: c Page: 79

52. The formula weight in amu of aluminum sulfate is
    a) 342.14 amu
    b) 123.04 amu
    c) 59.04 amu
    d) 150.14 amu
    e) 273.06 amu

    Answer: a Page: 79

53. The formula weight in amu of silver chromate is
    a) 159.87 amu
    b) 223.87 amu
    c) 331.73 amu
    d) 339.86 amu
    e) 175.87 amu

    Answer: c Page: 79

54. What is the formula weight of $(NH_4)_2SO_4$?
    a) 100 amu
    b) 118 amu
    c) 116 amu
    d) 132 amu

    Answer: d Page: 79

55. What is the molecular weight of the compound CH_3CO_2H?
    a) 60 amu
    b) 48 amu
    c) 44 amu
    d) 32 amu

    Answer: a Page: 79

56. What is the molecular weight of the compound C_2H_5OH?
    a) 34 amu
    b) 41 amu
    c) 30 amu
    d) 46 amu

    Answer: d Page: 79

57. What is the percentage of carbon in dimethylsulfoxide, C_2H_6SO?
 a) 60.0%
 b) 20.6%
 c) 30.7%
 d) 7.74%
 e) 79.8%

 Answer: c Page: 80

58. The mass percentage of H in CH_4 is
 a) 25.13%
 b) 4.032%
 c) 74.87%
 d) 92.26%
 e) 7.743%

 Answer: a Page: 80

59. The mass percentage of Al in aluminum sulfate is
 a) 7.886%
 b) 15.77%
 c) 21.93%
 d) 45.70%
 e) 35.94%

 Answer: b Page: 80

60. The mass percentage of C in CH_4 is
 a) 25.13%
 b) 133.6%
 c) 74.87%
 d) 92.26%
 e) 7.743%

 Answer: c Page: 80

61. The mass percentage of F in KrF_2 is
 a) 18.48%
 b) 145.3%
 c) 68.80%
 d) 81.52%
 e) 31.20%

 Answer: e Page: 80

62. 2.1043 moles of which one of the following has the largest number of atoms?
    a) S_8
    b) $C_{10}H_8$
    c) $Al_2(SO_4)_3$
    d) Na_3PO_4

    Answer: b Page: 82

63. How many moles of carbon atoms are contained in 4 moles of dimethylsulfoxide, C_2H_6SO?
    a) 2
    b) 6
    c) 8
    d) 4

    Answer: c Page: 82

64. One million argon atoms is how many moles of argon atoms?
    a) 3
    b) 1.7×10^{-18}
    c) 6.0×10^{23}
    d) 1.0×10^{-6}

    Answer: b Page: 82

65. How many sulfur atoms are there in 25 molecules of $C_4H_4S_2$?
    a) $1.5 \text{ X } 10^{25}$
    b) $4.8 \text{ X } 10^{25}$
    c) $3.0 \text{ X } 10^{25}$
    d) 50

    Answer: d Page: 84

66. How many hydrogen atoms are there in 25 molecules of $C_4H_4S_2$?
    a) 25
    b) $3.8 \text{ X } 10^{24}$
    c) $6.0 \text{ X } 10^{25}$
    d) 100

    Answer: d Page: 84

67. How many carbon atoms are there in 200 molecules of C_3H_8O?
    a) 600
    b) 200
    c) 3.61×10^{26}
    d) 1.20×10^{26}

    Answer: a Page: 84

68. How many atoms of oxygen are in 300 molecules of CH_3CO_2H?
   a) 300
   b) 600
   c) 3.01×10^{24}
   d) 3.61×10^{26}

   Answer: b Page: 84

69. How many molecules of CH_4 are in 48.2 g of this compound?
   a) 5.00×10^{-24}
   b) 3.00
   c) 2.90×10^{25}
   d) 1.81×10^{24}

   Answer: d Page: 84

70. How many atoms of fluorine are in 19 g of CH_2F_2?
   a) 2.2×10^{23}
   b) 38
   c) 3.3×10^{24}
   d) 4.4×10^{23}

   Answer: d Page: 70

71. How many grams of hydrogen are in 46 g of CH_4O?
   a) 5.8
   b) 1.5
   c) 2.8
   d) 0.36

   Answer: a Page: 84

72. How many molecules of CH_4O are in 32.0 g of CH_4O?
   a) 5.32×10^{-23}
   b) 1.00
   c) 1.88×10^{22}
   d) 6.00×10^{23}

   Answer: d Page: 84

73. How many grams of oxygen are in 65 g of $C_2H_2O_2$?
   a) 18
   b) 29
   c) 9.0
   d) 36

   Answer: d Page: 84

74. How many atoms of nitrogen are in 10 g of NH_4NO_3?
    a) 3.5
    b) 1.5 X 10^{23}
    c) 3.0 X 10^{23}
    d) 1.8

    Answer: b Page: 84

75. Argon gas has a density of 1.40 g/L at standard conditions. How many argon atoms are in 1.0 L of argon gas?
    a) 4.7 X 10^{22}
    b) 3.4 X 10^{25}
    c) 2.1 X 10^{22}
    d) 1.5 X 10^{25}

    Answer: c Page: 84

76. What is the empirical formula of a compound that contains 27.0% S, 13.4% O, and 59.6% Cl?
    a) SOCl
    b) $SOCl_2$
    c) S_2OCl
    d) SO_2Cl

    Answer: b Page: 86

77. What is the properly written empirical formula of a compound of molecular formula C_8H_{16} of molecular weight 112.21 amu?
    a) C_8H_{16}
    b) CH_3
    c) C_2H_8
    d) C_3H
    e) CH_2

    Answer: e Page: 86

78. What is the properly written empirical formula of a hydrocarbon 89.94% by mass carbon?
    a) C_3H_4
    b) C_4H_3
    c) C_9H_{10}
    d) C_9H
    e) C_8H_6

    Answer: a Page: 86

79. What is the empirical formula for a compound that is 29% by weight Na, 41% S, and 30% O?
a) $Na_2S_2O_3$
b) $NaSO_2$
c) $NaSO$
d) $NaSO_3$

Answer: a Page: 86

80. What is the empirical formula of a compound that is 49.4% K, 20.3% S, and 30.3% O?
a) KSO_2
b) KSO_3
c) K_2SO_4
d) K_2SO_3

Answer: d Page: 86

81. A compound was found to be 40.0% carbon, 6.7% hydrogen, and 53.3% oxygen by weight. What is the empirical formula of the compound?
a) CH_2O
b) C_6HO_8
c) $C_2H_4O_2$
d) C_3H_6O

Answer: a Page: 86

82. Determine the molecular formula of a compound that contains 40.0% C, 6.71% H, and 53.29% O and has a molecular mass of 60.05.
a) $C_2H_4O_2$
b) CH_2O
c) $C_2H_3O_4$
d) $C_2H_2O_4$

Answer: a Page: 88

83. A nitrogen oxide (contains only N and O) 63.65% by mass nitrogen might have which molecular formula(s)?
a) NO
b) NO_2
c) N_2O
d) N_2O_4
e) both NO_2 and N_2O_4

Answer: c Page: 88

84. A sulfur oxide (contains only S and O) 50.0% by mass sulfur might have which molecular formula(s)?
a) SO
b) SO_2
c) S_2O
d) S_2O_4
e) both SO_2 and S_2O_4

Answer: e Page: 88

85. What is the properly written empirical formula of a compound of molecular formula C_2H_6 of molecular weight 30.07 amu?
a) CH_2
b) CH_3
c) C_2H_6
d) C_3H
e) C_8H^{24}

Answer: b Page: 88

86. What is the molecular formula of a compound of empirical formula NO_2 and formula weight 89 ± 6 amu?
a) NO
b) NO_2
c) N_2O
d) N_2O_4
e) N_3O_6

Answer: d Page: 88

87. What is the properly written empirical formula of a compound of molecular formula C_6H_{12} of molecular weight 84.16 amu?
a) CH_2
b) CH_3
c) C_6H_{12}
d) C_2H
e) $C_{12}H_{24}$

Answer: a Page: 88

88. What is the molecular formula of a compound of empirical formula CH and formula weight 81 ± 6 amu?
a) CH
b) C_4H_4
c) C_6H_6
d) C_4H_4S
e) C_5H_5O

Answer: c Page: 88

89. A compound containing only carbon, hydrogen, and oxygen is analyzed and found to be 70.6% carbon, 5.9% hydrogen, and 23.5% oxygen. The molecular weight of the compound is 136. What is the molecular formula?
a) $C_8H_8O_2$
b) C_8H_4O
c) C_4H_4O
d) $C_9H_{12}O$

Answer: a Page: 88

90. $H_2C{=}CH_2$ and $H_2C{=}CH{-}CH_3$ have the same ________ formula(s).
a) empirical
b) molecular
c) structural
d) empirical and molecular
e) empirical, molecular, and structural

Answer: a Page: 86

91. A compound containing only carbon and hydrogen is 85.7% by weight carbon and 14.3% by weight hydrogen. What is the empirical formula of the compound?
a) CH_2
b) C_2H_4
c) CH_4
d) C_4H_8

Answer: a Page: 86

92. A compound containing only carbon and hydrogen is 80.0% by weight carbon and 20.0% by weight hydrogen. What is the empirical formula of the compound?
a) $C_{20}H_{60}$
b) C_7H_{20}
c) CH_3
d) C_2H_6

Answer: c Page: 86

93. A compound containing potassium, nitrogen, and oxygen was found to be 38.7% by weight potassium, 13.9% nitrogen, and 47.4% oxygen. What is the empirical formula of the compound?
a) KNO_3
b) $K_2N_2O_3$
c) KNO_2
d) K_2NO_3

Answer: a Page: 86

94. Which hydrocarbon pair below has identical mass percentage C?
    a) C_3H_4 and C_3H_6
    b) C_2H_4 and C_3H_4
    c) C_2H_4 and C_4H_2
    d) C_2H_4 and C_3H_6
    e) none of the above

    Answer: d Page: 80

95. The combustion of 3.42 g of a compound known to contain only nitrogen and hydrogen was burned in oxygen. The result was the formation of 9.82 g of NO_2 and 3.85 g of water. Determine the empirical formula of this compound.
    a) NH
    b) NH_2
    c) N_2H
    d) NH_3

    Answer: b Page: 89

96. A compound with a molecular weight of 110.1 that contained only C, H, and O was analyzed by combustion. The combustion of a 5.19 g sample of the compound resulted in the formation of 12.4 g of carbon dioxide and 2.55 g of water. What is the molecular formula of this compound?
    a) $C_6H_6O_2$
    b) C_3H_3O
    c) CH_3O
    d) $C_2H_6O_5$

    Answer: a Page: 89

97. What mass of magnesium nitride can be made from reaction of 1.22 g of magnesium with excess nitrogen? Do not forget to balance the reaction.

    $$Mg + N_2 \rightarrow Mg_3N_2$$

    a) 1.69 g
    b) 15.2 g
    c) 5.07 g
    d) 5.02 g

    Answer: a Page: 90

98. What mass of magnesium is required to react with 9.27 g of nitrogen? Be sure to balance the reaction.

    $$Mg + N_2 \rightarrow Mg_3N_2$$

    a) 8.04 g
    b) 24.1 g
    c) 16.1 g
    d) 0.92 g

    Answer: b Page: 90

99. How many grams of oxygen are required to burn 28.8 g of ammonia? Be sure to balance the reaction.

$$NH_3 + O_2 \rightarrow NO_2 + H_2O$$

a) 94.7 g
b) 54.1 g
c) 108 g
d) 15.3 g

Answer: a Page: 90

100. What mass of NO_2 can be produced by combustion of 43.9 g of ammonia? Be sure to balance the reaction.

$$NH_3 + O_2 \rightarrow NO_2 + H_2O$$

a) 2.58 g
b) 178 g
c) 119 g
d) 0.954 g

Answer: c Page: 90

101. How many grams of H_2O are formed by complete conversion of 32.00 g O_2 with excess H_2 according to $2H_2 + O_2 \rightarrow 2H_2O$?

a) 18.02
b) 36.03
c) 32.00
d) 2.016
e) 4.032

Answer: b Page: 90

102. How many moles of GeF_4 are needed to form 8.00 mol GeF_3H according to the reaction $GeH_4 + 3GeF_4 \rightarrow 4GeF_3H$ if the product is obtained in 92.6% yield?
a) 1.85
b) 2.00
c) 8.64
d) 7.41
e) 2.16

Answer: e Page: 90

103. How many moles of H_2O are produced when 2.5 moles of O_2 react according to the following equation?

$$C_3H_8 + 5O_2 \rightarrow 3CO_2 + 4H_2O$$

a) 4
b) 3
c) 2.5
d) 2

Answer: d Page: 90

104. How many moles of CO_2 are produced when 2.5 moles of O_2 react according to the following equation?

$$C_3H_8 + 5O_2 \rightarrow 3CO_2 + 4H_2O$$

a) 1.5
b) 3
c) 5
d) 6

Answer: a Page: 90

105. How many moles of NH_3 can be produced by the complete reaction of six moles of H_2O according to the following equation?

$$Li_3N + 3H_2O \rightarrow 3LiOH + NH_3$$

a) 2
b) 1
c) 6
d) 3

Answer: a Page: 90

106. Consider the equation shown below. If 3.0 g of O_2 produces 3.4 g of H_2O, how many grams of H_2O would be produced by 6.0 g of O_2?

$$2H_2 + O_2 \rightarrow 2H_2O$$

a) 3.4
b) 6.8
c) 1.7
d) 6.4

Answer: b Page: 90

107. How many grams of H_2O are required to produce 13 g of C_2H_2 according to the following equation?

$$CaC_2 + 2H_2O \rightarrow Ca(OH)_2 + C_2H_2$$

a) 4.5
b) 9.0
c) 18
d) 4.7×10^2

Answer: c Page: 90

108. How many grams of CH_4 are required to produce 43 g of Cu according to the following equation?

$$4CuO + CH_4 \rightarrow CO_2 + 2H_2O + 4Cu$$

a) 0.17
b) 2.7
c) 11
d) 43

Answer: b Page: 90

109. Determine the number of grams of CO_2 produced according to the following equation when 7.3 g of C_3H_8 burns in excess O_2.

$$C_3H_8 + 5O_2 \rightarrow 3CO_2 + 4H_2O$$

a) 22
b) 7.3
c) 8.0×10^2
d) 2.4

Answer: a Page: 90

110. How many grams of N_2 will be required to completely react with 9.3 g of H_2 according to the following equation?

$$N_2 + 3H_2 \rightarrow 2NH_3$$

a) 1.3×10^2
b) 2.0
c) 43
d) 3.9×10^2

Answer: c Page: 90

111. Using the balanced equation shown below, calculate the number of grams of H_2O that would be produced by the complete reaction of 5.0 g of O_2.

$$2H_2(g) + O_2(g) \rightarrow 2H_2O(l)$$

a) 5.6
b) 2.8
c) 2.3×10^2
d) 0.31

Answer: a Page: 90

112. Determine the number of grams of SO_2 that would be produced by the reaction of 15 g of CS_2 according to the following equation.

$$CS_2 + 3O_2 \rightarrow CO_2 + 2SO_2$$

a) 13
b) 6.3
c) 6.5×10^2
d) 25

Answer: d Page: 90

113. How many grams of PbI_2 could be made from the complete reaction of 6.5 g of KI according to the following balanced equation?

$$Pb(NO_3)_2 + 2KI \rightarrow PbI_2 + 2KNO_3$$

a) 2.3
b) 9.0
c) 18
d) 36

Answer: b Page: 90

114. How many grams of H_2 would be required to completely react with 7.1 g of N_2?

$$N_2 + 3H_2 \rightarrow 2NH_3$$

a) 0.51
b) 0.76
c) 1.2
d) 1.5

Answer: d Page: 90

115. Why is carbon dioxide called a greenhouse gas?
  a) it is needed in large quantities by plants growing in greenhouses
  b) it is a major product of greenhouses
  c) lead carbonate is a common pigment used in green house paint
  d) it absorbs heat energy radiated away from the surface of the earth, effectively trapping it in the atmosphere, much like the glass of a greenhouse
  e) bacterial degradation of fertilizers in a greenhouse environment produce large quantities of carbon dioxide

  Answer: d Page: 94

116. What mass of hydrogen can be produced by reaction of 4.73 g of magnesium with 1.83 g of water? Be sure to balance the reaction.

$$Mg + H_2O \rightarrow Mg(OH)_2 + H_2$$

  a) 0.102 g
  b) 0.0162 g
  c) 0.0485 g
  d) 0.219 g

  Answer: a Page: 94

117. What mass of silver chloride can be made by reaction of 4.22 g of silver nitrate with 7.73 g of aluminum chloride? Be sure to balance the reaction.

$$AgNO_3 + AlCl_3 \rightarrow Al(NO_3)_3 + AgCl$$

  a) 17.6 g
  b) 4.22 g
  c) 24.9 g
  d) 3.56 g

  Answer: d Page: 94

118. How many moes of magnesium oxide are produced by reaction of 3.82 g of magnesium nitride with 7.73 g of water? The reaction must be balanced.

$$Mg_3N_2 + H_2O \rightarrow NH_3 + MgO$$

  a) 0.114
  b) 0.0378
  c) 0.429
  d) 0.0756

  Answer: a Page: 94

119. If the reaction of 3.82 g of magnesium nitride with 7.73 g of water produced 3.60 g of magnesium oxide, what is the percent yield of this reaction?

$$Mg_3N_2 + H_2O \rightarrow NH_3 + MgO$$

a) 94.5%
b) 78.6%
c) 46.6%
d) 49.4%

Answer: b Page: 94

120. For $Fe(CO)_5 + 2PF_3 + H_2 \rightarrow Fe(CO)_2(PF_3)_2(H)_2 + 3CO$, how many moles of CO can form from a mixture of 5.0 mol $Fe(CO)_5$, 8.0 mol PF_3, and 6.0 mol H_2?

a) 15
b) 5.0
c) 24
d) 6.0
e) 12

Answer: e Page: 94

121. For $Ru_3(CO)_{12} + 9AsF_3 \rightarrow 3Ru(CO)_2(AsF_3)_3 + 6CO$, how many millimoles of $Ru(CO)_2(AsF_3)_3$ can form from a mixture of 2.0 mmol $Ru_3(CO)_{12}$ and 24 mmol AsF_3?

a) 2.0
b) 6.0
c) 12
d) 54
e) 8.0

Answer: b Page: 94

122. C_2H_4 burns in O_2 to produce CO_2 and H_2O according to the following equation.

$$C_2H_4 + 3O_2 \rightarrow 2CO_2 + 2H_2O$$

How many grams of CO_2 will be formed when 3.0 g of C_2H_4 reacts with 3.0 g of O_2?

a) 2.8
b) 4.1
c) 6.2
d) 9.4

Answer: a Page: 94

123. What is the maximum number of grams of NH_3 that can be produced by the reaction of 1.0 g of N_2 with 3.0 g of H_2 according to the following equation?

$$N_2 + 3H_2 \rightarrow 2NH_3$$

a) 2.0
b) 1.2
c) 0.61
d) 17

Answer: b Page: 94

124. Determine the number of grams of SO_3 that can be produced by the reaction of 1.0 g of S with 1.0 g of O_2 according to the equation shown.

$$2S(s) + 3O_2(g) \rightarrow 2SO_3(g)$$

a) 0.27
b) 1.7
c) 2.5
d) 3.8

Answer: b Page: 94

125. Calculate the number of grams of Al_2O_3 that could be produced if 2.5 g of aluminum and 2.5 g of oxygen were allowed to react according to the following balanced equation.

$$4Al(s) + 3O_2(g) \rightarrow 2Al_2O_3(s)$$

a) 9.4
b) 7.4
c) 4.7
d) 5.3

Answer: c Page: 94

126. How many grams of SF_6 could be produced by the reaction of 3.5 g of sulfur with 4.5 g of fluorine according to the following equation?

$$S + 3F_2 \rightarrow SF_6$$

a) 12
b) 3.2
c) 5.8
d) 16

Answer: c Page: 94

127. What is the maximum number of grams of Cu that could be produced by the reaction of 30.0 g of CuO and 20.0 g of CH_4?

$$4CuO + CH_4 \rightarrow 2H_2O + 4Cu + CO_2$$

a) 6.00
b) 24.0
c) 95.9
d) 318

Answer: b Page: 98

128. If the reaction of 2.5 g of aluminum with 2.5 g of oxygen produced 3.5 g of aluminum oxide, what is the percent yield of aluminum oxide?

$$4Al + 3O_2 \rightarrow 2Al_2O_3$$

a) 74%
b) 37%
c) 47%
d) 66%
e) 26%

Answer: a Page: 97

129. If the reaction of 1.0 g of sulfur with 1.0 g of oxygen according to the reaction below produced 0.80 g of sulfur trioxide, what is the percent yield of sulfur dioxide?

$$2S + 3O_2 \rightarrow 2SO_3$$

a) 30%
b) 296%
c) 21%
d) 88%
e) 47%

Answer: e Page: 97

130. The percent yield of sulfur hexafluoride in the reaction below is 79%. Calculate the theoretical yield of sulfur hexafluoride if 7.9 g of fluorine reacts with excess sulfur.

$$S + 3F_2 \rightarrow SF_6$$

a) 30. g
b) 10. g
c) 7.9 g
d) 24 g
e) 0.11 g

Answer: b Page: 97

131. The percent yield of sulfur hexafluoride in the reaction below is 79%. Calculate the actual yield of sulfur hexafluoride if 7.9 g of fluorine reacts with excess sulfur.

$$S + 3F_2 \rightarrow SF_6$$

a) 30. g
b) 10. g
c) 7.9 g
d) 24 g
e) 0.11 g

Answer: c Page: 97

132. What is the mass of 9.76×10^{12} atoms of sodium?
a) 22.99 g
b) 1.62×10^{-11} g
c) 3.73×10^{-10} g
d) 7.05×10^{-13} g

Answer: c Page: 82

133. How many moles of pyridine, C_5H_5N, are contained in 3.13 g of pyridine?
a) 0.0396 mol
b) 25.3 mol
c) 0.319 mol
d) 0.00404 mol

Answer: a Page: 82

134. How many oxygen atoms are contained in 2.74 g of $Al_2(SO_4)_3$?
a) 12
b) 6.02×10^{23}
c) 7.22×10^{24}
d) 5.78×10^{22}

Answer: d Page: 82

135. The total number of atoms in 0.111 mol of $Fe(CO)_3(PH_3)_2$ is
a) 15
b) 1.00×10^{2}
c) 4.46×10^{21}
d) 1.67
e) 2.76×10^{-24}

Answer: b Page: 82

136. A 1.29 g sample of a compound composed of C, H, and O was burned in oxygen. If 1.26 g of CO_2 and 0.258 g of water were produced, what is the percentage composition of the compound?
a) 34.4% C, 2.90% H, 92.0% O
b) 12.6% C, 25.8% H, 61.6% O
c) 26.7% C, 2.24% H, 71.3% O
d) 12.0% C, 72.0% H, 16.0% O

Answer: c Page: 89

Chapter 4: Aqueous Reactions and Solution Stoichiometry

MULTIPLE CHOICE

1. A homogeneous mixture consists of 12% ethanol, 38% methanol, 10% butanol, and 40% pentanol. The solvent in this mixture is
   a) ethanol
   b) methanol
   c) butanol
   d) pentanol
   e) water

   Answer: d Page: 107

SHORT ANSWER

2. What is the solvent in an aqueous solution?

   Answer: water Page: 107

MULTIPLE CHOICE

3. Which one of the following is a correct expression for molarity?
   a. mol solute/L solvent
   b. mol solute/mL solvent
   c. mmol solute/mL solution
   d. mol solute/kg solvent
   e. μmol solute/L solution

   Answer: c Page: 107

4. Which one of the following is not true concerning 2.00 L of 0.100 M $Ca_3(PO_4)_2$ solution?
   a) this solution contains 0.200 moles of $Ca_3(PO_4)_2$
   b) this solution contains 0.800 mole of oxygen atoms
   c) 1.00 L of this solution is required to furnish 0.300 mole of calcium atoms
   d) 500.0 mL of this solution contains 6.02×10^{22} phosphorus atoms

   Answer: b Page: 107

5. The temperature of a 0.847 M solution of NaBr was increased from 25°C to 40°C. What effect did this temperature change have on the molarity of NaBr in this solution?
   a) the molarity increased
   b) the molarity decreased
   c) the molarity did not change

   Answer: b Page: 107

6. What is the molarity of sodium ions in 4.57 L of 0.847 M Na_3P solution?
   a) 0.847 M
   b) 3.87 M
   c) 0.185 M
   d) 2.54 M

   Answer: d Page: 107

7. Which one of the following results in the formation of 0.200 M K_2SO_4 solution?
   a) dilution of 250.0 mL of 1.00 M K_2SO_4 to 1.00 L
   b) dissolving 43.6 g of K_2SO_4 in water and diluting to a total volume of 250.0 mL
   c) diluting 20.0 mL of 5.00 M K_2SO_4 solution to 500.0 mL
   d) dissolving 20.2 g of K_2SO_4 in water and diluting to 250.0 mL, then diluting 25.0 mL of this solution to a total volume of 500.0 mL

   Answer: c Page: 107

8. What is the molarity of NaCl in a solution made by mixing 25.0 mL of 0.100 M NaCl with 50.0 mL of 0.100 M NaCl?
   a) 0.100 M
   b) 0.0500 M
   c) 0.0333 M
   d) 0.0250 M

   Answer: a Page: 107

9. What is the molarity of CH_3OH in a solution prepared by dissolving 11.7 g of CH_3OH in 230 mL of solution?
   a) 11.9 M
   b) 1.59×10^{-3} M
   c) 0.0841 M
   d) 1.59 M

   Answer: d Page: 107

10. How many grams of H_3PO_4 are in 175 mL of a 3.5 M solution of H_3PO_4?
    a) 0.61
    b) 60
    c) 20
    d) 4.9

    Answer: b Page: 107

11. What is the molarity of a NaCl solution prepared by dissolving 9.3 g of NaCl in 350 mL of solution?
a) 18
b) 0.16
c) 0.46
d) 27

Answer: c Page: 107

12. How many grams of NaOH (MW = 40.0) are there in 500 mL of 0.175 M NaOH solution?
a) 2.19×10^{-3}
b) 114
c) 14.0
d) 3.50

Answer: d Page: 107

13. How many grams of CH_3OH would have to be added to water to prepare 150 mL of a solution that is 2.0 M CH_3OH?
a) 9.6×10^3
b) 4.3×10^2
c) 2.4
d) 9.6

Answer: d Page: 107

14. How many moles of Br^- are present in 0.500 L of 0.300 M $AlBr_3$?
a) 0.150
b) 0.0500
c) 0.450
d) 0.167
e) 0.500

Answer: c Page: 107

15. How many moles of Co^{2+} are present in 0.200 L of 0.400 M CoI_2?
a) 2.00
b) 0.500
c) 0.160
d) 0.0800
e) 0.0400

Answer: d Page: 107

16. How many moles of K^+ are present in 343 mL of 1.27 M K_3PO_4?
a) 0.436
b) 1.31
c) 0.145
d) 3.70
e) 11.1

Answer: b Page: 107

17. What are the respective molar concentrations of Fe^{3+} and I^- afforded by dissolving 0.200 mol FeI_3 in water and diluting to 725 mL?
a) 0.276 and 0.828
b) 0.828 and 0.276
c) 0.276 and 0.276
d) 0.145 and 0.435
e) 0.145 and 0.0483

Answer: a Page: 107

18. What are the respective molar concentrations of Na^+ and SO_4^{2-} afforded by dissolving 0.500 mol Na_2SO_4 in water and diluting to 1.33 L?
a) 0.665 and 0.665
b) 0.665 and 1.33
c) 1.33 and 0.665
d) 0.376 and 0.752
e) 0.752 and 0.376

Answer: e Page: 107

19. Calculate the molarity of sodium ions in a solution made by diluting 50.0 mL of 0.874 M sodium sulfide solution to a total volume of 250.0 mL.
a) 0.175 M
b) 4.37 M
c) 0.525 M
d) 0.350 M
e) 0.874 M

Answer: d Page: 110

20. Dilution causes ________ in the concentration of the solute in a solution.
a) an increase
b) a decrease
c) no change

Answer: b Page: 110

21. What is the concentration in M of an aqueous ethanol solution if 400 mL thereof diluted to 4.00 L affords a concentration of 0.0400 M?
a) 0.400
b) 0.200
c) 2.00
d) 1.60
e) 4.00

Answer: a Page: 110

22. What is the new concentration in M of aqueous methanol if 0.200 L of a 2.00 M solution thereof is diluted to 0.800 L?
a) 0.800
b) 0.200
c) 0.500
d) 0.400
e) 8.00

Answer: c Page: 110

23. What procedure should be used in diluting a concentrated acid or base in order to avoid spattering due to the intense heat generated?

Answer:
The acid or base should be added to water and then further diluted by adding more water.

Page: 111

24. Solutions are typically made or diluted in what piece of glassware?
a) pipet
b) buret
c) volumetric flask
d) beaker

Answer: c Page: 112

25. Which one of the following will not break into ions upon dissolving in water?
a) C_2H_6SO
b) KBr
c) Cs_3PO_3
d) WC_{16}
e) AIP

Answer: a Page: 113

SHORT ANSWER

26. Explain why water is a good solvent for ionic substances.

Answer:
The oxygen of water has a slight negative charge that is attracted to and surrounds the cation of the ionic substance, stabilizing it in solution. The hydrogens of water have a slight positive charge and thus are attracted to and surround the anion of the ionic substance stabilizing it in solution.

Page: 113

MULTIPLE CHOICE

27. Which one of the following is not an electrolyte?
a) HCl
b) Rb_2SO_4
c) Ar
d) KOH

Answer: c Page: 113

28. The reaction between strontium hydroxide and chloric acid produces
a) a molecular compound and a weak electrolyte
b) two weak electrolytes
c) two strong electrolytes
d) a molecular compound and a strong electrolyte
e) two molecular compounds

Answer: d Page: 118

29. A 0.100 M solution of which one of the following will contain the highest concentration of potassium ions?
a) potassium phosphite
b) potassium hydrogen carbonate
c) potassium hypochlorite
d) potassium iodide
e) potassium oxide

Answer: a Page: 114

30. For a substance to be considered a strong electrolyte, it must
a) be an ionic compound
b) dissociate virtually completely to its ions in solution
c) be highly soluble in water
d) contain both metal and nonmetal atoms

Answer: b Page: 115

SHORT ANSWER

31. What is the concentration of HCl in a 0.100 M solution of HCl? Why?

Answer:
Essentially zero because HCl is a strong electrolyte and will be virtually completely ionized in solution leaving no intact HCl molecules.

Page: 115

MULTIPLE CHOICE

32. Which one of the following is a diprotic acid?
a) nitric acid
b) chloric acid
c) phosphoric acid
d) hydrofluroric acid
e) sulfuric acid

Answer: e Page: 116

SHORT ANSWER

33. What ions should be present in a solution of sulfuric acid?

Answer:
H^+, HSO_4^-, and SO_4^{2-}

Page: 116

MULTIPLE CHOICE

34. The color of litmus is changed from ___ to ___ by base.
a) red, blue
b) blue, red
c) yellow, green
d) colorless, pink

Answer: a Page: 116

35. Which one of the following solutions will have the greatest concentration of hydroxide ions?
a) 0.100 M rubidium hydroxide
b) 0.100 M magnesium hydroxide
c) 0.100 M ammonia
d) 0.100 M beryllium hydroxide

Answer: a Page: 117

36. Which one of the following is a weak acid?
    a) HNO_3
    b) HCl
    c) HI
    d) HF
    e) $HClO_4$

    Answer: d Page: 117

37. The hydroxide of which of the following is a weak base?
    a) magnesium
    b) calcium
    c) barium
    d) strontium

    Answer: a Page: 117

38. $Ca(OH)_2$ is a
    a) strong base
    b) weak base
    c) strong acid
    d) weak acid

    Answer: a Page: 117

39. $HClO_4$ is a
    a) strong base
    b) weak base
    c) strong acid
    d) weak acid

    Answer: c Page: 117

40. HNO_2 is a
    a) strong base
    b) weak base
    c) strong acid
    d) weak acid

    Answer: d Page: 117

41. NH_4Cl is a
    a) strong base
    b) weak base
    c) strong acid
    d) weak acid

    Answer: d Page: 117

SHORT ANSWER

42. Write the net ionic equation for the reaction between an acid and a metal hydroxide.

Answer: $H^+ + OH^- \rightarrow H_2O$ Page: 120

MULTIPLE CHOICE

43. What are the spectator ions in the reaction between KOH and HNO_3?
a) K^+ and H^+
b) H^+ and OH^-
c) K^+ and $NO^-{}_3$
d) H^+ and $NO^-{}_3$

Answer: c Page: 120

44. The net ionic equation for the reaction between aqueous solutions of HF and KOH is
a) $HF + KOH \rightarrow H_2O + K^+ + F^-$
b) $HF + OH^- \rightarrow H_2O + F^-$
c) $HF + K^+ + OH^- \rightarrow H_2O + KF$
d) $H^+ + OH^- \rightarrow H_2O$
e) $H^+ + F^- + K^+ + OH^- \rightarrow H_2O + K^+ + F^-$

Answer: b Page: 120

45. Which ion(s) is/are spectator ions in the formation of a precipitate of $BaSO_4$ via combining aqueous solutions of BaI_2 and K_2SO_4?
a) Ba^{2+} only
b) K^+ only
c) Ba^{2+} and $SO_4{}^{2-}$
d) K^+ and I^-
e) $SO_4{}^{2-}$ and I^-

Answer: d Page: 120

46. Which ion(s) is/are spectator ions in the formation of a precipitate of AgBr via combining aqueous solutions of $CoBr_2$ and $AgNO_3$?
a) Co^{2+} and $NO_3{}^-$
b) $NO_3{}^-$ and Br^-
c) Co^{2+} and Ag^+
d) Br^-
e) $NO_3{}^-$

Answer: a Page: 120

47. The balanced net ionic equation for precipitation of $CaCO_3$ when aqueous solutions of Li_2CO_3 and $CaCl_2$ are mixed is
a) $2Li^+(aq) + CO_3^{2-}(aq) \rightarrow Li_2CO_3(aq)$
b) $2Li^+(aq) + 2Cl^-(aq) \rightarrow 2LiCl(aq)$
c) $Li^+(aq) + Cl^-(aq) \rightarrow LiCl(aq)$
d) $Ca^{2+}(aq) + CO_3^{2-}(aq) \rightarrow CaCO_3(s)$
e) $Li_2CO_3(aq) + CaCl_2(aq) \rightarrow 2LiCl(aq) + CaCO_3(s)$

Answer: d Page: 120

48. The balanced net ionic equation for precipitation of AgI when aqueous solutions of $AgNO_3$ and NaI are mixed is
a) $Ag^+(aq) + I^-(aq) \rightarrow AgI(s)$
b) $Ag^+(aq) + NO_3^-(aq) \rightarrow AgNO_3(s)$
c) $Ag^+(aq) + NO_3^-(aq) \rightarrow AgNO_3(aq)$
d) $AgNO_3(aq) + NaI(aq) \rightarrow AgI(s) + NaNO_3(aq)$
e) $AgNO_3(aq) + NaI(aq) \rightarrow AgI(aq) + NaNO_3(s)$

Answer: a Page: 120

49. The balanced molecular equation for precipitation of AgI when aqueous solutions of $AgNO_3$ and NaI are mixed is
a) $AgNO_3(aq) + NaI(aq) \rightarrow AgI(s) + NaNO_3(aq)$
b) $AgNO_3(aq) + NaI(aq) \rightarrow AgI(aq) + NaNO_3(s)$
c) $AgNO_3(s) + NaI(s) \rightarrow AgI(aq) + NaNO_3(aq)$
d) $AgNO_3(aq) + NaI(aq) \rightarrow AgI(s) + NaNO_3(s)$
e) $AgNO_3(s) + NaI(s) \rightarrow AgI(s) + NaNO_3(aq)$

Answer: a Page: 120

50. The balanced net ionic equation for complete neutralization of H_2SO_4 by KOH in aqueous solution is
a) $SO_4^{2-}(aq) + 2K^+(aq) \rightarrow K_2SO_4(aq)$
b) $SO_4^{2-}(aq) + 2K^+(aq) \rightarrow K_2SO_4(s)$
c) $2H^+(aq) + 2OH^-(aq) \rightarrow 2H_2O(l)$
d) $H_2SO_4(aq) + 2OH^-(aq) \rightarrow 2H_2O(l) + SO_4^{2-}(aq)$
e) $2H^+(aq) + 2KOH(aq) \rightarrow 2H_2O(l) + 2K^+(aq)$

Answer: c Page: 120

51. The balanced molecular equation for complete neutralization of H_2SO_4 by KOH in aqueous solution is
a) $2H^+(aq) + 2OH^-(aq) \rightarrow 2H_2O(l)$
b) $2H^+(aq) + 2KOH(aq) \rightarrow 2H_2O(l) + 2K^+(aq)$
c) $H_2SO_4(aq) + 2OH^-(aq) \rightarrow 2H_2O(l) + SO_4^{2-}(aq)$
d) $H_2SO_4(aq) + 2KOH(aq) \rightarrow 2H_2O(l) + K_2SO_4(s)$
e) $H_2SO_4(aq) + 2KOH(aq) \rightarrow 2H_2O(l) + K_2SO_4(aq)$

Answer: e Page: 120

52. Aqueous sodium chloride will react with which one of the following in a metathesis reaction?
a) calcium nitrate
b) potassium bromide
c) lead nitrate
d) barium nitrate

Answer: c Page: 120

53. Which one of the following forms an insoluble bromide, iodide, and sulfate but a soluble chloride?
a) Ag^+
b) Hg^{2+}
c) Hg_2^{2+}
d) Pb^{2+}

Answer: b Page: 120

54. The formation of which one of the compounds below will act as the driving force for metathesis reactions?
a) $HC_2H_3O_2$
b) $MgCl_2$
c) $NaNO_3$
d) KOH

Answer: a Page: 120

55. A solid was found to be highly soluble in water. Treating separate portions of a solution of this solid with NaCl, NaBr, NaI, Na_2SO_4, Na_2CO_3, Na_3PO_4, NaOH, and Na_2S produced no precipitates. Treatment of an aqueous solution of this solid with acid resulted in the formation of the foul smelling gas, H_2S. This solid was
a) $Pb(No_3)_2$
b) $(NH_4)_2S$
c) KBr
d) Li_2CO_3

Answer: b Page: 120

56. A compound was found to be soluble in water. It was also found that addition of acid to an aqueous solution of this compound resulted in the formation of carbon dioxide. Which one of the following cations would form a precipitate when added to an aqueous solution of this compound?
a) NH^+_4
b) K^+
c) Cr^{3+}
d) Rb^+
e) Na^+

Answer: c Page: 120

57. A solid, X, was found to be water soluble. An aqueous solution of this solid evolved bubbles of CO_2 when HCl was added. An aqueous solution of which one of the following salts would form a precipitate when added to an aqueous solution of X?
a) K^+
b) Ag^+
c) $NH^+{}_4$
d) Rb^+
e) Li^+

Answer: b Page: 120

58. The balanced net ionic equation for formation of an aqueous solution of NiI_2 accompanied by evolution of CO_2 gas via mixing solid $NiCO_3$ and aqueous hydriodic acid is
a) $2NiCO_3(s) + HI(aq) \rightarrow 2H_2O(l) + CO_2(g) + 2Ni^{2+}(aq)$
b) $NiCO_3(s) + I^-(aq) \rightarrow 2H_2O(l) + CO_2(g) + Ni^{2+}(aq) + HI(aq)$
c) $NiCO_3(s) + 2H^+(aq) \rightarrow H_2O(l) + CO_2(g) + Ni^{2+}(aq)$
d) $NiCO_3(s) + 2HI(aq) \rightarrow 2H_2O(l) + CO_2(g) + NiI_2(aq)$
e) $NiCO_3(s) + 2HI(aq) \rightarrow H_2O(l) + CO_2(g) + Ni^{2+}(aq) + 2I^-(aq)$

Answer: c Page: 120

59. The balanced net ionic equation for formation of an aqueous solution of $Al(NO_3)_3$ via mixing solid $Al(OH)_3$ and aqueous nitric acid is
a) $Al(OH)_3(s) + 3HNO_3(aq) \rightarrow 3H_2O(l) + Al(NO_3)_3(aq)$
b) $Al(OH)_3(s) + 3NO_3^-(aq) \rightarrow 3OH^-(aq) + Al(NO_3)_3(aq)$
c) $Al(OH)_3(s) + 3NO_3^-(aq) \rightarrow 3OH^-(aq) + Al(NO_3)_3(s)$
d) $Al(OH)_3(s) + 3H^+(aq) \rightarrow 3H_2O(l) + Al^{3+}(aq)$
e) $Al(OH)_3(s) + 3HNO_3(aq) \rightarrow 3H_2O(l) + Al^{3+}(aq) + NO_3^-(aq)$

Answer: d Page: 120

60. Which one of the following cannot act as a driving force for a matathesis reaction?
a) formation of a weak electrolyte
b) formation of a gas
c) formation of a molecular compound
d) formation of an insoluble compound
e) formation of a soluble, strong electrolyte

Answer: e Page: 121

61. Which of the following is very soluble in water at 25° C?
a) $Fe_3(PO_4)_2$
b) $Fe(OH)_2$
c) $Fe(NO_3)_2$
d) $FeCO_3$
e) FeS

Answer: c Page: 122

62. Solubility rules predict precipitate formation for mixing 0.1 M aqueous solutions of
    a) $NiBr_2$ and $AgNO_3$
    b) NaI and KBr
    c) K_2SO_4 and $CrCl_3$
    d) KOH and $Ba(NO_3)_2$
    e) Li_2CO_3 and CsI

    Answer: a Page: 122

63. Which one of the following compounds is insoluble in water?
    a) Na_2CO_3
    b) K_2SO_4
    c) $Fe(NO_3)_3$
    d) ZnS

    Answer: d Page: 122

64. Which one of the following will not result in the formation of a gas?
    a) adding acid to a sulfate
    b) adding acid to a nitrate
    c) adding base to a sulfide
    d) adding base to a sulfite
    e) adding base to an ammonium salt

    Answer: e Page: 126

65. Which one of the following is true concerning antacids?
    a) those containing aluminum hydroxide cause diarrhea
    b) those containing magnesium hydroxide cause constipation
    c) those containing calcium hydroxide cause an increase in acid production after absorbtion
    d) they act to decrease acid production in the stomach
    e) Milk of magnesia contains both magnesium and aluminum hydroxides

    Answer: c Page: 128

66. An example of an oxidation is
    a) ice melting in a soft drink
    b) table salt dissolving in water for cooking vegetables
    c) rusting of iron
    d) the reaction of sodium chloride with lead nitrate to form lead chloride and sodium nitrate

    Answer: c Page: 129

67. When zinc reacts with sulfuric acid, the zinc is oxidized and dissolves. What is reduced and what is the product of that reaction?
a) sulfate, $S_4O_6^{2-}$
b) sulfur, elemental sulfur
c) oxygen in sulfate, elemental oxygen
d) hydrogen in sulfuric acid, elemental hydrogen

Answer: d Page: 129

68. Of the choices below, which would be the best for the lining of a tank intended for use in storage of hydrochloric acid?
a) copper
b) zinc
c) nickel
d) iron
e) tin
f) cobalt

Answer: a Page: 131

69. One method for removal of metal ions from a solution is to convert the metal to its elemental form so it can be filtered out as a solid. Which metal can be used to remove aluminum ions from solution?
a) zinc
b) cobalt
c) lead
d) copper
e) nickel
f) none of these

Answer: f Page: 131

70. An aqueous solution of nickel ions will oxidize each of the following metals except
a) aluminum
b) chromium
c) barium
d) tin
e) potassium

Answer: d Page: 131

71. Which one of the following will produce hydrogen gas?
a) Cu + HNO_3
b) Co + HCl
c) Ag + HCl
d) Hg + HCl

Answer: b Page: 131

72. Based on the activity series, which reaction below will not occur?
a) $Mg(s) + 2HCl(aq) \rightarrow MgCl_2(aq) + H_2(g)$
b) $2Ag(s) + 2HNO_3(aq) \rightarrow 2AgNO_3(aq) + H_2(g)$
c) $2Ni(s) + H_2SO_4(aq) \rightarrow Ni_2SO_4(aq) + H_2(g)$
d) $2Al(s) + 6HBr(aq) \rightarrow 2AlBr_3(aq) + 3H_2(g)$
e) $Zn(s) + 2HI(aq) \rightarrow ZnI_2(aq) + H_2(g)$

Answer: b Page: 131

73. Based on the activity series, which reaction below will occur?
a) $Zn(s) + MnI_2(aq) \rightarrow ZnI_2(aq) + Mn(s)$
b) $SnCl_2(aq) + Cu(s) \rightarrow Sn(s) + CuCl_2(aq)$
c) $2AgNO_3(aq) + Pb(s) \rightarrow 2Ag(s) + Pb(NO_3)_2(aq)$
d) $3Hg(l) + 2Cr(NO_3)_3(aq) \rightarrow 3Hg(NO_3)_2 + 2Cr(s)$
e) $3FeBr_2(aq) + 2Au(s) \rightarrow 3Fe(s) + 2AuBr_3(aq)$

Answer: c Page: 131

74. The balanced net ionic equation for the dissolution of zinc metal in aqueous hydrobromic acid is
a) $Zn(s) + 2Br^-(aq) \rightarrow ZnBr_2(aq)$
b) $Zn(s) + 2HBr(aq) \rightarrow ZnBr_2(aq) + 2H^+(aq)$
c) $Zn(s) + 2HBr(aq) \rightarrow ZnBr_2(s) + 2H^+(aq)$
d) $Zn(s) + 2H^+(aq) \rightarrow Zn^{2+}(aq) + H_2(g)$
e) $2Zn(s) + H^+(aq) \rightarrow 2Zn^{2+}(aq) + H_2(g)$

Answer: d Page: 131

75. Which one of the following elements is <u>most</u> easily oxidized?
a) O
b) F
c) N
d) Al

Answer: d Page: 131

76. Which of these metals is the <u>least</u> easily oxidized?
a) Na
b) Au
c) Fe
d) Ca

Answer: b Page: 131

77. Based on the equations below, which metal is the most active?

$$Pb(NO_3)_2(aq) + Ni(s) \rightarrow Ni(NO_2)_2(aq) + (Pb(s)$$

$$Pb(NO_3)_2(aq) + Ag(s) \rightarrow \text{No reaction}$$

$$Cu(NO_3)_2(aq) + Ag(s) \rightarrow \text{No reaction}$$

a) Ni
b) Ag
c) Cu
d) Pb

Answer: a Page: 131

78. Consider the following reactions.

$$AgNO_3(aq) + Zn(s) \rightarrow Ag(s) + Zn(NO_3)_2$$

$$Zn(NO_3)_2(aq) + Co(s) \rightarrow \text{No reaction}$$

$$AgNO_3(aq) + Co(s) \rightarrow Co(NO_3)_2(aq) + Ag(s)$$

Which is the correct order of increasing activity for these metals?

a) Ag < Zn < Co
b) Co < Ag < Zn
c) Co < Zn < Ag
d) Ag < Co < Zn

Answer: d Page: 131

79. Zinc is more active than cobalt and iron but less active than aluminum. Cobalt is more active than nickel but less active than iron. Which of the following correctly lists the elements in order of increasing activity?

a) Co < Ni < Fe < Zn < Al
b) Ni < Fe < Co < Zn < Al
c) Ni < Co < Fe < Zn < Al
d) Fe < Ni < Co < Al < Zn

Answer: c Page: 131

80. When copper is reacted with nitric acid, the copper is oxidized to Cu^{2+}. What is reduced in this reaction and what is formed from it?
a. Cu, Cu^{2+}
b. H^+, H_2
c. NO_3^-, NO_2
d. H_2O, H_2

Answer: c Page: 133

81. Nitric acid will dissolve copper even though hydrochloric acid will not because
    a) oxidation of copper by HCl would result in the formation of copper chloride which is soluble, so there is no driving force for the reaction
    b) nitric acid is less viscous than HCl and so contacts the surface of the copper better
    c) the copper very rapidly reacts with the HCl to form an insulating layer of $CuCl_2$ on the surface of the metal that protects it from oxidation
    d) hydrogen ions are not strong enough oxidizing agents but the nitrate ions in nitric acid are

    Answer: d Page: 133

82. What volume of 0.827 M KOH solution is required to completely neutralize 35.00 mL of 0.737 M H_2SO_4? solution?
    a) 35.0 mL
    b) 1.12 mL
    c) 25.8 mL
    d) 62.4 mL
    e) 39.3 mL

    Answer: d Page: 133

83. Calculate the concentration of arsenic acid, H_3AsO_4, in a solution if 25.00 mL of that solution required 35.21 mL of 0.1894 M KOH for titration.
    a) 0.2668 M
    b) 0.8003 M
    c) 0.08892 M
    d) 0.1345 M

    Answer: c Page: 133

84. Calculate the concentration of mercury(1) ions, Hg_2^{2+}, in a solution given that 30.00 mL of that solution required 43.23 mL of 0.8283 M NaCl for titration.
    a) 1.194 M
    b) 0.5968 M
    c) 0.2984 M
    d) 2.387 M

    Answer: b Page: 133

85. Calculate the percent of oxalic acid, $H_2C_2O_4$, in a solid given that a 0.7984 g sample of that solid required 37.98 mL of 0.2283 M NaOH for titration.
a) 48.89%
b) 97.78%
c) 28.59%
d) 1.086%

Answer: a Page: 133

86. How many moles of $BaCl_2$ are formed via complete neutralization of 393 mL of 0.171 M $Ba(OH)_2$ with aqueous HCl?
a) 0.0672
b) 0.0336
c) 0.134
d) 2.30
e) 1.15

Answer: a Page: 133

87. How many grams of AgBr are formed when 35.5 mL of 0.184 M $AgNO_3$ is treated with an excess of aqueous hydrobromic acid?
a) 1.44
b) 1.23
c) 53.6
d) 34.5
e) 188

Answer: b Page: 133

88. How many grams of CaF_2 are formed when 47.8 mL of 0.334 M NaF is treated with an excess of aqueous calcium(II) nitrate?
a) 1.25
b) 0.472
c) 2.49
d) 0.943
e) 0.623

Answer: e Page: 133

89. A 17.5 mL sample of acetic acid (CH_3CO_2H) required 29.6 mL of 0.250 M NaOH to neutralize it. What was the molarity of the acetic acid solution?
a) 0.15
b) 0.42
c) 130
d) 6.8

Answer: b Page: 133

90. How many mL of 0.135 M NaOH would be required to neutralize 13.7 mL of 0.129 M HCl?
a) 13.1
b) 0.24
c) 14.3
d) 0.076

Answer: a Page: 133

91. Determine the number of liters of 0.250 M HNO_3 required to neutralize a solution prepared by dissolving 17.5 g of NaOH in 350 mL of solution.
a) 50.0
b) 0.44
c) 1.75
d) 0.070

Answer: c Page: 133

92. A 28.7 mL sample of KOH required 31.3 mL of 0.118 M HCl to neutralize it. How many grams of KOH were in the original sample?
a) 1.6
b) 7.2
c) 0.17
d) 0.21

Answer: b Page: 133

SHORT ANSWER

93. What is aqua regia?

Answer: a 3:1 mixture of concentrated hydrochloric and nitric acids

Page: 133

MULTIPLE CHOICE

94. When gold dissolves in aqua regia, what is reduced?
a) H^+
b) NO
c) Cl^-
d) H_2O
e) Au

Answer: b Page: 133

SHORT ANSWER

95. When gold dissolves in aqua regia, into what form is the gold converted?

Answer:

$AuCl_4^-$

Page: 133

MULTIPLE CHOICE

96. The point in a titration at which the indicator changes is called the
    a) equivalence point
    b) indicator point
    c) standard point
    d) end point
    e) volumetric point

    Answer: d Page: 136

97. Which one of the following would require the largest amount of 0.100 M sodium hydroxide solution for neutralization?
    a) 10.0 mL of 0.0500 M phosphoric acid
    b) 20.0 mL of 0.0500 M nitric acid
    c) 5.0 mL of 0.0100 M sulfuric acid
    d) 15.0 mL of 0.0500 M hydrobromic acid
    e) 10.0 mL of 0.0500 M perchloric acid

    Answer: a Page: 133

98. Which one of the following substances is produced during the reaction of an acid with a metal hydroxide?
    a) H_2
    b) H_2O
    c) CO_2
    d) NaOH

    Answer: b Page: 123

Chapter 5: Energy Relationships in Chemistry: Thermochemistry

MULTIPLE CHOICE

1. Which one of the following will have a greater kinetic energy?
   a) a 10 kg object traveling at 5 m/s
   b) a 5 kg object traveling at 10 m/s
   c) both of these have the same kinetic energy

   Answer: b Page: 146

2. Calculate the kinetic energy in J of an electron (mass = 9.11×10^{-28} kg) moving at 6.00×10^{6} m/s.
   a) 4.98×10^{-48}
   b) 3.28×10^{-14}
   c) 1.64×10^{-14}
   d) 2.49×10^{-48}
   e) 6.56×10^{-14}

   Answer: c Page: 146

3. Determine the kinetic energy of an automobile weighing 2135 pounds traveling at 55 mph. (1 mile = 5280 ft)
   a) 1.2×10^{4} J
   b) 2.9×10^{5} J
   c) 5.9×10^{5} J
   d) 3.2×10^{6} J

   Answer: b Page: 146

4. Calculate the kinetic energy of a 7.3 kg steel ball traveling at 18.0 m/s.
   a) 1.2×10^{3} J
   b) 66 J
   c) 2.4×10^{3} J
   d) 1.3×10^{2} J

   Answer: a Page: 146

5. Calculate the kinetic energy of a 150 lb jogger (68.1 kg) traveling at 12.0 mile/hr (5.36 m/s).
   a) 1.96×10^{3} J
   b) 365 J
   c) 978 J
   d) 183 J

   Answer: c Page: 146

6. Determine the kinetic energy (in J) of an 80 g bullet traveling at 300 m/s.
   a) 3.6×10^6
   b) 1.2×10^4
   c) 3.6×10^3
   d) 12

   Answer: c Page: 146

7. Work equals force _____ distance.
   a) plus
   b) times
   c) minus
   d) divided by

   Answer: b Page: 146

SHORT ANSWER

8. Define energy.

   Answer: Energy is the capacity to do work or to transfer heat.

   Page: 146

MULTIPLE CHOICE

9. What type of energy is chemical energy?
   a) kinetic
   b) potential

   Answer: b Page: 146

10. One Joule equals
   a) $1\ kg \cdot m^2/s^2$
   b) 2 kg
   c) 4.184 cal
   d) $1\ g \cdot cm/s$
   e) none of these

   Answer: a Page: 147

11. At what velocity must a 20.0 g object be moving in order to possess a kinetic energy of 1.00 J?
   a) 1 m/s
   b) 100 m/s
   c) 10 m/s
   d) 1000 m/s
   e) 50 m/s

   Answer: c Page: 147

12. According to the first law of thermodynamics
    a) all spontaneous processes are accompanied by an increase in disorder
    b) energy is conserved during any process
    c) the entropy of a pure, crystalline substance at absolute zero is zero
    d) the amount of work done during a change is independent of the pathway of that change
    e) none of these

    Answer: b Page: 147

SHORT ANSWER

13. What type of system can exchange energy with the surroundings but cannot exchange matter with the surroundings?

    Answer: A closed system Page: 148

MULTIPLE CHOICE

14. Which one of the following is false concerning internal energy, ΔE ?
    a. it is a state function
    b. it can be measured exactly
    c. $\Delta E = E_{final} - E_{initial}$
    d. $\Delta E = q + w$
    e. when a system undergoes a process in which it gains energy from the surrounding, the ΔE for the process is positive

    Answer: b Page: 148

15. What is the ΔE of a system that releases 12.4 J of heat and does 4.2 J of work on the surroundings?
    a) 16.6 J
    b) 12.4 J
    c) 4.2 J
    d) -16.6 J
    e) -8.2 J

    Answer: d Page: 148

16. Consider a balloon that was left in a car with newspaper strewn on top of it. As the car heats up, the balloon expands and pushes the newspapers up. In this process what is the sign of q?
    a) +
    b) -

    Answer: a Page: 148

17. Consider a balloon that was left in a car with newspaper strewn on top of it. As the car heats up, the balloon expands and pushes the newspapers up. In this process what is the sign of w?
a) +
b) -

Answer: b Page: 148

18. Calculate the value of ΔE for a system that performs 213 kJ of work on its surroundings and loses 79 kJ of heat?
a) +292 kJ
b) -292 kJ
c) +134 kJ
d) -134 kJ
e) -213 kJ

Answer: b Page: 148

19. The energy of a system can be increased by
a) adding heat to the system
b) having the system do work on the surroundings
c) withdrawing heat from the system
d) adding heat to the system and having the system do work on the surroundings

Answer: a Page: 148

20. Which one of the following conditions would always result in an increase in ΔE for a system?
a) the system loses heat and does work on the surroundings
b) the system gains heat and does work on the surroundings
c) the system loses heat and has work done on it by the surroundings
d) the system gains heat and has work done on it by the surroundings

Answer: d Page: 148

21. Calculate the value of ΔE for a system that loses 50 J of heat and has 150 J of work performed on it by the surroundings.
a) 50 J
b) 100 J
c) -100 J
d) -200 J

Answer: b Page: 148

22. Which of the following changes always results in a negative ΔE?
a) the system absorbs heat and does work
b) the system gives off heat and does work
c) the system absorbs heat and has work done on it
d) the system gives off heat and has work done on it

Answer: b Page: 148

23. Which one of the following is not an endothermic process?
    a) ice melting
    b) water evaporating
    c) boiling soup
    d) condensation of water vapor

    Answer: d Page: 149

24. Of the following, which one is a state function?
    a) H
    b) q
    c) w
    d) none of these

    Answer: a Page: 150

25. The energy change of a system occurring at constant pressure is given by _____ and the energy change of a system occurring at constant volume is given by _____.
    a) ΔH, ΔE
    b) ΔE, ΔH
    c) ΔH, ΔH
    d) ΔE, ΔE

    Answer: a Page: 151

26. In which type of process does the enthalpy of a system increase?
    a) endothermic
    b) exothermic

    Answer: a Page: 152

27. Which one of the following is true concerning enthalpy?
    a) it is an intensive property, always having the units energy per mole
    b) it usually is largely different in magnitude than the internal energy of a process
    c) it is a state function
    d) it is measured under conditions of constant volume
    e) the enthalpy change of a reaction is the inverse of the enthalpy change of the reverse reaction

    Answer: c Page: 152

28. A chemical reaction that absorbs heat from the surroundings is said to be __________ and has a ________ value of ΔH.
    a) endothermic, positive
    b) endothermic, negative
    c) exothermic, negative
    d) exothermic, positive

    Answer: a Page: 152

29. Which one of the following processes is endothermic?
a) $2H_2(g) + O_2(g) \rightarrow 2H_2O(g)$
b) $H_2O(g) \rightarrow H_2O(l)$
c) $CH_4(g) + 2O_2(g) \rightarrow CO_2(g) + 2H_2O(g)$
d) $H_2O(s) \rightarrow H_2O(l)$

Answer: d Page: 152

30. Which one of the following changes will have a positive value of $\Delta H°$?
a) $CO_2(s) \rightarrow CO_2(g)$
b) $C(s) + O_2(g) \rightarrow CO_2(g)$
c) $2H_2O(l) \rightarrow 2H_2(g) + O_2(g)$
d) $NH_3(l) \rightarrow 2H_2(g) + O_2(g)$

Answer: c Page: 152

31. Which one of the following reactions has a negative value for $\Delta H°$?
a) $CO_2(s) \rightarrow CO_2(g)$
b) $C(s) + O_2(g) \rightarrow CO_2(g)$
c) $2H_2O(l) \rightarrow 2H_2(g) + O_2(g)$
d) $NH_3(l) \rightarrow 2H_2(g) + O_2(g)$

Answer: b Page: 152

32. $2Al(s) + 3O_2(g) \rightarrow 2Al_2O_3(s)$ $\Delta H° = -3351$ kJ

The reaction shown above is _______ and therefore heat is _______ by the reaction.
a) endothermic, evolved
b) endothermic, absorbed
c) exothermic, evolved
d) exothermic, absorbed

Answer: c Page: 152

33. For the hypothetical reaction $3X_2(g) \rightarrow 2X_3(g)$, $\Delta H°$ is -333 kJ and the atomic weight of X is 66.6 amu. ΔH for conversion of 11.1 g of X_3 gas into X_2 gas in kJ is
a) -2.00 kJ
b) +2.00 kJ
c) -333 kJ
d) +9.25 kJ
e) -9.25 kJ

Answer: d Page: 154

34. The value of $\Delta H°$ for the following reaction is -72 kJ. How many kJ of heat will be evolved when 1.0 mole of HBr is formed in this reaction?

$$H_2(g) + Br_2(g) \rightarrow 2HBr(g)$$

a) 144
b) 72
c) 0.44
d) 36

Answer: d Page: 154

35. The value of $\Delta H°$ for the following reaction is -126 kJ. How much heat will be evolved when 2.00 mol of $NaOH_{(s)}$ is formed in the reaction?

$$2Na_2O_2(s) + 2H_2O(l) \rightarrow 4NaOH(s) + O_2(g)$$

a) 252 kJ
b) 63 kJ
c) 3.9 kJ
d) 7.8 kJ

Answer: b Page: 154

36. The value of $\Delta H°$ for the following reaction is -126 kJ. Determine the amount of heat (in kJ) that would be evolved by the reaction of 25.0 g of Na_2O_2 with water.

$$2Na_2O_2(s) + 2H_2O(l) \rightarrow 4NaOH(s) + O_2(g)$$

a) 20.2
b) 40.4
c) 67.5
d) 80.8

Answer: a Page: 154

37. The value of ΔH for the following reaction is -790 kJ. What is the enthalpy change (in kJ) accompanying the reaction of 0.95 g of S according to this equation?

$$2S(s) + 3O_2(g) \rightarrow 2SO_3(g)$$

a) 23
b) -23
c) -12
d) 12

Answer: c Page: 154

38. The value of ΔH° for the following reaction is -6535 kJ. How many kJ of heat will be evolved during the combustion of 16.0 g of $C_6H_6(l)$?

$$2C_6H_6(l) + 15O_2(g) \rightarrow 12CO_2(g) + 6H_2O(l)$$

a) 1.34×10^3
b) 5.23×10^4
c) 670
d) 2.68×10^3

Answer: c Page: 154

39. The value of ΔH° for the following reaction is -482 kJ. Determine the amount of heat (in kJ) exchanged with the surroundings when 12.0 g of CO(g) completely reacts.

$$2CO(g) + O_2(g) \rightarrow 2CO_2(g)$$

a) 2.89×10^3
b) 207
c) 103
d) 65.7

Answer: c Page: 154

40. The value of ΔH° for the following reaction is -336 kJ. Determine the amount of heat (in kJ) exchanged with the surroundings when 23.0 g of HCl is formed.

$$CH_4(g) + 3Cl_2(g) \rightarrow CHCl_3(l) + 3HCl(g)$$

a) 177
b) 2.57×10^3
c) 70.7
d) 211

Answer: c Page: 154

41. The value of ΔH° for the following reaction is -186 kJ. How many kJ of heat would be evolved from the reaction of 25 g of Cl_2?

$$H_2(g) + Cl_2(g) \rightarrow 2HCl(g)$$

a) 65
b) 5.3×10^2
c) 33
d) 47

Answer: a Page: 154

42. The value of $\Delta H°$ for the following reaction is -186 kJ. Calculate the value of $\Delta H_f°$ (in kJ/mol) for HCl(g).

$$H_2(g) + Cl_2(g) \rightarrow 2HCl(g)$$

a) -3.72×10^2
b) -1.27×10^2
c) -93.0
d) -186

Answer: c Page: 154

43. $2\ Al(s)\ 3O_2(g) \rightarrow 2Al_2O_3(s)$ $\Delta H° = -3351$ kJ

What would $\Delta H°$ (in kJ) be for the formation of 75.0 g of $Al_2O_3(s)$?
a) -2.51×10^5
b) -1.26×10^5
c) -2464
d) -1232

Answer: d Page: 154

44. $2Al(s) + 3O_2(g) \rightarrow 2Al_2O_3(s)$ $\Delta H° = -3351$ kJ

Determine the value of $\Delta H_f°$ (in kJ) for $Al_2O_3(s)$.

a) -3351
b) -1676
c) -32.86
d) -16.43

Answer: b Page: 154

45. An object initially at 25°C absorbed 382 J of heat and experienced a temperature increase. Of the choices below for the final temperature of the object, which one would indicate the object with the greatest heat capacity?
a) 45°C
b) 36°C
c) 79°C
d) 91°C

Answer: b Page: 157

46. If the molar heat capacity of a compound with the formula C_2H_6SO is 88.0 J/mol•K, what is the specific heat of this substance?
a) 88.0 J/g•K
b) 1.13 J/g•K
c) 4.89 J/g•K
d) 6.88×10^3 J/g•K

Answer: b Page: 157

47. A sample of aluminum absorbed 9.86 J of heat and its temperature increased from 23.2°C to 30.5°C. What was the mass of the aluminum sample? The specific heat of aluminum is 0.90 J/g·K.
a) 72 g
b) 1.5 g
c) 65 g
d) 8.1 g
e) 6.6 g

Answer: b Page: 157

48. $\Delta H°$ for $HCl(aq) + KOH(aq) \rightarrow H_2O(l) + KCl(aq)$ is -56.0 kJ.
If the specific heat of the solution resulting from neutralization of 50.0 mL of 0.220 M HCl with 0.400 M KOH is 4.18 J/g· °C and its density is assumed to be 1.01 g/mL, what is the final solution temperature if the initial temperature is 22.2°C?
a) 3.4°C
b) 36.9°C
c) 24.1°C
d) 27.8°C
e) 41.1°C

Answer: c Page: 157

49. An iron sphere of diameter 4.00 cm and density 7.86 g/cm^3 at 20.0°C is dropped into a perfectly insulated beaker containing 90.0 g of H_2O at 50.0°C. [$V = (4/3)\pi r^3$.] The respective specific heats of Fe and H_2O are 0.45 and 4.18 J/g· °C. What is the final temperature in °C of the iron sphere?
a) 7
b) 73
c) 29
d) 48
e) 43

Answer: c Page: 157

50. The heat capacity of lead is 0.13 J/g· °C. How many joules of heat would be required to raise the temperature of 15 g of lead from 22°C to 37°C?
a) 2.0
b) -0.13
c) 5.8×10^{-4}
d) 29

Answer: d Page: 157

51. When 72 g of a metal at 97.0°C is added to 100 g of water at 25.0°C, the final temperature is found to be 29.1°C. What is the heat capacity per gram of the metal? (Heat capacity of H_2O = 4.184 J/g• °C)
   a) 0.46 J/g• °C
   b) 2.8 J/g• °C
   c) 0.35 J/g• °C
   d) 2.0 J/g• °C

   Answer: c Page: 157

52. When 29 J of heat is transferred to 15 g of lead at 22°C, the temperature of the lead increases to 37°C. What is the heat capacity (in J/g• °C) of lead?
   a) 7.8
   b) 1.9
   c) 29
   d) 0.13

   Answer: d Page: 157

53. Calculate the heat capacity per gram (C_g) for metal X from the following information. 95 g of metal at 75°C are placed in 50 g of water (C_g = 4.184) at 18°C. The final temperature of the water is 23°C.
   a) 23
   b) 0.21
   c) 0.76
   d) 3.6

   Answer: b Page: 157

54. What is the resulting temperature when 35 g of water at 75°C is mixed with 15 g of water at 15°C? (Heat capacity of H_2O = 4.184 J/g• °C)
   a) 33 °C
   b) 48 °C
   c) 57 °C
   d) 120 °C

   Answer: c Page: 157

55. 55.0 g of water at 69.0°C is added to an unknown amount of water at 22.0° C. The final temperature is 31.0°C. How many grams of water were there initially at 22.0°C?
   a) 232
   b) 13.0
   c) 7.68×10^{-2}
   d) 4.31×10^{-3}

   Answer: a Page: 157

56. The heat capacity of copper metal is 0.38 J/g·°C. Assume you had a 75 g cube of copper at 25.0°C. What would the final temperature of the copper be (in °C) if it absorbed 150 J of heat?
a) 19.7
b) 5.3
c) 30.3
d) 25.8

Answer: c Page: 157

57. The density of gold is 19.3 g/cm^3. The heat capacity of gold is 0.13 J/g·°C. A cube of gold at 75.0°C is dropped into 150 g of water at 25.0°C. The final temperature of the mixture is 27.5°C. What is the length of an edge of the gold cube? (Heat capacity of H_2O = 4.184 J/g·°C)
a) 13 cm
b) 6.3 cm
c) 2.4 cm
d) 0.42 cm

Answer: c Page: 157

58. 50.0 mL of 1.0 M HCl were mixed with 50.0 mL of 1.0 M NaOH in a coffee cup calorimeter. The resulting solution changed temperature from 23.0°C to 29.8°C. Which one of the following is not true concerning this experiment? Assume the resulting solution had the density and specific heat of pure water.
a) the reaction was exothermic
b) 2.8 kJ of heat were transferred during the process
c) for this reaction, q_{rxn} = -2.84 kJ
d) the heat flow monitored during this process was monitored under constant pressure

Answer: c Page: 158

59. A 1.96 g sample of titanium was burned in a bomb calorimeter that had a heat capacity of 9.84 kJ/°C. The temperature of the calorimeter increased from 36.84°C to 98.82°C. Calculate the amount of heat that would be released from the combustion of one mole of titanium.
a) 62.0 kJ
b) 610 kJ
c) 1.49 x 10^4 kJ
d) 311 kJ
e) 1200 kJ

Answer: c Page: 160

60. Using the thermochemical equations below, which one of the following choices is correct for calculation of the ΔH of the following reaction?

$Mg_3N_2 + 3H_2O \rightarrow 3MgO + 2NH_3$ $\Delta H_{rxn} = ?$
$Mg + N_2 \rightarrow Mg_3N_2$ ΔH_1
$H_2 + (1/2)O_2 \rightarrow H_2O$ ΔH_2
$Mg + (1/2)O_2 \rightarrow MgO$ ΔH_3
$(1/2)N_2 + (3/2)H_2 \rightarrow NH_3$ ΔH_4

a) $\Delta H_{rxn} = \Delta H_1 + \Delta H_2 + \Delta H_3 + \Delta H_4$
b) $\Delta H_{rxn} = \Delta H_1 + \Delta H_2 - \Delta H_3 - \Delta H_4$
c) $\Delta H_{rxn} = 2\Delta H_4 + 4\Delta H_3 - \Delta H_2 - 3\Delta H_1$
d) $\Delta H_{rxn} = \Delta H_1 - \Delta H_2 - \Delta H_3 - \Delta H_4$
e) $\Delta H_{rxn} = 3\Delta H_3 + 2\Delta H_4 - \Delta H_1 - 3\Delta H_2$

Answer: e Page: 161

61. Given the values of ΔH° for the two reactions below, what is ΔH° in kJ for the reaction $IF_5(g) \rightarrow IF_3(g) + F_2(g)$?

$IF(g) + F_2(g) \rightarrow IF_3(g)$ $\Delta H° = -390$ kJ

$IF(g) + 2F_2(g) \rightarrow IF_5(g)$ $\Delta H° = -745$ kJ

a) +355
b) -1135
c) +1135
d) +35
e) -35

Answer: a Page: 161

62. The following reactions occur for the hypothetical element E:

$2E(l) + O_2(g) \rightarrow 2EO(g)$ $\Delta H° = -333$ kJ
$EO(g) + O_2(g) \rightarrow EO (s)$ $\Delta H° = -196$ kJ

What is ΔH° in kJ for the reaction $2E(l) + 3O_2(g) \rightarrow 2EO_3(s)$?

a) -526
b) +526
c) +725
d) -725
e) -137

Answer: d Page: 161

63. Given the following thermochemical equation

$Fe_2O_3 + 3CO \rightarrow 2Fe + 3CO_2$ $\Delta H° = -28.0$ kJ
$3Fe + 4CO_2 \rightarrow 4CO + Fe_3O_4$ $\Delta H° = +12.5$ kJ

Calculate the value of $\Delta H°$ for:

$3Fe_2O_3 + CO \rightarrow CO_2 + 2Fe\ O_4$ $\Delta H° = ?$

a) -59.0 kJ
b) 40.5 kJ
c) -15.5 kJ
d) -109 kJ

Answer: a Page: 161

64. Consider the following reactions and their associated values of $\Delta H°$.

$N_2(g) + 2O_2(g) \rightarrow 2NO_2(g)$ $\Delta H° = 66.4$ kJ $2NO(g) + O_2(g) \rightarrow 2NO_2(g)$ $\Delta H° = -114.2$ kJ

What is the value of $\Delta H°$ for the equation shown below?

$N_2(g) + O_2(g) \rightarrow 2NO(g)$

a) 181 kJ
b) -47.8 kJ
c) 47.8 kJ
d) 90.3 kJ

Answer: a Page: 161

65. Use the ΔH values for equations 1 and 2 to determine the value of ΔH for equation 3.

(1) $2NO \rightarrow N_2 + O_2$ $\Delta H = -180$ kJ
(2) $2NO + O_2 \rightarrow 2NO_2$ $\Delta H = -112$ kJ
(3) $N_2 + 2O_2 \rightarrow 2NO_2$ $\Delta H = ?$

a) 68
b) -68
c) -292
d) 292

Answer: a Page: 161

66. Use the information shown for equations 1 and 2 to determine the value of $\Delta H°$ (in kJ) for equation 3.

    (1) $2S(s) + 3O_2(g) \rightarrow 2SO_3(g)$ $\Delta H° = -790$ kJ
    (2) $S(s) + O_2(g) \rightarrow SO_2(g)$ $\Delta H° = -297$ kJ
    (3) $2SO_2(g) + O_2(g) \rightarrow 2SO_3(g)$ $\Delta H° = ?$

    a) 196
    b) -196
    c) 1087
    d) -1384

    Answer: b Page: 161

67. For which one of the following reactions is the $\Delta H°$ a heat of formation?
    a) $N_{2(g)} + 3H_{2(g)} \rightarrow 2NH_{3(g)}$
    b) $(1/2)N_{2(g)} + O_{2(g)} \rightarrow NO_{2(g)}$
    c) $6C_{(s)} + 6H_{(g)} \rightarrow C_6H_{6(1)}$
    d) $P_{(g)} + 4H_{(g)} + Br_{(g)} \rightarrow PH_4Br_{(1)}$
    e) $12C_{(g)} + 11H_{2(g)} + 11O_{(g)} \rightarrow C_6H_{22}O_{11}(g)$

    Answer: b Page: 165

68. Which one of the following is not in its most stable form at 25°C and 1 atmosphere of pressure?
    a) $P_{4(s)}$
    b) $Br_{2(1)}$
    c) $N_{2(g)}$
    d) $F_{2(s)}$

    Answer: d Page: 165

69. For which one of the following is $\Delta H_f°$ zero?
    a) $O_{2(s)}$
    b) $diamond_{(s)}$
    c) $N_{2(g)}$
    d) $F_{2(s)}$

    Answer: c Page: 165

70. For which species below would $\Delta H_f°$ be zero?

    $Ni(s) + 2CO(g) + 2PF_3(g) \rightarrow Ni(CO)_2(PF_3)_2(1)$

    a) Ni(s)
    b) CO(g)
    c) $PF_3(g)$
    d) $Ni(CO)_2(PF_3)_2(1)$
    e) both CO(g) and $PF_3(g)$

    Answer: a Page: 165

71. For which species below would $\Delta H_f°$ be zero?

$2Co(s) + H_2(g) + 8PF_3(g) \rightarrow 2HCo(PF_3)_4(l)$

a) $Co(s)$
b) $H_2(g)$
c) $PF_3(g)$
d) $HCo(PF_3)_4(l)$
e) both $Co(s)$ and $H_2(g)$

Answer: e Page: 165

72. For which one of the following equations is $\Delta H°_{rxn}$ equal to $\Delta H_f°$ for the product?

a) $Xe(g) + 2F_2(g) \rightarrow XeF_4(g)$
b) $CH_4(g) + 2Cl_2(g) \rightarrow CH_2Cl_2(l) + 2HCl(g)$
c) $N_2(g) + O_3(g) \rightarrow N_2O_3(g)$
d) $2CO(g) + O_2(g) \rightarrow 2CO_2(g)$

Answer: a Page: 165

73. For which one of the following reactions is the value of $\Delta H°$ equal to $\Delta H_f°$ for the product?
a) $2Ca(s) + O_2(g) \rightarrow 2CaO(s)$
b) $C_2H_2(g) + H_2(g) \rightarrow C_2H_4(g)$
c) $2C(s) + O_2(g) \rightarrow 2CO(g)$
d) $3Mg(s) + N_3(g) \rightarrow Mg_3N_2(s)$

Answer: d Page: 165

74. Calculate the $\Delta H°$ for the reaction below.
$Ca(OH)_2 + 2H_3AsO_4 \rightarrow Ca(H_2AsO_4)_2 + 2\ H_2O$

Substance	$\Delta H_f°$, kJ/mol
$Ca(OH)_2$	-986.6
H_3AsO_4	-900.4
$Ca(H_2AsO_4)_2$	-2346
H_2O	-258.9

a) -744.9 kJ
b) -4519 kJ
c) -4219 kJ
d) -130.4 kJ
e) none of these

Answer: d Page: 165

75. Calculate the $\Delta H°$ for the dissolution of 0.8327 g of H_3AsO_4 in water.

Substance	$\Delta H_f°$, kJ/mol
$H_3AsO_{4(s)}$	-900.4
$H_3AsO_{4(aq)}$	-899.7

a) 0.004 kJ
b) 0.7 kJ
c) 0.006 kJ
d) 1800.1 kJ

Answer: a Page: 166

76.

Substance	$\Delta H°_f$ (kJ/mol)
$H_2O(l)$	-286
$NO(g)$	90
$NO_2(g)$	34
$HNO_3(aq)$	-207
$NH_3(g)$	-46

Calculate the value of $\Delta H°$ (in kJ) for the following reaction.

$$4NH_3(g) + 5O_2(g) \rightarrow 4\ NO(g) + 6H_2O(l)$$

a) -1172
b) -150
c) -1540
d) -1892

Answer: a Page: 166

77.

Substance	$\Delta H°_f$ (kJ/mol)
$IF(g)$	-95
$IF_5(g)$	-840
$IF_7(g)$	-941

What is the value of $\Delta H°$ for the following reaction?

$$IF_7(g) + I_2(g) \rightarrow IF_5(g) + 2IF(g)$$

a) 69 kJ
b) 311 kJ
c) -1991 kJ
d) -69 kJ

Answer: d Page: 166

78.

Substance	ΔH°_f (kJ/mol)
$IF(g)$	-95
$IF_5(g)$	-840
$IF_7(g)$	-941

ΔH° for the following reaction is -390 kJ. What is the value of ΔH_f° (in kJ/mol) for $IF_3(g)$?

$$IF(g) + F(g) \rightarrow IF(g)$$

a) 295
b) -485
c) -295
d) 485

Answer: b Page: 166

79.

Substance	ΔH°_f (kJ/mol)
C_2H_4 (g)	52.3
$C_2H_5OH(l)$	-277.7
$CH_3CO_2H(l)$	-484.5
$H_2O(l)$	-285.8

Determine the value of ΔH° for the following reaction.

$$C_2H_5OH(l) + O_2(g) \rightarrow CH_3CO_2H(l) + H_2O(l)$$

a) -79.0 kJ
b) -1048.0 kJ
c) -476.4 kJ
d) -492.6 kJ

Answer: b Page: 166

80.

Substance	ΔH°_f (kJ/mol)
$H_2O(l)$	-286
$NO(g)$	90
$NO_2(g)$	34
$HNO_3(aq)$	-207
$NH_3(g)$	-46

Calculate the value of ΔH° (in kJ) for the following reaction.

$$3NO_2(g) + H_2O(l) \rightarrow 2HNO_3(aq) + NO(g)$$

a) 64
b) 140
c) -140
d) -508

Answer: c Page: 166

81. The value of $\Delta H°$ for the reaction shown below is 44 kJ. What is the value of $\Delta H_f°$ for $H_2O(g)$?

$$H_2O(l) \rightarrow H_2O(g)$$

a) 330
b) -242
c) -330
d) 242

Answer: b Page: 166

82.

Substance	$\Delta H°_f$ (kJ/mol)
$IF(g)$	-95
$IF_5(g)$	-840
$IF_7(g)$	-941

What is the value of $\Delta H°$ for the following reaction?

$$IF_5(g) + F_2(g) \rightarrow IF_7(g)$$

a) 1801 kJ
b) -1801 kJ
c) 121 kJ
d) -121 kJ

Answer: d Page: 166

83.

Substance	$\Delta H°_f$ (kJ/mol)
C_2H_4 (g)	52.3
$C_2H_5OH(l)$	-277.7
$CH_3CO_2H(l)$	-484.5
$H_2O(l)$	-285.8

The value of $\Delta H°$ for the following reaction is -137.0 kJ. What is the value of $\Delta H_f°$ for $C_2H_6(g)$?

$$C_2H_4(g) + H_2(g) \rightarrow C_2H_6(g)$$

a) 189.3 kJ/mol
b) -84.7 kJ/mol
c) -189.3 kJ/mol
d) 84.7 kJ/mol

Answer: b Page: 166

84.

Substance	ΔH°_f (kJ/mol)
$CO(g)$	-110.5
$CO_2(g)$	-393.7
$CaCO_3(s)$	-1207

Compute ΔH° in kJ for the following reaction.

$$2CO(g) + O_2(g) \rightarrow 2CO_2(g)$$

a) -566.4
b) -283.3
c) 283.3
d) -677.0

Answer: a Page: 166

85.

Substance	ΔH°_f (kJ/mol)
$CO(g)$	-110.5
$CO_2(g)$	-393.7
$CaCO_3(s)$	-1207

If ΔH° for the following reaction is 177.8 kJ, what is ΔH_f° for $CaO(s)$

$$CaCO_3(s) \rightarrow CaO(s) + CO_2(g)$$

a) -1600 kJ/mol
b) -813.4 kJ/mol
c) -635.5 kJ/mol
d) 813.4 kJ/mol

Answer: c Page: 166

86.

Substance	ΔH°_f (kJ/mol)
$Ag_2O(s)$	-31.0
$Ag_2S(s)$	-32.6
$H_2S(g)$	-20.6
$H_2O(l)$	-286

What is the value of ΔH° (in kJ) for the following reaction?

$$2Ag_2S(s) + O_2(g) \rightarrow 2Ag_2O(s) + 2S(s)$$

a) -1.6
b) 1.6
c) -3.2
d) 3.2

Answer: d Page: 166

87.

Substance	ΔH°_f (kJ/mol)
$Ag_2O(s)$	-31.0
$Ag_2S(s)$	-32.6
$H_2S(g)$	-20.6
$H_2O(l)$	-286

What is the value of ΔH° (in kJ) for the following reaction?

$$Ag_2O(s) + H_2S(g) \rightarrow Ag_2S(s) + H_2O(l)$$

a) -267
b) -370
c) -202
d) -308

Answer: a Page: 166

88.

Substance	ΔH°_f (kJ/mol)
$SO_2(g)$	-297
$SO_3(g)$	-396
$SO_2Cl_2(g)$	-364
$H_2SO_4(l)$	-814
$H_2O(l)$	-286

Determine the value of ΔH° (in kJ) for the following reaction.

$$2SO_2(g) + O_2(g) \rightarrow 2SO_3(g)$$

a) -99
b) 99
c) -198
d) 198

Answer: c Page: 166

89.

Substance	ΔH°_f (kJ/mol)
$SO_2(g)$	-297
$SO_3(g)$	-396
$SO_2Cl_2(g)$	-364
$H_2SO_4(l)$	-814
$H_2O(l)$	-286

Determine the value of ΔH° (in kJ) for the following reaction.

$$SO_3(g) + H_2O(l) \rightarrow H_2SO_4(l)$$

a) -132
b) 1496
c) 704
d) -704

Answer: a Page: 166

90.

Substance	$\Delta H°_f$ (kJ/mol)
$SO_2(g)$	-297
$SO_3(g)$	-396
$SO_2Cl_2(g)$	-364
$H_2SO_4(l)$	-814
$H_2O(l)$	-286

The value of $\Delta H°$ for the following reaction is -62 kJ. What is the value of $\Delta H°$ (in kJ/mol) for HCl(g)?

$$SO_2Cl_2(g) + 2H_2O(l) \rightarrow H_4SO_4(l) + 2HCl(g)$$

a) -184
b) 60
c) -92
d) 30

Answer: c Page: 166

91.

Substance	$\Delta H°_f$ (kJ/mol)
$SO_2(g)$	-297
$SO_3(g)$	-396
$SO_2Cl_2(g)$	-364
$H_2SO_4(l)$	-814
$H_2O(l)$	-286

Calculate the amount of heat (in kJ) evolved when 7.5 g of SO_2 reacts according to the following equation.

$$SO_2(g) + Cl_2(g) \rightarrow SO_2Cl_2(g)$$

a) 77
b) 5.7×10^2
c) 19
d) 7.9

Answer: d Page: 166

92. The energy released by combustion of 1 g of a substance is called that substance's
a) specific heat
b) fuel value
c) nutritional calorie content
d) heat capacity

Answer: b Page: 170

93. A 5 ounce cup of raspberry yogurt contains 6.0 g of protein, 2.0 g of fat, and 26.9 g of carbohydrate. The respective fuel values in kJ/g for fat, protein, and carbohydrate are 38, 17, and 17. What is the fuel value in kJ of this cup of yogurt?
a) 640
b) 830
c) 600
d) 720

Answer: a Page: 170

94. A 25.5 g piece of cheddar cheese contains 37% fat, 28% protein, and 4% carbohydrate. The respective fuel values in kJ/g for fat, protein, and carbohydrate are 38, 17, and 17. What is the fuel value in kJ for this piece of cheese?
a) 500
b) 330
c) 790
d) 99
e) 260

Answer: a Page: 170

95. Fuel values of hydrocarbons in kJ/g increase as the H/C atomic ratio increases. Which of the following compounds has the highest fuel value in kJ/g?
a) C_2H_6
b) C_2H_4
c) C_2H_2
d) CH_4
e) C_6H_6

Answer: d Page: 170

96. The average fuel value of sugar is 17 kJ/g. A 2.0 L pitcher of sweetened Kool-Aid contains 400 g of sugar. What is the fuel value (in kJ) of a 500 mL serving of Kool-Aid? (Assume the sugar is the only fuel source.)
a) 4.2×10^4
b) 1.7×10^3
c) 1.7×10^6
d) 1.7×10^2

Answer: b Page: 170

97. An explosive used in commercial blasting is known as ANFO. ANFO is a mixture of
a. picric acid and nitroglycerine
b. gasoline and kerosene
c. potassium nitrate and diesel fuel
d. TNT and gun powder
e. ammonium nitrate and fuel oil

Answer: e Page: 169

SHORT ANSWER

98. At 250°C, ammonium nitrate decomposes to form nitrous oxide and water. What is formed when ammonium nitrate decomposes at 300°C?

Answer: N_2, O_2, and H_2O Page: 169

99. What function does fuel oil serve in ANFO?

Answer:
I has a high heat content and thus greatly increases the energy released when the ammonium nitrate explodes.

Page: 169

MULTIPLE CHOICE

100. Ammonium nitrate is a commonly available compound. What is the primary use of this compound?
a) fertilizer
b) cleaning agent
c) instant cold packs
d) food preservative
e) antioxidant

Answer: a Page: 169

101. The metabolism of which one of the following produces the greatest amount of energy per gram?
a) carbohydrates
b) fats
c) proteins

Answer: b Page: 170

102. Which one of the following produces a different amount of energy when burned in a calorimeter than when metabolized?
    a) fats
    b) carbohydrates
    c) proteins

    Answer: c Page: 170

103. Of the substances below, which one has the highest fuel value?
    a) charcoal
    b) bituminous coal
    c) natural gas
    d) hydrogen
    e) wood

    Answer: d Page: 172

104. Which one of the choices below is not considered a fossil fuel?
    a) anthracite coal
    b) crude oil
    c) natural gas
    d) hydrogen

    Answer: d Page: 172

105. Natural gas is composed primarily of
    a) methane
    b) butane
    c) propane
    d) ethane

    Answer: a Page: 172

106. What was the primary source of energy consumed in the United States in 1995?
    a) nuclear
    b) petroleum
    c) coal
    d) natural gas
    e) hydroelectric

    Answer: b Page: 172

SHORT ANSWER

107. What is the physical state of petroleum at 25°C and of what is it primarily composed?

    Answer: liquid, hydrocarbons Page: 172

108. Coal is a solid that is composed of

Answer:
high molecular weight hydrocarbons as well as compounds containing S, O, and N

Page: 172

MULTIPLE CHOICE

109. What is the main problem with harnessing solar energy for practical uses?
   a) its high intensity too rapidly destroys devices utilized for capture of the energy
   b) solar energy is too valuable to the polarization of the Earth for food production to be able to harvest in other ways
   c) it is diffuse and it fluctuates with time and weather conditions
   d) only the short wavelengths are useful and they are too penetrating to be captured efficiently

   Answer: c Page: 174

110. The most abundant fossil fuel is
   a) natural gas
   b) petroleum
   c) coal
   d) uranium
   e) hydrogen

   Answer: c Page: 172

111. Syngas is produced by treating _____ with superheated steam.
   a) natural gas
   b) graphite
   c) uranium
   d) coal
   e) hydrogen

   Answer: d Page: 181

SHORT ANSWER

112. Syngas is a mixture of what three substances?

   Answer: CH_4, H_2, and CO Page: 172

113. Hydrogen cannot be used as a primary energy source. Why?

   Answer: There is too little free H_2 in nature. Page: 173

114. Hydrogen can be obtained from coal and from natural gas. How?

Answer: By treatment of coal or natural gas with superheated steam.

Page: 172

MULTIPLE CHOICE

115. Hydrogen can be produced by the decomposition of hydrocarbons or of water. What is the main drawback associated with these sources of hydrogen for commercial uses?
a) these compounds themselves are very expensive to sufficiently purify prior to their decomposition
b) the byproducts of the decomposition of these compounds are very hazardous to the environment
c) these compounds are very expensive to obtain themselves and processing them further is not financially feasible
d) these processes can use more energy than is subsequently reclaimed when the hydrogen is used as a fuel
e) these decomposition processes are generally explosive and are highly regulated by the federal government for safety reasons

Answer: d Page: 173

116. In a hydrogen-powered vehicle in which the hydrogen is stored in an alloy such as iron-titanium alloy, how is the hydrogen released from the alloy?
a) by heating
b) by reaction with steam
c) by electrolysis
d) by reaction with gasoline
e) the alloy itsel is burned

Answer: a Page: 173

Chapter 6: Electronic Structure of Atoms

MULTIPLE CHOICE

1. Electromagnetic radiation travels through a vacuum at a rate of
   a. 186,000 m/s
   b. 125 m/s
   c. 3.00 x 108 m/s
   d. 10,000 m/s
   e. it depends on wavelength

   Answer: c Page: 183

2. Which one of the following is correct?
   a. $\nu + \lambda = c$
   b. $\nu \div \lambda = c$
   c. $\nu = c\lambda$
   d. $\lambda = c\nu$
   e. $\nu\lambda = c$

   Answer: e Page: 184

SHORT ANSWER

3. What wavelengths correspond to the visible region of the electromagnetic spectrum?

   Answer: About 400 to 700 nm. Page: 184

MULTIPLE CHOICE

4. What is the wavelength of light that has a frequency of $1.20 \times 10^{13} s^{-1}$?
   a) 25.0 µm
   b) 2.50×10^{-5} µm
   c) 0.0400 µm
   d) 12.0 µm

   Answer: a Page: 184

5. Ham radio operators often broadcast on the 6 meter band. What is the frequency of this electromagnetic radiation in MHz?
   ($c = 3.0 \times 10^{8}$ m/s.)
   a) 500 s^{-1}
   b) 200 s^{-1}
   c) 50 s^{-1}
   d) 20 s^{-1}

   Answer: c Page: 184

6. What is the frequency of electromagnetic radiation with a wavelength of 0.53 m? ($c = 3.00 \times 10^8$ m/s.)
   a) $5.7 \times 10^8\ s^{-1}$
   b) $1.8 \times 10^{-9}\ s^{-1}$
   c) $1.6 \times 10^8\ s^{-1}$
   d) $1.3 \times 10^{-33}\ s^{-1}$

   Answer: a Page: 184

7. The energy of a photon of light is _____ proportional to its frequency and ______ proportional to its wavelength.
   a) directly, directly
   b) inversely, inversely
   c) inversely, directly
   d) directly, inversely

   Answer: d Page: 184

8. Of the following regions of the electromagnetic spectrum, which one has the shortest wavelength?
   a) x-rays
   b) radio waves
   c) microwaves
   d) gamma rays
   e) ultraviolet
   f) infrared

   Answer: d Page: 185

9. To Planck is attributed the
   a) Uncertainty Principle
   b) hydrogen atom model
   c) line spectra equation
   d) concept of matter waves
   e) quantum concept

   Answer: e Page: 185

10. Which one of the following forms of electromagnetic radiation has the <u>shortest</u> wavelength?
    a) ultraviolet
    b) X-ray
    c) microwave
    d) infrared

    Answer: b Page: 185

11. Who earned the Nobel Prize in physics in 1918 for his work on quantum theory?
a) Roald Hoffman
b) Max Planck
c) William Lipscomb
d) Linus Pauling
e) Georg Mendelssohn

Answer: b Page: 186

12. Electromagnetic radiation of which of the following wavelengths (in nm) is of the lowest energy?
a) 526
b) 493
c) 623
d) 277
e) 532

Answer: c Page: 186

13. Electromagnetic radiation of which of the following wavelengths (in nm) is of the highest energy?
a) 617
b) 233
c) 623
d) 597
e) 486

Answer: b Page: 186

14. Which one of the following forms of electromagnetic radiation possesses the greatest energy per photon?
a) ultraviolet
b) X-ray
c) infrared
d) microwave

Answer: b Page: 186

15. What is the wavelength (in meters) of a photon with an energy of 5.25×10^{-19} J? ($c = 3.00 \times 10^{8}$ m/s, $h = 6.63 \times 10^{-34}$ J•s.)
a) 3.79×10^{-7}
b) 2.64×10^{6}
c) 2.38×10^{23}
d) 4.21×10^{-24}

Answer: a Page: 186

16. The photoelectric effect
    a) is the total reflection of light by metals giving them their typical luster
    b) is the production of current by silicon solar cells when exposed to sunlight
    c) is the ejection of electrons by a metal when struck by light
    d) is the darkening of photographic film when exposed to an electric field

    Answer: c Page: 187

17. Which one of the following is considered to be ionizing radiation?
    a) visible light
    b) radio waves
    c) x-rays
    d) microwaves
    e) infrared radiation

    Answer: c Page: 188

18. Radiation called ELF or extremely-low-frequency radiation has frequencies in the range of
    a) 10^{-3} - 10^{-5} Hz
    b) 10^{-5} - 10^{-9} Hz
    c) 100 - 10,000 Hz
    d) 400 - 700 nm
    e) 1 - 1000 Hz

    Answer: e Page: 188

19. Bohr described the possible paths followed by the electron in his model of the hydrogen atom as
    a) orbits
    b) orbitals

    Answer: a Page: 189

20. Which of the following transitions in the Bohr hydrogen atom model affords emission of the highest-energy photon?
    a) $n_i = 1 \rightarrow n_f = 6$
    b) $n_i = 6 \rightarrow n_f = 1$
    c) $n_i = 6 \rightarrow n_f = 3$
    d) $n_i = 3 \rightarrow n_f = 6$
    e) $n_i = 4 \rightarrow n_f = 1$

    Answer: b Page: 189

21. Which of the following Bohr H-atom transitions would afford emission of a photon of electromagnetic radiation in the Balmer series?
a) $n_i = 1 \rightarrow n_f = 2$
b) $n_i = 2 \rightarrow n_f = 1$
c) $n_i = 1 \rightarrow n_f = 6$
d) $n_i = 2 \rightarrow n_f = 4$
e) $n_i = 6 \rightarrow n_f = 2$

Answer: e Page: 189

22. Which one of the following electron transitions in a hydrogen atom results in the greatest release of energy from the atom?
a) n=3 to n=4
b) n=1 to n=3
c) n=6 to n=4
d) n=7 to n=5

Answer: c Page: 189

23. Which one of the following electron transitions would result in the loss of energy from a hydrogen atom?
a) n=7 to n=9
b) n=7 to n=5
c) n=5 to n=6
d) n=1 to n=2

Answer: b Page: 189

24. What is the maximum number of different spectral lines that could be produced by electrons going from n=3 to the ground state by all possible paths in hydrogen atoms?
a) 1
b) 2
c) 3
d) 4

Answer: c Page: 189

25. Using Bohr's equation for the energy levels of the hydrogen atom, determine the energy of an electron (in J) in the fourth level of hydrogen.

($R_H = 2.18 \times 10^{-18}$ J.)
a) -1.362×10^{-19}
b) -5.448×10^{-19}
c) -7.343×10^{18}
d) -1.836×10^{-29}

Answer: a Page: 189

26. An electron in a hydrogen atom is found to have an energy of -1.362 X 10 J. What orbit would the electron be in according to the Bohr model of the hydrogen atom? (R_H = 2.18 X 10^{-18} J.)
    a) 1
    b) 2
    c) 3
    d) 4

    Answer: d Page: 189

27. Calculate the energy change (in J) that would accompany an electronic transition in a hydrogen atom from n=2 to n=3.

    (R_H = 2.18 X 10^{-18} J.)
    a) 4.0 X 10^{-19}
    b) 3.0 X 10^{-19}
    c) -3.0 X 10^{-19}
    d) -7.9 X 10^{-19}

    Answer: b Page: 189

28. Calculate the energy change (in J) associated with an electron transition from n=2 to n=5 in a hydrogen atom.
    (R_H = 2.18 X 10^{-18} J.)
    a) 6.5 X 10^{-19}
    b) 5.5 X 10^{-19}
    c) 8.7 X 10^{-20}
    d) 4.6 X 10^{-19}

    Answer: d Page: 189

29. What is the frequency (in Hz) of electromagnetic radiation necessary to move an electron from n=2 to n=4 in a hydrogen atom?
    (h = 6.63 X 10^{-34} J•s, R_H = 2.18 X 10^{-18} J.)
    a) 4.1 X 10^{-19}
    b) 6.2 X 10^{14}
    c) 5.4 X 10^{-19}
    d) 8.2 X 10^{14}

    Answer: b Page: 189

30. According to the Bohr model, the maximum number of electrons that can exist at the n=3 level of an atom is:
    a) 18
    b) 12
    c) 8
    d) 4

    Answer: a Page: 189

31. Calculate the radius (in m) of the third orbit in a hydrogen atom ($r_1 = 5.3 \times 10^{-11}$ m.)
    a) 4.8×10^{-10}
    b) 2.5×10^{-20}
    c) 1.6×10^{-10}
    d) 8.4×10^{-21}

    Answer: a Page: 189

32. Calculate the radius (in m) of the fourth orbit in a hydrogen atom ($r_1 = 5.3 \times 10^{-11}$ m.)
    a) 2.1×10^{-10}
    b) 4.5×10^{-20}
    c) 1.1×10^{-20}
    d) 8.5×10^{-10}

    Answer: d Page: 189

33. A spectrum containing only specific wavelengths is called a ______ spectrum.
    a) line
    b) continuous
    c) visible
    d) Balmer

    Answer: a Page: 190

34. In the Bohr model of the atom, the radius of the orbit for n = 3 is larger than that of the orbit for n = 1 by what factor?
    a) 1
    b) 2
    c) 4
    d) 6
    e) 9

    Answer: e Page: 191

35. Which one of the following is a correct expression for calculation of the wavelength of a particle?
    a) $\lambda = h + mv$
    b) $\lambda = hmv$
    c) $\lambda = \frac{h}{mv}$
    d) $\lambda = \frac{mv}{c}$
    e) $\lambda = mv$

    Answer: c Page: 194

36. Which one of the following should have the shortest wavelength when traveling at 30 cm/s?
a) a marble
b) a car
c) a planet
d) a uranium atom

Answer: c Page: 194

37. The scientist to whom the wave nature of matter is attributed is
a) Schrodinger
b) Heisenberg
c) de Broglie
d) Einstein
e) Bohr

Answer: c Page: 194

38. The de Broglie wavelength of an electron is 8.7×10^{-11} m. The mass of this electron is 9.1×10^{-31} kg. What is the velocity (in m/s) of this electron? ($h = 6.63 \times 10^{-31}$ j•s.)
a) 8.4×10^{3}
b) 1.2×10^{-7}
c) 6.9×10^{-54}
d) 8.4×10^{6}

Answer: d Page: 194

39. Determine the wavelength (in m) of a 7.5 g bullet traveling at 700 m/s. ($h = 6.63 \text{ X } 10^{-34}$ J•s.)
a) $7.7 \text{ X } 10^{33}$
b) $1.3 \text{ X } 10^{-34}$
c) $6.2 \text{ X } 10^{-29}$
d) $1.3 \text{ X } 10^{-27}$

Answer: b Page: 194

40. Determine the wavelength (in m) of a 1000 kg auto traveling at 75 km/hr. ($h = 6.63 \text{ X } 10^{-34}$ J•s.)
a) $3.2 \text{ X } 10^{-38}$
b) $8.8 \text{ X } 10^{-39}$
c) $3.2 \text{ X } 10^{-35}$
d) $1.4 \text{ X } 10^{-35}$

Answer: a Page: 194

41. What is the wavelength (in m) of an electron whose velocity is 1.7 X 10^4 m/s and whose mass is 9.1 X 10^{-28} g?
(h = 6.63 X 10^{-34} J•s.)
a) 4.3 X 10^{-11}
b) 12
c) 4.3 X 10^{-8}
d) 2.3 X 10^7

Answer: c Page: 194

42. The Heisenberg Uncertainty Principle states that it is impossible to precisely know both the position and the _________ of an electron in an atom.
a) mass
b) color
c) momentum
d) shape

Answer: c Page: 195

43. The probability of finding an electron at a given point in space is given by the value of _____ at that point.

a) H
b) Ψ
c) Ψ^2
d) λ
e) $\frac{hc}{\lambda}$

Answer: c Page: 195

SHORT ANSWER

44. In the Bohr model of the atom, electrons are located in ________. In the quantum mechanical model of the atom, electrons are located in __________.

Answer: orbits, orbitals Page: 197

45. How many quantum numbers are used in the quantum mechanical model of the atom? Identify these quantum numbers.

Answer: 3, n, l, and m_l Page: 197

MULTIPLE CHOICE

46. All of the orbitals in a given electron shell have the same value of which quantum number?
    a) principal
    b) azimuthal
    c) magnetic
    d) spin
    e) psi

    Answer: a Page: 197

47. All of the orbitals in a given subshell have the same value of which quantum number?
    a) principal
    b) azimuthal
    c) magnetic
    d) a and b
    e) b and c

    Answer: d Page: 197

48. Which quantum number defines the shape of an orbital?
    a) spin
    b) magnetic
    c) principal
    d) azimuthal

    Answer: d Page: 197

49. Which quantum number describes the orientation of an orbital in space?
    a) spin
    b) magnetic
    c) principal
    d) azimuthal

    Answer: b Page: 197

50. The values of the principal quantum number and the azimuthal quantum number of the electrons in a 3d subshell are
    a) 3,3
    b) 2,3
    c) 3,2
    d) 2,2

    Answer: c Page: 197

51. Which one of the following is not a valid value for the magnetic quantum number of the electrons in a 5d subshell?
a) 2
b) 5
c) 0
d) 1
e) -1
f) -2

Answer: b Page: 197

52. How many values does the magnetic quantum number have for a 5f subshell?
a) 1
b) 5
c) 3
d) 14
e) 7

Answer: e Page: 197

53. How many orbitals are in the third shell?
a) 25
b) 4
c) 9
d) 16
e) 1

Answer: c Page: 197

54. Which one of the following subshells only contains one orbital?
a) 5d
b) 6f
c) 4s
d) 3d

Answer: c Page: 197

55. Two electrons in the same atom which have identical values of quantum numbers n, l, and m_l are said to be in
a) the same shell and subshell, but different orbitals
b) the same shell, but different subshells and orbitals
c) the same shell, subshell, and orbital
d) the same subshell and orbital, but different shells
e) different shells, subshells, and orbitals

Answer: c Page: 197

56. Which of the subshells below do not exist due to the mathematical constraints upon the quantum number "l"?
 a) 2d
 b) 2s
 c) 2p
 d) all of the above
 e) none of the above

 Answer: a Page: 197

57. Which orbital type below does not exist due to wave-mechanical quantum number restrictions?
 a) 4f
 b) 4d
 c) 4p
 d) 4s
 e) none of the above

 Answer: e Page: 197

58. Which set of quantum numbers <u>cannot</u> be correct?
 a) $n=2,\ l=0,\ m_l=0$
 b) $n=2,\ l=1,\ m_l=-1$
 c) $n=3,\ l=1,\ m_l=-1$
 d) $n=1,\ l=1,\ m_l=1$

 Answer: d Page: 197

59. Which set of quantum numbers <u>cannot</u> be correct?
 a) $n=6,\ l=0,\ m_l=0$
 b) $n=3,\ l=2,\ m_l=3$
 c) $n=3,\ l=2,\ m_l=-2$
 d) $n=1,\ l=0,\ m_l=0$

 Answer: b Page: 197

60. What is the maximum number of orbitals possible at the second principal energy level of an atom?
 a) 1
 b) 2
 c) 4
 d) 8

 Answer: c Page: 197

61. Which one of the following orbitals has an azimuthal quantum number of 3?
   a) s
   b) p
   c) d
   d) f

   Answer: d Page: 197

62. Which quantum number indicates that there will be three orbitals of the p type at n=2?
   a) n
   b) l
   c) m_l
   d) p

   Answer: c Page: 197

63. The n = 1 shell contains ___ p orbitals and the other shells each contain ___ p orbitals.
   a) 3, 6-9
   b) 0,3
   c) 6,2
   d) 3,3

   Answer: b Page: 197

64. The lowest energy shell that contains f orbitals is the shell with n =
   a) 3
   b) 2
   c) 4
   d) 1

   Answer: c Page: 197

65. In the quantum-mechanical model, the spatial orientation of an orbital is determined by quantum number(s)
   a) n
   b) l
   c) m_l
   d) m_s
   e) m_l and m_s

   Answer: c Page: 197

66. Which one of the following is an incorrect orbital notation?
   a) 4f
   b) 2d
   c) 3s
   d) 2p

   Answer: b Page: 197

67. Which one of the following is an incorrect orbital notation?
    a) 2s
    b) $3p_y$
    c) 3f
    d) $4d_{xy}$

    Answer: c Page: 197

68. Which quantum number determines the energy of an electron in a hydrogen atom?
    a) n
    b) E
    c) m_l
    d) l

    Answer: a Page: 197

69. At maximum, an f subshell can hold ___ electrons, a d subshell can hold ___ electrons, and a p subshell can hold ___ electrons.
    a) 14,10,6
    b) 2,8,18
    c) 18,8,2
    d) 2,12,21

    Answer: a Page: 197

70. The principal quantum number of the first d subshell is
    a) 1
    b) 2
    c) 3
    d) 4

    Answer: c Page: 197

71. In the quantum-mechanical model, the general shape of an orbital is determined by quantum number(s)
    a) n
    b) l
    c) m_l
    d) m_s
    e) m_l and m_s

    Answer: b Page: 197

72. How many subshells does the shell with the prinicpal quantum number of 9 contain?
   a) 3
   b) 5
   c) 7
   d) 9
   e) 1

   Answer: d Page: 198

73. The total number of orbitals in a shell is given by
   a. l^2
   b. n^2
   c. $2n$
   d. $2n + 1$
   e. $2l + 1$

   Answer: b Page: 198

74. The places where the value of Ψ^2 is zero are called a(n)
   a. orbital
   b. orbit
   c. node
   d. wave function
   e. azimuth

   Answer: c Page: 200

75. Which type of orbital is spherically symmetrical?
   a) s
   b) p
   c) d
   d) f

   Answer: a Page: 200

76. The probability of finding an electron at a node in a hydrogen-atom 2s orbital is
   a) 0.00
   b) 0.25
   c) 0.50
   d) 0.75
   e) 1.00

   Answer: a Page: 200

77. Which sketch represents an orbital that can have a principal quantum number of 2?
    a) 1
    b) 2
    c) 3
    d) 1, 2, and 3

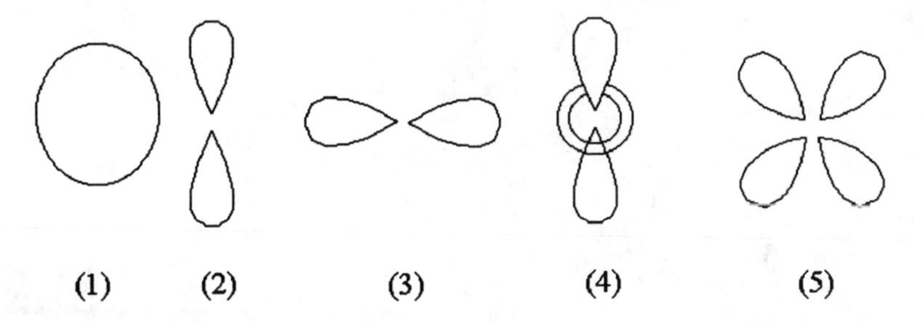

Answer: d Page: 200

78. Which sketch represents an orbital with the quantum numbers $n=3$, $l=0$, $m_l=0$?

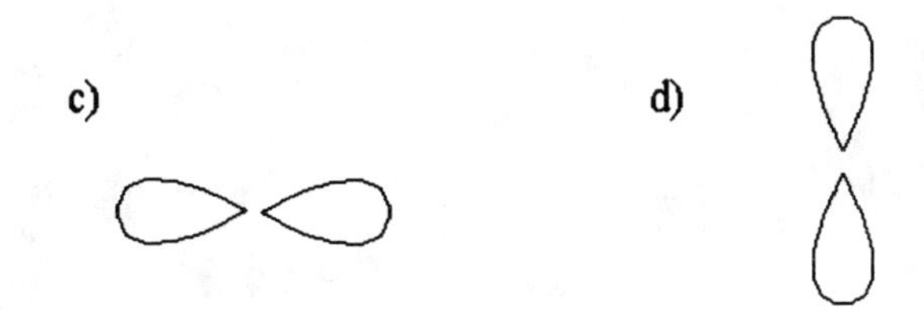

Answer: a Page: 200

79. Which sketch represents an orbital that <u>cannot</u> have a principal quantum number of 2?

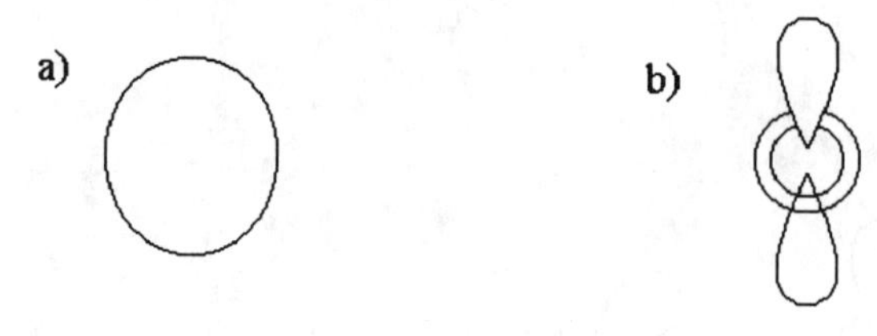

Answer: b Page: 200

80. In the symbol, p_x, what is the meaning of x?
    a. the energy
    b. the spin of the electrons
    c. the probability of the shell
    d. the size of the orbital
    e. the axis along which the orbital is aligned

Answer: e Page: 201

SHORT ANSWER

81. On the axes below, draw the general shape of a p_y orbital.

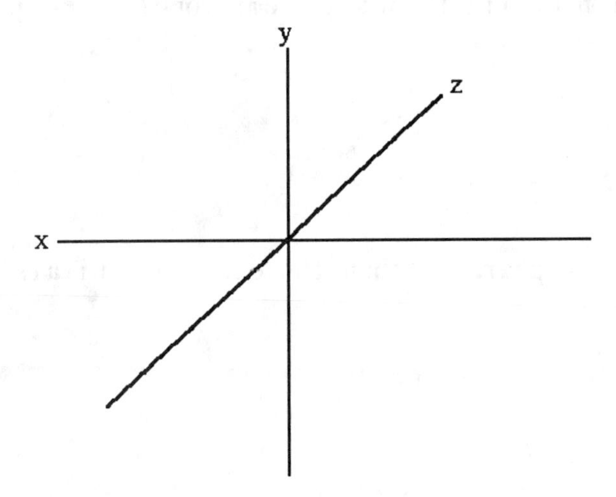

Answer:

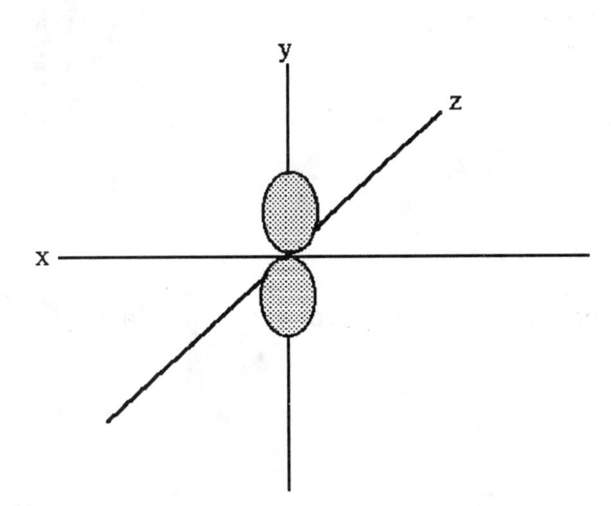

Page: 201

82. All of the subshells in a given shell have the same energy. In a many-electron atom, the subshells in a given shell do not have the same energy. Why?

Answer:
Hydrogen atoms have only one electron. Therefore, in a hydrogen atom, the energy of orbitals depends only on *n*. In many-electron atoms, electron-electron repulsion causes the energies of subshells in a given shell to differ.

Page: 201

Chapter 6: Electronic Structure of Atoms

MULTIPLE CHOICE

83. Which one of the following electron configurations would allow a hydrogen atom to absorb a photon of light, but not emit one?
   a) 3s
   b) 2s
   c) 3p
   d) 1s

   Answer: d Page: 202

84. Which d orbital has a different appearance than the other d orbitals?
   a) xy
   b) x^2-y^2
   c) xz
   d) yz
   e) z^2

   Answer: e Page: 202

85. For the $4d_{yz}$ orbital, the "yz" specifies its
   a) size
   b) shape
   c) spatial orientation
   d) electron spin
   e) degree of degeneracy

   Answer: c Page: 202

86. Which one of the following orbitals is degenerate with $5p_y$ in a many-electron atom?
   a) 5s
   b) $5p_x$
   c) $4p_y$
   d) $5d_{xy}$

   Answer: b Page: 201

87. In a many-electron atom, for a given value of n, effective nuclear charge _____ with increasing value of l.
   a) increases
   b) decreases
   c) does not change

   Answer: b Page: 203

88. In a many-electron atom, for a given value of n, the energy of an orbital increases with _____ value of l.
   a. increasing
   b. decreasing

   Answer: a Page: 203

89. Orbitals that are degenerate have the same
    a. shape
    b. spatial orientation
    c. size
    d. energy
    e. value of n

    Answer: d Page: 203

90. Which one of the following experiences the greatest effective nuclear charge in a many electron atom?
    a) 4f
    b) 4p
    c) 4d
    d) 4s

    Answer: d Page: 203

91. Which orbital of those listed below is of the highest energy in atomic tellurium?
    a) 2s
    b) 3s
    c) 4d
    d) 3p
    e) 3d

    Answer: c Page: 203

92. The tin atom has 50 electrons. Electrons in which of its orbitals below experience the lowest effective nuclear charge?
    a) 1s
    b) 3p
    c) 3d
    d) 5s
    e) 5p

    Answer: e Page: 203

93. Which of the following orbitals is degenerate with $5d_z2$ in a many-electron atom?
    a) $5p_z$
    b) $4d_z2$
    c) 5a
    d) $5d_{xy}$

    Answer: d Page: 203

94. Which one of the following has the orbitals listed in order of increasing energy?
a) 1s2s2p3s3p4s3d4p
b) 1s2s3s4s2p3p4p3d
c) 1s2s2p3s3p3d4s4p
d) 1s2s2p3s3p4s4p3d

Answer: a Page: 203

SHORT ANSWER

95. Write the orbitals 1s through 4d in the order in which they are filled.

Answer: 1s,2s,3s,3d,4s,3d,4p,5s,4d Page: 203

MULTIPLE CHOICE

96. The spin quantum number can take on values of
a) 1,2,3,...
b) -1,...,0,...,+1
c) 0 to n-1
d) + or - $\frac{1}{2}$

Answer: d Page: 204

97. According to constraints imposed by wave-mechanical model mathematics and by the Pauli Exclusion rule, if electrons A and B in the same atom have quantum numbers as shown in the table below, which value(s) of ? is/are not allowed?

Electron	n	l	m_l	m_s
A	4	1	-1	+1/2
B	4	1	?	+1/2

a) 4
b) -2
c) 2
d) -1
e) all of the above

Answer: e Page: 205

98. According to constraints imposed by wave-mechanical model mathematics and by the Pauli Exclusion rule, if electrons A and B in the same atom have quantum numbers as shown in the table below, which value of ? is allowed?

Electron	n	l	m_l	m_s
A	3	1	-1	+1/2
B	3	1	?	-1/2

a) 3
b) -3
c) 4
d) -1
e) none of the above

Answer: d Page: 205

99. A major effect of the Pauli Exclusion rule is to allow
a) only one subshell in the first electron shell
b) only seven electron shells total for any atom
c) three orbitals in the 3p subshell
d) three orbitals in any p subshell
e) no more than two electrons per orbital

Answer: e Page: 205

100. Which one of the following represents a correct set of quantum numbers for an electron in an atom?
(arranged as n, l, m_l, and m_s)
a) 2,2,-1,-1/2
b) 1,0,0,1/2
c) 3,3,3,1/2
d) 5,4,-5,1/2

Answer: b Page: 205

101. Which one of the following represents a possible set of quantum numbers (in the order n, l, m_l, m_s) for an electron in an atom?
a) 2,1,-1,1/2
b) 2,1,0,0
c) 2,2,0,1/2
d) 2,0,1,-1/2

Answer: a Page: 205

102. Which one of the following represents an <u>incorrect</u> set of quantum numbers for an electron in an atom?
(arranged as n, l, m_l, and m_s)
a) 2,1,-1,-1/2
b) 1,0,0,1/2
c) 3,3,3,1/2
d) 5,4,-3,1/2

Answer: c Page: 205

103. What is the maximum number of electrons in an atom that can have the following quantum numbers: n=2, m_s=+1/2 ?
a) 1
b) 2
c) 4
d) 8

Answer: c Page: 205

104. What is the maximum number of electrons in an atom that can have the following quantum numbers: n=1, m =+1/2_s?
a) 1
b) 2
c) 4
d) 8

Answer: a Page: 205

105. What is the maximum number of electrons in an atom that can have the quantum numbers n=4, l=2, m_l=-1?
a) 2
b) 5
c) 10
d) 32

Answer: a Page: 205

106. How many electrons in an atom can have the following set of quantum numbers: n=3, l=2, m_l=0?
a) 1
b) 2
c) 6
d) 10

Answer: b Page: 205

107. Which diagram represents a violation of the Pauli Exclusion Principle?

a) 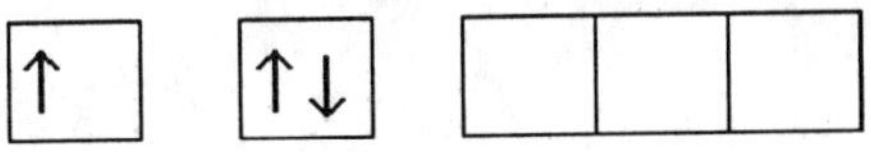 [↑] [↑↓] [| |]

b) 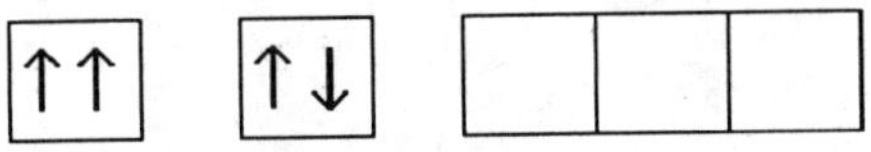 [↑↑] [↑↓] [| |]

c) 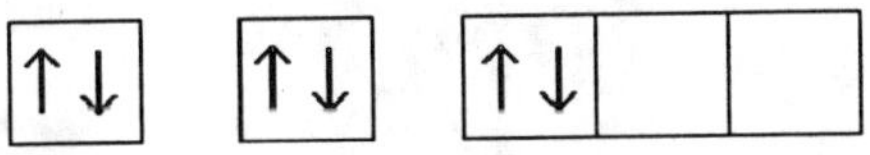 [↑↓] [↑↓] [↑↓| |]

d) 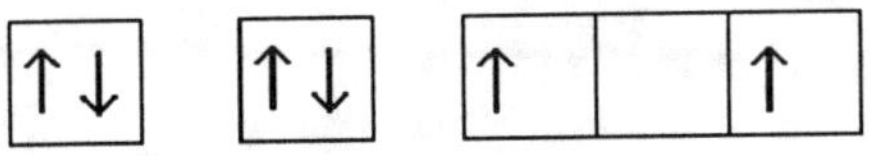 [↑↓] [↑↓] [↑| |↑]

Answer: b Page: 205

108. Which set of orbital diagrams shows a violation of the Pauli Exclusion Principle?

a) 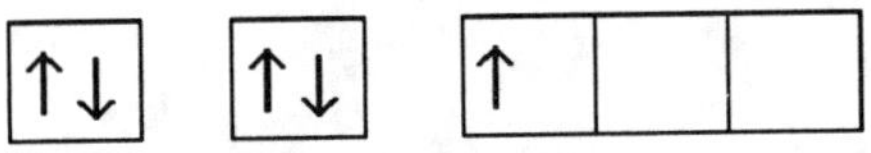 [↑↓] [↑↓] [↑| |]

b) 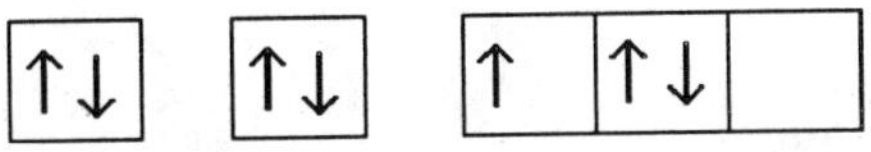 [↑↓] [↑↓] [↑|↑↓|]

c) 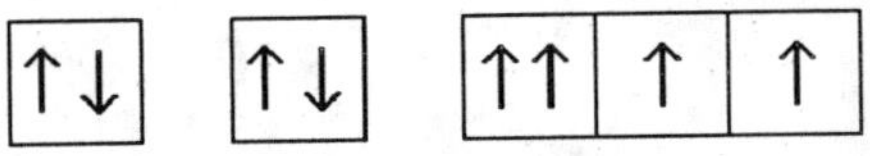 [↑↓] [↑↓] [↑↑|↑|↑]

d) 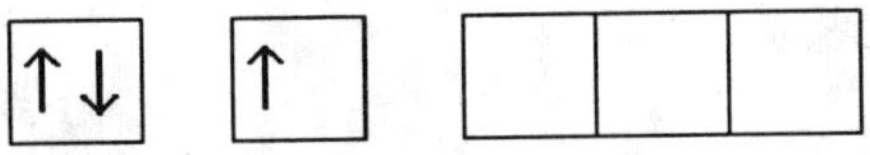 [↑↓] [↑] [| |]

Answer: c Page: 205

109. Which orbital diagram represents a violation of the Pauli Exclusion Principle?

a) | ↑↓ | | ↑↓ | | ↑↓ | | |

b) | ↑↓ | | ↑ | | | | |

c) | ↑↓ | | ↑↑ | | ↑ | | |

d) | ↑↓ | | ↑↓ | | ↑ | | ↑ |

Answer: c Page: 205

110. Which one of the following orbital diagrams violates the Pauli Exclusion Principle?

a) | ↑↓ | | ↑↓ | | ↑ | ↑ | |

b) | ↑↓ | | ↑↓ | | ↑ | | ↑ |

c) | ↑↓ | | ↑ | | ↑ | ↑ | |

d) | ↑↓ | | ↑↓↑ | | ↑ | | |

Answer: d Page: 205

111. Which set of orbital diagrams shows a violation of the Pauli Exclusion Principle?

a) [↑↓] [↑↑] [↑ | |]

b) [↑↓] [↑↓] [↑ | |]

c) [↑↓] [↑↓] [↑↓ | ↑ |]

d) [↑] [ ] [| |]

Answer: a Page: 205

112. Which orbital diagram represents a violation of the Pauli Exclusion Principle?

a) [↑↓] [↑↓] [↑ | ↑ | ↓]

b) [↑↓] [↓] [| |]

c) [↑↓] [↑↓] [↑↑ | |]

d) [↑↓] [↑↓] [↑ | ↑ |]

Answer: c Page: 205

113. The Stern-Gerlach experiment provided experimental evidence for
a) the spin of protons
b) the existence of the atomic nucleus
c) the spin of electrons
d) the shape of s orbitals

Answer: c Page: 206

114. Which one of the following orbitals can hold two electrons?
   a) $2p_x$
   b) 3s
   c) $4d_{xy}$
   d) all of the above

   Answer: d Page: 206

115. A 3p orbital can hold ___ electrons
   a) 1
   b) 2
   c) 3
   d) 4
   e) 8

   Answer: b Page: 206

116. Which one of the following elements has one or more unpaired electrons in the ground state?
   a) neon
   b) calcium
   c) zirconium
   d) cadmium
   e) mercury

   Answer: c Page: 206

117. Which one of the following is the correct orbital diagram for ground state nitrogen?

	1s	2s	2p	2p	2p
a)	↑↓	↑↓	↑↓	↑	
b)	↑↓	↑↑	↑	↑	↑
c)	↑↑	↑↓	↑	↑	↑
d)	↑↓	↑↓	↑	↑	↑

   Answer: d Page: 206

ESSAY

118. Write the electron configuration for a ground state phosphorus atom. Use long hand notation and label both core electrons and valence electrons.

Answer:

```
          valence
          |     |
1s²2s²2p⁶3s²3p³
| core |
```

Page: 206

MULTIPLE CHOICE

119. How many electrons populate the (complete) 3p electron subshell in the ground state of atomic xenon?
a) 2
b) 6
c) 8
d) 10
e) 36

Answer: b Page: 206

120. How many electrons populate the (complete) 2nd electron shell in the ground state of atomic argon?
a) 2
b) 6
c) 8
d) 18
e) 36

Answer: c Page: 206

121. How many electrons populate the (complete) 4d electron subshell in the ground state of atomic xenon?
a) 2
b) 6
c) 8
d) 10
e) 36

Answer: d Page: 206

122. Which one of the following orbital diagrams represents an excited atom?

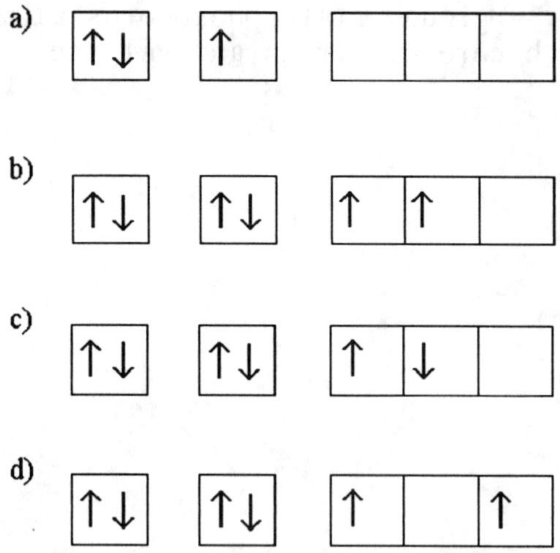

a) [↑↓] [↑] [| |]

b) [↑↓] [↑↓] [↑ | ↑ |]

c) [↑↓] [↑↓] [↑ | ↓ |]

d) [↑↓] [↑↓] [↑ | | ↑]

Answer: c Page: 206

123. $[Ar]4s^2 3d^{10} 4p^3$ is the electron configuration of
a) As
b) V
c) P
d) Sb

Answer: a Page: 206

124. The electron configuration of Ag is
a) $[Ar]4s^2 4d^9$
b) $[Kr]5s^1 4d^{10}$
c) $[Kr]5s^2 3d^9$
d) $[Ar]4s^1 4d^{10}$

Answer: b Page: 206

125. Which diagram represents an atom in the ground state?

a) 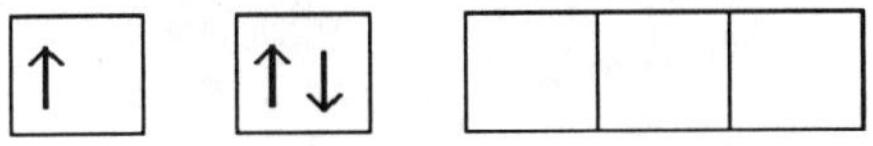 [↑] [↑↓] [| |]

b) 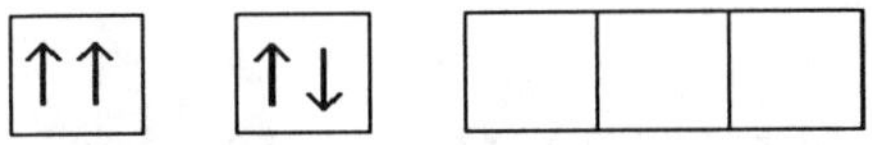 [↑↑] [↑↓] [| |]

c) 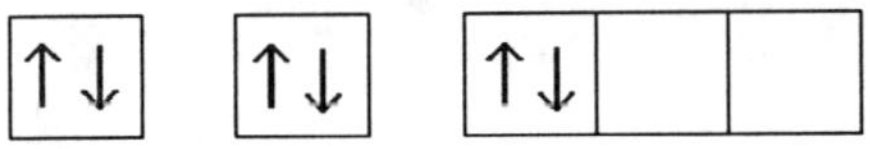 [↑↓] [↑↓] [↑↓| |]

d) 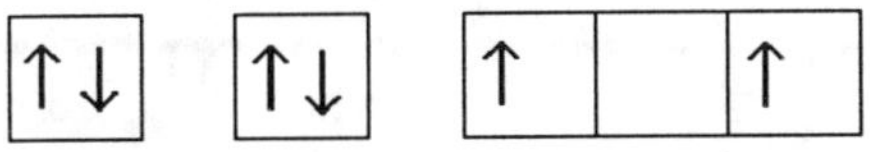 [↑↓] [↑↓] [↑| |↑]

Answer: d Page: 206

126. Which orbital diagram represents an atom in its ground state?
a) both w and x
b) both x and z
c) both x and y
d) both w and y

w) 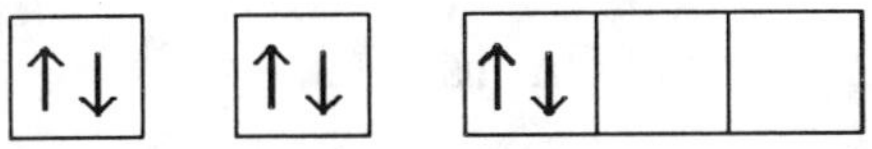 [↑↓] [↑↓] [↑↓| |]

x) 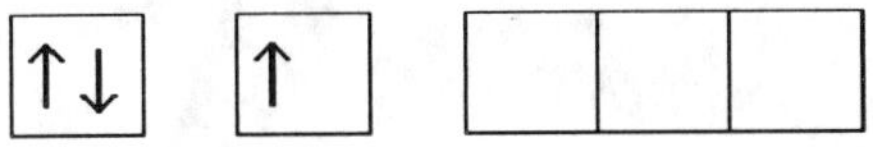 [↑↓] [↑] [| |]

y) 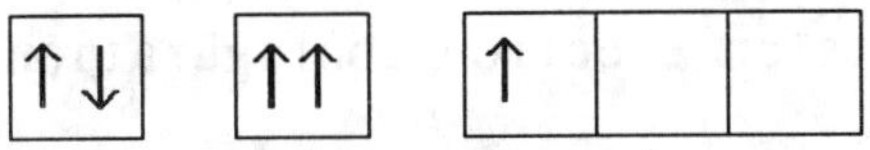 [↑↓] [↑↑] [↑| |]

z) 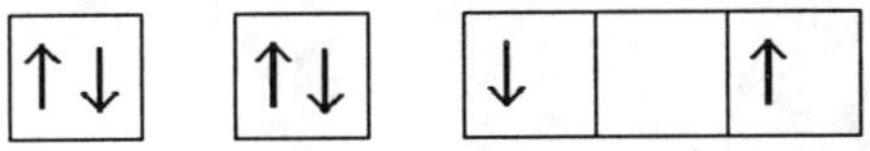 [↑↓] [↑↓] [↓| |↑]

Answer: b Page: 206

127. The electron configuration of Fe is given by
a) $1s^2 2s^2 3s^2 3p^6 3d^6$
b) $1s^2 2s^2 2p^6 3s^2 3p^6 3d^6 4s^2$
c) $1s^2 2s^2 2p^6 3s^2 3p^6 4s^2$
d) $1s^2 2s^2 2p^6 3s^2 3p^6 4s^2 4d^6$

Answer: b Page: 206

128. The electron configuration of Ga is given by
a) $1s^2 2s^2 3s^2 3p^6 3d^{10} 4s^2 4p^1$
b) $1s^2 2s^2 2p^6 3s^2 3p^6 4s^2 4d^{10} 4p^1$
c) $1s^2 2s^2 2p^6 3s^2 3p^6 3d^{10} 4s^2 4p^1$
d) $1s^2 2s^2 2p^6 3s^2 3p^6 3d^{10} 4s^2 4d^1$

Answer: c Page: 206

129. Which one of the following elements has the ground state electron configuration $[Kr]5s^1 4d^5$?
a) Nb
b) Mo
c) Cr
d) Mn

Answer: b Page: 206

130. Which one of the following elements has the ground state electron configuration $[Ar]4s^1 3d^5$?
a) V
b) Mn
c) Fe
d) Cr

Answer: d Page: 206

131. The ground state electron configuration for Zn is
a) $[Kr]4s^2 3d^{10}$
b) $[Ar]4s^2 3d^{10}$
c) $[Ar]4s^1 3d^{10}$
d) $[Ar]3s^2 3d^{10}$

Answer: b Page: 206

132. Which one of the following represents an electron configuration for an excited oxygen atom?
a) $1s^2 2s^2 2p^2$
b) $1s^2 2s^2 2p^2 3s^2$
c) $1s^2 2s^2 2p^1$
d) $1s^2 2s^2 2p^4$

Answer: b Page: 206

133. Which one of the following represents an excited carbon atom?
a) $1s^2 2s^2 2p^1 3s^1$
b) $1s^2 2s^2 2p^3$
c) $1s^2 2s^2 2p^1$
d) $1s^2 2s^2 3s^1$

Answer: a Page: 206

134. How many unpaired electrons are there in a ground state phosphorus atom?
   a) 0
   b) 1
   c) 2
   d) 3

   Answer: d Page: 206

135. How many unpaired electrons are there in a ground state fluorine atom?
   a) 0
   b) 1
   c) 2
   d) 3

   Answer: b Page: 206

136. For the $_{25}Mn$ atom, which subshell is partially filled?
   a) 3s
   b) 4s
   c) 4p
   d) 3d
   e) 4d

   Answer: d Page: 206

137. Which set of orbital diagrams shows a violation of Hund's Rule for an atom in its ground state?

   a) [↑↓] [↑↑] [↑ | |]

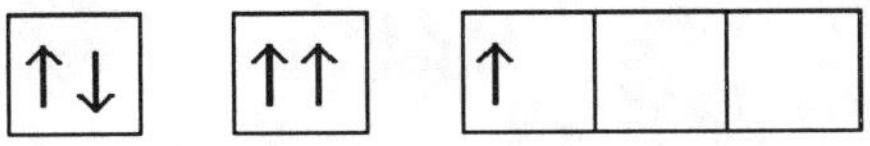

   b) [↑↓] [↑↓] [↑ | |]

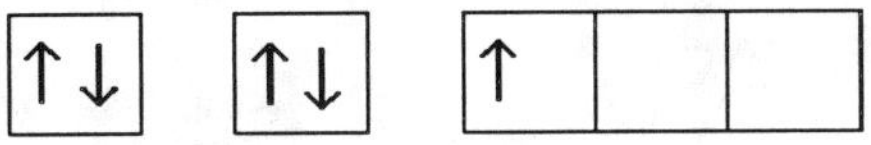

   c) [↑↓] [↑↓] [↑↓ | ↑ |]

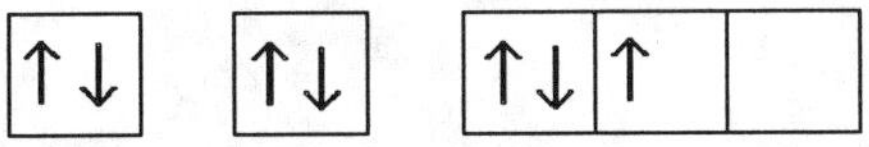

   d) [↑] [ ] [| |]

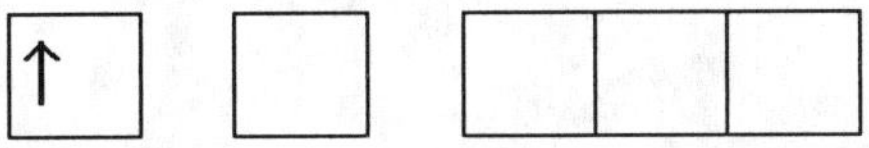

   Answer: c Page: 208

138. Which diagram represents a violation of Hund's Rule?

a) [↑] [↑↓] [| |]

b) [↑↑] [↑↓] [| |]

c) [↑↓] [↑↓] [↑↓ | |]

d) [↑↓] [↑↓] [↑ | | ↑]

Answer: c Page: 208

139. Which set of orbital diagrams shows a violation of Hund's Rule for an atom in its ground state?

a) [↑↓] [↑↓] [↑ | |]

b) [↑↓] [↑↓] [↑ | ↑↓ |]

c) [↑↓] [↑↓] [↑↑ | ↑ | ↑]

d) [↑↓] 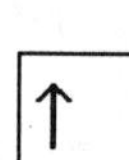 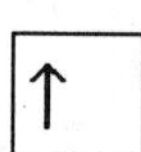 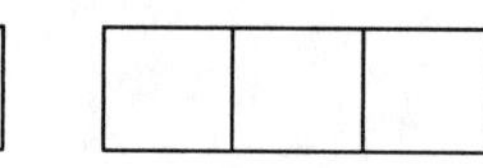

Answer: b Page: 208

140. Which one of the following ground state orbital diagrams violates Hund's Rule?

a) [↑↓] [↑↓] [↑ | ↑ |]

b) [↑↓] [↑↓] [↑ | | ↑]

c) [↑↓] [↑↓] [↓ | ↓ |]

d) [↑↓] [↑↓] [↑↓ | |]

Answer: d Page: 208

141. Which orbital diagram represents a violation of Hund's Rule?

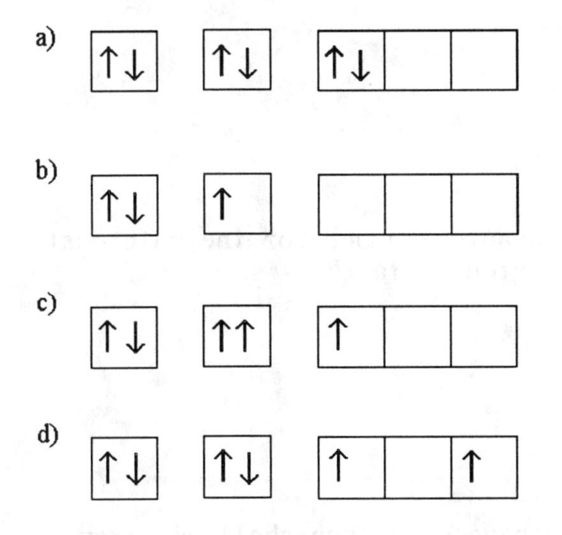

Answer: a Page: 208

142. Which orbital diagram represents a violation of Hund's Rule?

a) [↑↓] [↑↓] [↑ | ↑ | ↓]

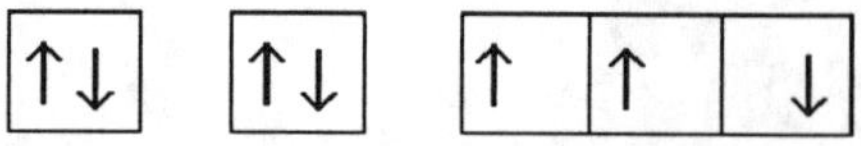

b) [↑↓] [↓] [| |]

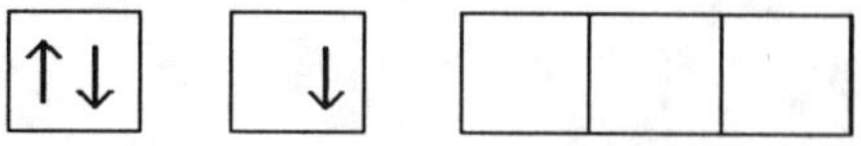

c) [↑↓] [↑↓] [↑↑ | |]

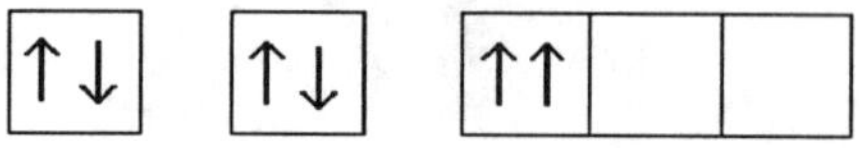

d) [↑↓] [↑↓] [↑ | ↑ |]

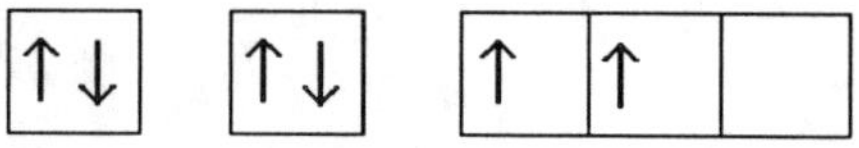

Answer: a Page: 208

143. What is the value of the n quantum number for the outermost electrons in a Br atom in the ground state?
a) 2
b) 3
c) 4
d) 5

Answer: c Page: 211

144. What is the value of the azimuthal quantum number for the outermost electrons in a nitrogen atom in the ground state?
a) 0
b) 1
c) 2
d) 3

Answer: b Page: 211

145. All of the elements in which column have a valence shell electron configuration ns^1?
a) noble gases
b) halogens
c) chalcogens
d) pnictogens
e) alkali metals
f) alkaline earth metals

Answer: e Page: 211

146. The valence shell of the element X contains 2 electrons in a 5s orbital. Below that shell, element X has a partially filled 4d subshell. What type of element is X?
a) main group element
b) chalcogen
c) halogen
d) transition metal
e) alkali metal

Answer: d Page: 211

147. The elements in the ___ period of the periodic table have a core electron configuration that is the same as the electron configuration of Ne.
a) first
b) second
c) third
d) fourth
e) fifth

Answer: c Page: 211

148. Which group of elements has p^6 as its outermost electron configuration?
a) 4A
b) 6A
c) 7A
d) noble gases

Answer: d Page: 211

149. Elements with the outermost electron configuration ns^2np^1 are found in which portion of the periodic table?
a) q
b) r
c) s
d) t

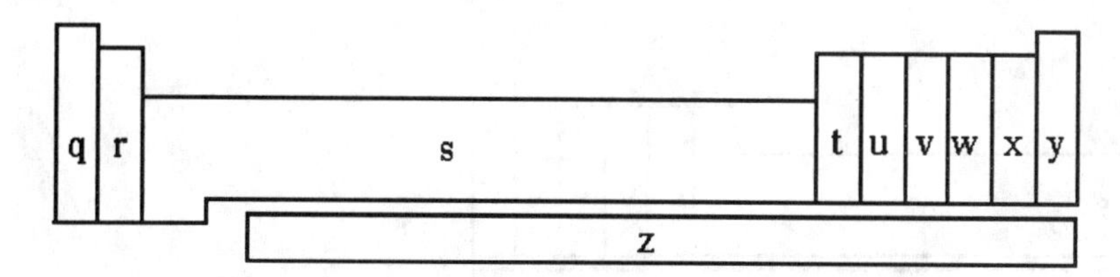

Answer: d Page: 211

150. What is the value of the azimuthal quantum number for the orbitals being filled in the portion of the periodic table labeled s?
a) 0
b) 1
c) 2
d) 3

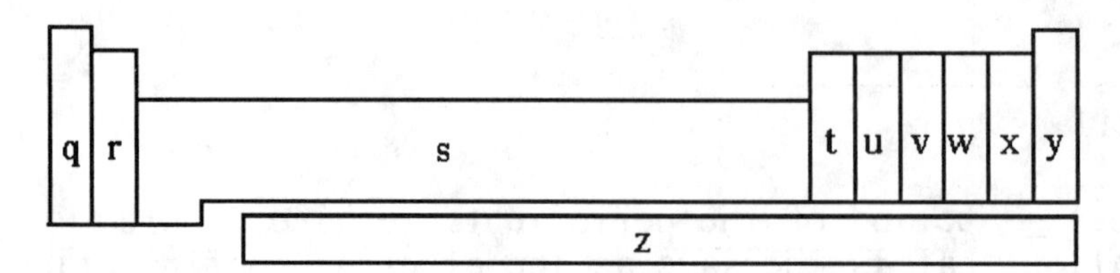

Answer: c Page: 211

151. Elements with the outermost electron configuration ns^2 are found in which portion of the periodic table?
a) q
b) r
c) s
d) t

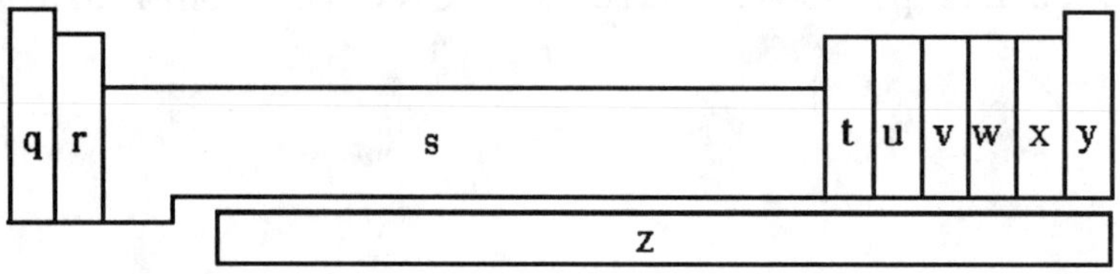

Answer: b Page: 211

152. What is the value of the azimuthal quantum number for the orbitals being filled in the portion of the periodic table labeled t?
a) 0
b) 1
c) 2
d) 3

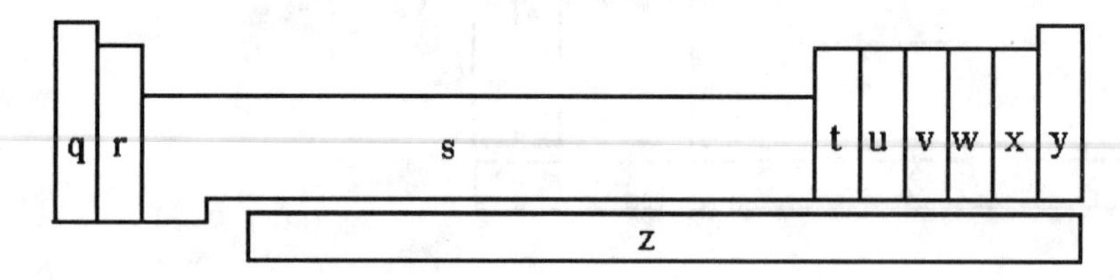

Answer: b Page: 211

153. What is the value of the azimuthal quantum number for the orbitals being filled in the portion of the periodic table labeled z?
   a) 0
   b) 1
   c) 2
   d) 3

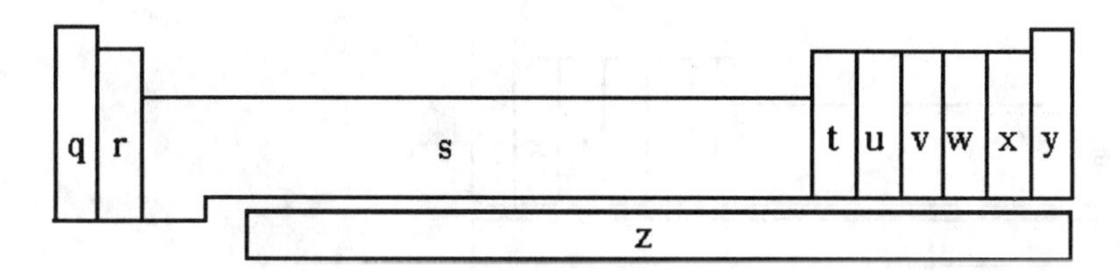

Answer: d Page: 211

154. Which group of the periodic table contains elements with valence shell electron configuration of ns^2np^1?
   a) 1A
   b) 2A
   c) 3A
   d) 4A

Answer: c Page: 211

155. Elements with the outermost electron configuration ns^2np^3 are found in which portion of the periodic table?
   a) s
   b) t
   c) u
   d) v

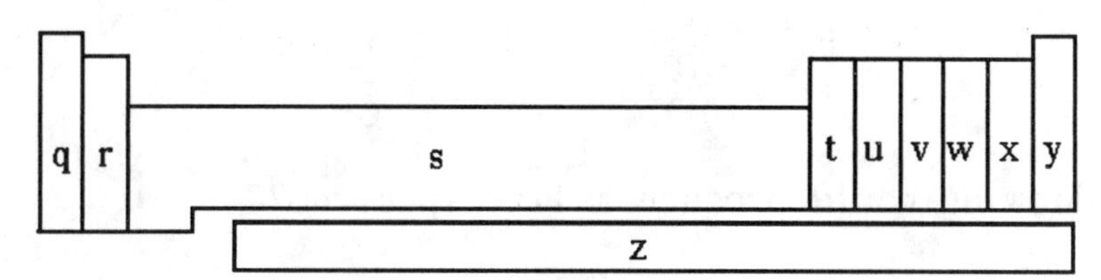

Answer: d Page: 211

156. What is the value of the azimuthal quantum number for the orbitals being filled in the portion of the periodic table labeled r?
a) 0
b) 1
c) 2
d) 3

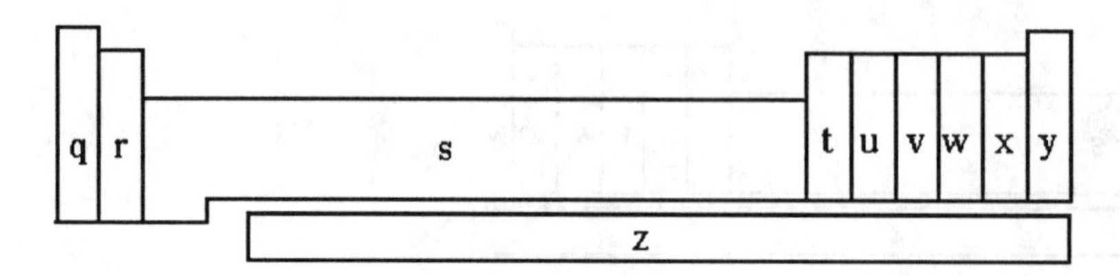

Answer: a Page: 211

157. What is the energy (in J) of a photon of electromagnetic radiation that has a wavelength of 9.0 meters?
($c = 3.00 \times 10^{8}$ m/s, $h = 6.63 \times 10^{-34}$ J•s.)
a) 2.2×10^{-26}
b) 4.5×10^{25}
c) 6.0×10^{-23}
d) 2.7×10^{9}

Answer: a Page: 197

158. What is the frequency of a photon with an energy of 3.7×10^{-18} J?
($h = 6.63 \times 10^{-34}$ J•s.)
a) 5.6×10^{15} s^{-1}
b) 1.8×10^{-16} s^{-1}
c) 2.5×10^{-15} s^{-1}
d) 5.4×10^{-8} s^{-1}

Answer: a Page: 197

159. Which one of the following would produce a line spectrum?
a) C_2H_6
b) Ar
c) $(CH_3)_3Al$
d) NH_3

Answer: b Page: 200

160. In the Bohr model of the atom
a) electrons travel in circular paths called orbitals
b) electrons can travel in paths of any energy
c) electron path energies are quantized
d) electron paths are designated by the Rydberg constant R_H

Answer: c Page: 200

161. An atom in the ground state
    a) has all electrons in the n = 1 orbit
    b) is finely divided
    c) will not absorb electromagnetic radiation of any wavelength
    d) has all electrons in the lowest energy orbits possible

    Answer: d Page: 200

SHORT ANSWER

162. Write the ground state electron configuration for copper.

    Answer: $[Ar]3d^{10}4s^1$ Page: 227

Chapter 7: Periodic Properties of the Elements

MULTIPLE CHOICE

1. Who is responsible for developing the concept of atomic numbers?
   a) Mendeleev
   b) Meyer
   c) Moseley
   d) Rutherford
   e) Faraday

   Answer: c Page: 224

2. Mendeleev's strategy for interpreting the periodic table would predict the chemical properties of element 32 to strongly resemble those of which element below?
   a) Zn
   b) Se
   c) Cu
   d) As
   e) Si

   Answer: e Page: 224

3. Which scientist was responsible for showing that the periodic table was arranged most logically by atomic number?
   a) Mendeleev
   b) Meyer
   c) Moseley
   d) Bohr
   e) Rutherford

   Answer: c Page: 224

4. What is the valence shell electron configuration of the halogens?
   a) ns^2np^6
   b) ns^1
   c) ns^2
   d) ns^2np^5
   e) ns^2np^3

   Answer: d Page: 226

5. In which one of the following atoms is the 1s orbital the smallest?
   a) Cl
   b) F
   c) Br
   d) I
   e) the 1s orbitals in all of these atoms are the same size

   Answer: d Page: 226

6. The 1s subshell is much closer to the nucleus in Ar than in He due to
   a) nuclear charge
   b) paramagnetism
   c) diamagnetism
   d) Hund's rule
   e) azimuthal quantum number

   Answer: a Page: 226

7. Atomic radius generally increases
   a) down a group and from right to left across a period
   b) up a group and from left to right across a period
   c) down a group and from left to right across a period
   d) up a group and from right to left across a period

   Answer: a Page: 227

8. Rank the elements below in order of decreasing atomic radius.
   Mg, Na, P, Si, Ar

   a) Mg,Na,P,Si,Ar
   b) Ar,Si,P,Na,Mg
   c) Si,P,Ar,Na,Mg
   d) Na,Mg,Si,P,Ar

   Answer: d Page: 227

9. Screening by valence electrons for representative elements is
   a) less efficient than that by core electrons
   b) more efficient than that by core electrons
   c) essentially identical to that by core electrons
   d) responsible for a general increase in atomic radius going across a period
   e) <u>both</u> more efficient than that by core electrons <u>and</u> responsible for a general increase in atomic radius going across a period

   Answer: a Page: 227

10. Atomic radius for the main-group elements generally increases down a group because
    a) effective nuclear charge increases down a group
    b) effective nuclear charge decreases down a group
    c) effective nuclear charge zigzags down a group
    d) the principal quantum number of the valence orbitals increases
    e) <u>both</u> effective nuclear charge increases down a group <u>and</u> the principal quantum number of the valence orbitals increases

    Answer: d Page: 227

11. Screening by core electrons for representative elements is
    a) less efficient than that by valence electrons
    b) more efficient than that by valence electrons
    c) essentially identical to that by valence electrons
    d) responsible for a general decrease in atomic radius going down a group
    e) both essentially identical to that by valence electrons and responsible for a general decrease in atomic radius going down a group

    Answer: b Page: 227

12. Which one of the following atoms has the largest radius?
    a) O
    b) F
    c) S
    d) Cl

    Answer: c Page: 227

13. Which one of the following atoms has the largest radius?
    a) Sr
    b) Ca
    c) K
    d) Rb

    Answer: d Page: 227

14. Select the smallest atom from the following list.
    a) Na
    b) Cl
    c) Fe
    d) P

    Answer: b Page: 227

15. Which one of the following atoms has the largest radius?
    a) I
    b) Co
    c) Ba
    d) Sr

    Answer: c Page: 227

16. Which one of the following elements has the largest atomic radius?
    a) Se
    b) As
    c) S
    d) Sb

    Answer: d Page: 227

17. Which one of the following elements has the largest atomic radius?
    a) O
    b) F
    c) Al
    d) P

    Answer: c Page: 227

18. The equation for the first ionization energy of fluorine is
    a) $F_2 + 2e^- \rightarrow 2F^-$
    b) $F_{(g)} + e^- \rightarrow F^-_{(g)}$
    c) $F_{(g)} \rightarrow F^+_{(g)} + e^-$
    d) $F^+_{(g)} \rightarrow F^{2+}_{(g)} + e^-$

    Answer: c Page: 229

19. Which ionization energy is the greatest?
    a) first
    b) second
    c) third
    d) fourth

    Answer: d Page: 229

20. In general, ____ have higher first ionization energies than ____.
    a) metals, nonmetals
    b) nonmetals, metals

    Answer: b Page: 229

21. In which choice below are the elements ranked in order of increasing first ionization energy?
    a) P,Cl,S,Al,Ar,Si
    b) Ar,Cl,S,P,Si,Al
    c) Al,Si,P,S,Cl,Ar
    d) Al,Si,S,P,Cl,Ar

    Answer: d Page: 229

ESSAY

22. Why is the first ionization energy of nitrogen greater than that of oxygen?

    Answer:
    The first electron lost from nitrogen is removed from a half filled 2p subshell which is more stable than the partially filled 2p subshell from which the first electron is removed in oxygen. Thus more energy is required to remove the first electron from nitrogen than from oxygen.
    Page: 229

MULTIPLE CHOICE

23. The first ionization energies of the elements ______ as you go from left to right across a period of the periodic table, and _______ as you go from the bottom to the top of a group in the table.
 a) increase, increase
 b) increase, decrease
 c) decrease, increase
 d) decrease, decrease

 Answer: a Page: 229

24. Which one of the following atoms has the largest <u>first</u> ionization energy?
 a) Br
 b) O
 c) C
 d) P

 Answer: b Page: 229

25. Which one of the following elements has the largest <u>first</u> ionization energy?
 a) Na
 b) Al
 c) Se
 d) Cl

 Answer: d Page: 229

26. Which one of the following elements has the largest <u>first</u> ionization energy?
 a) K
 b) Rb
 c) Sr
 d) Ca

 Answer: d Page: 229

27. Which one of the following elements has the largest <u>first</u> ionization energy?
 a) Se
 b) As
 c) S
 d) Sb

 Answer: c Page: 229

28. Which one of the following elements would have the largest <u>first</u> ionization energy?
    a) B
    b) N
    c) P
    d) Si

    Answer: b Page: 229

29. Which one of the following elements has the largest <u>second</u> ionization energy?
    a) Rb
    b) Sr
    c) Y
    d) Cs

    Answer: a Page: 229

30. Which one of the following elements has the largest <u>second</u> ionization energy?
    a) K
    b) Rb
    c) Sr
    d) Ca

    Answer: a Page: 229

31. Which one of the following elements would have the largest <u>second</u> ionization energy?
    a) Ca
    b) Sr
    c) Sc
    d) K

    Answer: d Page: 229

32. Which one of the following elements has the largest <u>third</u> ionization energy?
    a) As
    b) Sc
    c) Ti
    d) Ca

    Answer: d Page: 229

33. Periodic trends are most pronounced across the periods of
    a) main group elements
    b) transition elements
    c) alkali metals
    d) noble gases

    Answer: a Page: 230

34. Electron affinity is generally
    a) endothermic
    b) exothermic

    Answer: b Page: 233

ESSAY

35. Explain the reason that the electron affinity of carbon is more exothermic than that of nitrogen.

    Answer:
    The electron added to carbon converts the 2p subshell from partially filled, $2p^2$, to half-filled, $2p^3$, thus adding stability to the atom. The electron added to nitrogen converts a half filled 2p subshell to a partially filled subshell, increasing the energy of the atom.
    Page: 233

MULTIPLE CHOICE

36. The ___ have the most negative electron affinities.
    a) alkaline earth metals
    b) alkali metals
    c) halogens
    d) transition metals

    Answer: c Page: 233

ESSAY

37. Explain why electron affinity does not change appreciably down a group.

    Answer:
    Proceeding down a group, atomic radius increases. Thus the added electron is farther from the nucleus. This decreases the energy released. Counterbalancing this decrease in energy release is the decrease in energy consumed to overcome electron electron repulsion in the outer shell because of its increasing size in proceeding down a group.
    Page: 233

MULTIPLE CHOICE

38. Which of the following elements has the most exothermic electron affinity?
a) Na
b) Li
c) Be
d) N
e) F

Answer: e Page: 233

39. Which one of the following elements has the largest (most exothermic) electron affinity?
a) S
b) Cl
c) Se
d) Br

Answer: b Page: 233

40. Which one of the following elements has the greatest (most exothermic) electron affinity?
a) P
b) Al
c) Si
d) Cl

Answer: d Page: 233

41. Which one of the following elements would have the largest (most exothermic) electron affinity?
a) O
b) K
c) B
d) Na

Answer: a Page: 233

42. In general, as you go across a period from left to right in the periodic table the atomic radius ______, the exothermicity of the electron affinity ________, and the first ionization energy _________.
a) decreases, decreases, increases
b) increases, increases, decreases
c) increases, increases, increases
d) decreases, increases, increases

Answer: d Page: 233

43. What value for the electron affinity of an element would indicate that its anion is unstable?
a. 0
b. >0
c. <0

Answer: b Page: 233

44. The element with the most negative electron affinity is
a. oxygen
b. sodium
c. fluorine
d. hydrogen
e. chlorine

Answer: e Page: 233

45. Of the following choices, which element is the most metallic?
a) strontium
b) barium
c) magnesium
d) calcium

Answer: b Page: 235

46. Which element in the chromium group is the most metallic?
a) W
b) Cr
c) Mo

Answer: b Page: 235

47. Which one of the following is a transition metal?
a) V
b) Rb
c) Al
d) Be

Answer: a Page: 235

48. Which one of the following is a metalloid?
a) Ge
b) S
c) Br
d) Pb

Answer: a Page: 235

49. The series which correctly lists from left to right a halogen, an alkaline earth, a transition metal, and an active metal is
    a) Cl, K, V, Mg
    b) Br, Ba, Cr, Na
    c) O, Ca, Ce, Al
    d) F, Sr, Fe, Sn

    Answer: b Page: 235

50. Which of the following is the most metallic?
    a) Na
    b) Mg
    c) Al
    d) K

    Answer: d Page: 235

51. Which one of the following elements is the most metallic?
    a) Sr
    b) Ca
    c) K
    d) Rb

    Answer: d Page: 235

52. Which one of the following elements is the most metallic?
    a) Mg
    b) Na
    c) K
    d) Al

    Answer: c Page: 235

53. Which series correctly lists elements in order of <u>decreasing</u> metallic character from left to right?
    a) B, N, Si
    b) F, Cl, S
    c) P, N, O
    d) P, S, Se

    Answer: c Page: 235

54. The compound most likely to be a gas at room temperature and pressure is
    a) C_2H_6
    b) Al_2O_3
    c) NaF
    d) SiO_2

    Answer: a Page: 235

SHORT ANSWER

55. In their compounds, the charges on the alkali metals are _______ and on the alkaline earth metals are _____ .

Answer: 1+, 2+, respectively Page: 235

MULTIPLE CHOICE

56. If Na reacts with element X to form an ionic compound with the formula Na_3X, then Ca will react with X to form
a) CaX_2
b) CaX
c) Ca_2X_3
d) Ca_3X_2

Answer: d Page: 235

57. Element M reacts with chlorine to form a compound with the formula MCl_2. It is more reactive than magnesium and smaller than barium. This element is
a) Sr
b) K
c) Na
d) Ra

Answer: a Page: 235

58. Of the metals below, all have low melting points except
a) Cs
b) Ga
c) W
d) Hg

Answer: c Page: 235

59. The oxide of which element below can react with hydrochloric acid?
a) sulfur
b) selenium
c) nitrogen
d) sodium

Answer: d Page: 235

60. The element with the highest melting point is
a) Ca
b) K
c) Sc
d) Na

Answer: c Page: 235

61. All of the following are ionic compounds except
    a) K_2O
    b) Na_2SO_4
    c) SiO_2
    d) Li_3N

    Answer: c Page: 235

62. This element reacts with chlorine to form a compound with the formula XCl_2. The oxide of this element is basic. Element X is
    a) Rb
    b) Ca
    c) Al
    d) P

    Answer: b Page: 235

63. Which one of the following compounds would produce a basic solution when dissolved in water?
    a) SO_2
    b) Na_2O
    c) CO_2
    d) OF_2

    Answer: b Page: 235

64. Element M reacts with oxygen to form an oxide with the formula MO. When MO is dissolved in water, the resulting solution is basic. Element M is most likely
    a) Na
    b) Ba
    c) S
    d) N

    Answer: b Page: 235

65. Which one of the following metals is most likely to form several different positive ions?
    a) Al
    b) Cs
    c) V
    d) Ca

    Answer: c Page: 235

66. Which one of the elements below has the greatest first ionization energy?
a) Li
b) K
c) Na
d) H
e) Rb
f) Cs

Answer: d Page: 235

ESSAY

67. Write and balance the reaction between zinc oxide and sulfuric acid.

Answer: $ZnO + H_2SO_4 \rightarrow ZnSO_4 + H_2O$ Page: 236

68. Seven nonmetals exist as diatomic molecules in their elemental forms. List them.

Answer: hydrogen, oxygen, nitrogen, fluorine, chlorine, bromine, iodine

Page: 248

69. Seven nonmetals exist as diatomic molecules in their elemental forms. Which one is a liquid at room temperature?

Answer: bromine Page: 237

MULTIPLE CHOICE

70. The reaction of a metal with a nonmetal produces a(n)
a) base
b) salt
c) acid
d) oxide
e) hydroxide

Answer: b Page: 237

71. Which nonmetal exists as a diatomic volatile solid?
a) bromine
b) antimony
c) phosphorus
d) iodine
e) boron

Answer: d Page: 237

72. When a metal and a nonmetal react, which one tends to gain electrons?
    a) the metal
    b) the nonmetal
    c) neither

    Answer: b Page: 237

73. Which halogen is solid at room temperature?
    a) Cl
    b) F
    c) Br
    d) I

    Answer: d Page: 248

SHORT ANSWER

74. The oxides of metals are _____ in water whereas the oxides of nonmetals are _____ in water.

    Answer: bases, acids Page: 238

75. Write the balanced chemical equation for the reaction of sulfur trioxide with potassium hydroxide.

    Answer: $SO_3 + 2KOH \rightarrow K_2SO_4 + H_2O$ Page: 239

76. Nonmetal oxides react with bases to form

    Answer: salt + water Page: 239

MULTIPLE CHOICE

77. The elements with the lowest first ionization energies belong to what group?
    a) alkali metals
    b) transition elements
    c) halogens
    d) alkaline earth metals
    e) noble gases

    Answer: a Page: 239

78. What is the coefficient of M when the following equation is completed and balanced if M is an alkali metal?

$$M(s) + H_2O(l) \rightarrow$$

a) 1
b) 2
c) 3
d) 4

Answer: b Page: 239

79. Which of these oxides is most basic?
a) K_2O
b) Al_2O_3
c) CO_2
d) MgO

Answer: a Page: 239

80. Which of these oxides is most acidic?
a) CaO
b) CO_2
c) Al_2O_3
d) Li_2O

Answer: b Page: 239

81. Which one of the following compounds would produce an acidic solution when dissolved in water?
a) Na_2O
b) CaO
c) MgO
d) CO_2

Answer: d Page: 239

82. Which of the following traits characterizes the alkali metals?
a) very high melting point
b) existence as diatomic molecules
c) common formation of dianions
d) the lowest I_1 values of the elements in each period
e) the smallest atom in each period

Answer: d Page: 239

83. Which one of the following substances is <u>always</u> produced when an active metal reacts with water?
a) NaOH
b) H_2O
c) CO_2
d) H_2

Answer: d Page: 239

84. Which one of the following is an active metal?
a) Fe
b) Al
c) Ca
d) Mn

Answer: c Page: 239

85. This element is more reactive than lithium and magnesium but less reactive than potassium. This element is
a) Na
b) Rb
c) Ca
d) Be

Answer: a Page: 239

86. Which one of the following is not true about the alkali metals?
a) they are low density solids at room temperature
b) they all readily form ions with a +1 charge
c) they all have 2 electrons in their valence shells
d) they are very reactive elements
e) they have the lowest first ionization energies of the elements

Answer: c Page: 239

87. Elemental sodium is prepared commercially by
a. electrolysis of seawater
b. electrolysis of molten NaCl
c. reaction of sulfuric acid with brine
d. roasting of galena
e. pyrolysis of limestone

Answer: b Page: 239

SHORT ANSWER

88. When an alkali metal reacts with hydrogen, what form of hydrogen is produced and what is it called?

Answer: H-, hydride Page: 239

MULTIPLE CHOICE

89. The reaction of potassium metal with elemental hydrogen produces
    a) KH
    b) KH_2
    c) K_2H
    d) none of these; potassium will not react directly with hydrogen

    Answer: a Page: 239

90. Which alkali metal reacts with oxygen to form the oxide, M2O?
    a) Li
    b) Na
    c) K
    d) Rb
    e) Cs

    Answer: a Page: 240

91. Which alkali metal can react with oxygen to form the oxide or the peroxide?
    a) Li
    b) Na
    c) K
    d) Rb
    e) Cs

    Answer: b Page: 240

SHORT ANSWER

92. Which alkali metals can react with oxygen to form either the peroxide or the superoxide?

    Answer: K, Rb, and Cs Page: 252

93. Which two elements are the least reactive of the alkaline earth metals?

    Answer: Be and Mg Page: 241

MULTIPLE CHOICE

94. Which alkaline earth metal will not react with water or with steam?
    a) Be
    b) Mg
    c) Ca
    d) Ba
    e) Sr

    Answer: a Page: 243

95. What is the coefficient of H_2O when the following equation is completed and balanced?

$$Ba(s) + H_2O(l) \rightarrow$$

a) 1
b) 2
c) 3
d) 5

Answer: b Page: 243

96. Which onc of the following is the least reactive?
a) Mg
b) Sr
c) Ca
d) Ba

Answer: a Page: 243

97. What element is used to produce the red color in fireworks and flares?
a) Mg
b) Sr
c) Ca
d) Ba

Answer: b Page: 243

98. Which trait below characterizes the alkaline earth metals?
a) the smallest atom in each period
b) common formation of monoanions
c) formation of basic oxides
d) existence as triatomic molecules
e) formation of halides of formula MX

Answer: c Page: 243

99. Which one of the following beverages originally was billed to contain lithium?
a) Coca Cola
b) Pepsi Cola
c) Gatorade
d) Koolaid
e) Seven-Up

Answer: e Page: 242

100. The carbonate of which alkali metal is used in treatment of manic-depressive illness?
a) Li
b) Na
c) K
d) Rb
e) Cs

Answer: a Page: 242

101. Of the following elements, which one does not really belong to any particular group?
a) nitrogen
b) radium
c) hydrogen
d) tungsten
e) copper

Answer: c Page: 243

102. Which one of the following is not true about oxygen?
a) the most stable allotrope is O_2
b) ozone is toxic whereas O_2 is not
c) dry air is about 80% oxygen
d) it forms two unstable ions, peroxide and superoxide

Answer: c Page: 244

103. The most common allotropic form of sulfur is
a) S
b) S_2
c) S_4
d) S_8

Answer: d Page: 244

104. Which group 6A element is most metallic in character?
a) oxygen
b) sulfur
c) selenium
d) tellurium
e) polonium

Answer: e Page: 244

105. The reduction of sulfur atoms produces ions with a charge of
a) -2
b) -1
c) +4
d) +6

Answer: a Page: 244

106. Which one of the following elements has an allotropic form that is produced in the upper atmosphere by lightning?
a) N
b) O
c) S
d) Cl

Answer: b Page: 244

107. The element phosphorus exists in two forms in nature called white phosphorus and red phosphorus. These two forms are examples of __________.
a) isotopes
b) allotropes
c) oxidation
d) metalloids

Answer: b Page: 244

108. This element reacts with oxygen to form an oxide with the formula XO_3. When added to water, XO_3 forms an acidic solution. Element X is
a) K
b) C
c) Mg
d) S

Answer: d Page: 244

109. In nature, sulfur is most commonly found in what form?
a) pure elemental
b) the oxides
c) metal sulfides
d) sulfuric acid
e) H_2S

Answer: c Page: 245

110. Which one of the following groups contains only nonmetals?
a) 1A
b) 2A
c) 6A
d) 7A
e) 5A

Answer: d Page: 245

ESSAY

111. Write the correctly balanced equation for the reaction of elemental fluorine with water.

Answer: $2H_2O + 2F_2 \rightarrow 4HF + O_2$ Page: 245

112. Write the correctly balanced equation for the reaction of elemental chlorine with water.

Answer: $Cl_2 + H_2O \rightarrow HCl + HOCl$ Page: 245

MULTIPLE CHOICE

113. Which hydrogen halide is a weak acid?
a) HCl
b) HBr
c) HF
d) HI

Answer: c Page: 245

114. Which trait below characterizes the halogens?
a) existence of all under ambient conditions as diatomic gases
b) tendency to form positive ions of several different charges
c) tendency to form negative ions of several different charges
d) metallic character
e) formation of alkali metal salts of formula MX

Answer: e Page: 245

115. This element reacts with hydrogen to produce a gas with the formula HX. When dissolved in water, HX forms an acidic solution. Element X is
a) Na
b) H
c) C
d) Br

Answer: d Page: 245

116. Osteoporosis is associated with the deficiency of ____ in the diet.
a) Li
b) Na
c) Ca
d) Mg
e) Fe

Answer: c Page: 247

SHORT ANSWER

117. Give the name and formula for the primary mineral in bone and in teeth.

Answer: hydroxyapatite, $Ca_5(PO_4)_3OH$ Page: 247

MULTIPLE CHOICE

118. In nature, the noble gases exist as
    a) monatomic gaseous atoms
    b) the gaseous fluorides
    c) as solids in rocks and in minerals
    d) as alkali metal salts
    e) as the sulfides

    Answer: a Page: 247

119. The first noble gas to be incorporated into a compound was
    a) Ar
    b) Kr
    c) He
    d) Ne
    e) Xe

    Answer: e Page: 261

120. The trend for electron affinity going left to right across a period of main-group elements is best described as
    a) becoming linearly more exothermic
    b) becoming linearly less exothermic
    c) becoming generally more exothermic, but with considerable interruptions due to electron-configuration effects
    d) becoming generally less exothermic, but with considerable interruptions due to electron-configuration effects
    e) remaining essentially constant

    Answer: c Page: 233

Chapter 8: Basic Concepts of Chemical Bonding

MULTIPLE CHOICE

1. The type of compound that is most likely to contain a covalent bond is
   a) one that is composed of a metal from the far left of the periodic table and a nonmetal from the far right of the periodic table
   b) a solid metal
   c) one that is composed of only nonmetals
   d) is held together by the electrostatic forces between oppositely charged ions

   Answer: c Page: 255

2. Of the following choices, which one is possibly an alkaline earth metal?
   a) X·
   b) X:
   c)
   ..
   :X:
   ..
   d)
   ·
   :X:
   ·

   Answer: b Page: 255

ESSAY

3. Write the electron-dot symbol for phosphide ions.

   Answer:
   ..
   :P: $^{3-}$
   ..

   Page: 255

MULTIPLE CHOICE

4. How many electrons appear in the Lewis electron-dot symbol for a phosphorus atom?
   a) 4 paired and 2 unpaired
   b) 2 paired and 4 unpaired
   c) 2 paired and 3 unpaired
   d) 4 paired and 3 unpaired
   e) 0 paired and 3 unpaired

   Answer: c Page: 255

5. How many electrons appear in the Lewis electron-dot symbol for a fluorine atom?
a) 4 paired and 2 unpaired
b) 4 paired and 3 unpaired
c) 2 paired and 5 unpaired
d) 6 paired and 1 unpaired
e) 0 paired and 5 unpaired

Answer: d Page: 255

6. Based upon electron configuration, which ion would magnesium most likely form?
a) Mg^{2+}
b) Mg^{2-}
c) Mg^{6-}
d) Mg^{6+}
e) Mg^{-}

Answer: a Page: 255

7. Based upon electron configuration, which ion would phosphorus most likely form?
a) P^{3+}
b) P^{3-}
c) P^{5+}
d) P^{5-}
e) P^{+}

Answer: b Page: 255

8. Based upon electron configuration, which ion would iodine most likely form?
a) I^{2+}
b) I^{4+}
c) I^{4-}
d) I^{+}
e) I^{-}

Answer: e Page: 255

9. How many unpaired electrons are in the Lewis electron-dot symbol for an oxygen atom?
a) 0
b) 1
c) 2
d) 4

Answer: c Page: 255

10. How many unpaired electrons are there in a N^{3-} ion?
a) 0
b) 1
c) 2
d) 3

Answer: a Page: 255

11. How many unpaired electrons are there in a O^{2-} ion?
a) 0
b) 1
c) 2
d) 3

Answer: a Page: 255

12. Which step in the formation of KBr from gaseous potassium atoms and gaseous bromine atoms is endothermic?
a) the ionization of the gaseous potassium atoms to K^+
b) the addition of an electron to the gaseous bromine atoms to form Br^-
c) K^+ and Br^- ions coming together to form the KBr lattice
d) none of these

Answer: c Page: 258

13. The chloride of which of the following metals should have the greatest lattice energy?
a) potassium
b) rubidium
c) sodium
d) lithium
e) cesium

Answer: d Page: 258

14. Which one of the following reactions is endothermic?
a) $P_{(g)} + e^- \rightarrow P^-$
b) $P_{(g)} + 2e^- \rightarrow P^{2-}$
c) $P_{(g)} + 3e^- \rightarrow nP^{3-}$
d) $P_{(g)} + 4e^- \rightarrow P^{4-}$

Answer: d Page: 258

SHORT ANSWER

15. Write the chemical equation for the reaction that has a ΔH = lattice energy for potassium bromide.

Answer: $KBr(s) \rightarrow K+(g) + Br^-(g)$ Page: 259

MULTIPLE CHOICE

16. Lattice energy _____ as ionic radius increases and _____ as ionic charge increases.
a) decreases, increases
b) increases, decreases
c) increases, increases
d) decreases, decreases

Answer: a Page: 259

17. Which one of the following ionic compounds would have the highest melting point?
a) K_2O
b) KCl
c) $CaCl_2$
d) MgO

Answer: d Page: 259

18. Which compound below has the lowest melting point?
a) Na_2O
b) Na_2S
c) KCl
d) MgS

Answer: c Page: 259

19. Which one of the following has the highest melting point?
a) NaCl
b) Na_2S
c) KCl
d) KBr

Answer: b Page: 259

20. The diagram below is the Born-Haber cycle for the formation of potassium fluoride. Which energy change corresponds to the negative lattice energy of potassium fluoride?
a) 2
b) 5
c) 4
d) 1
e) 6

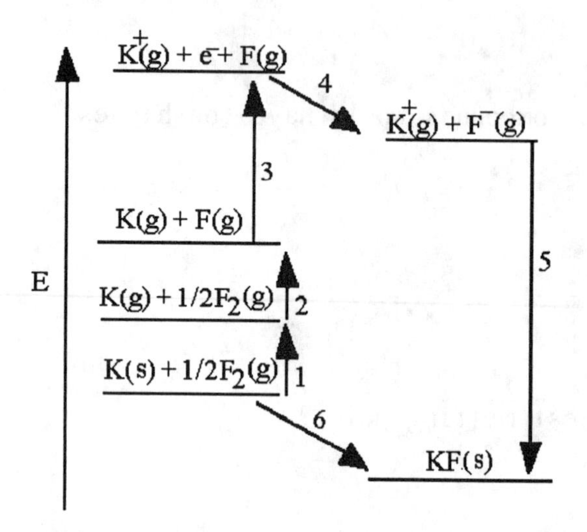

Answer: b Page: 260

21. The diagram below is the Born-Haber cycle for the formation of potassium fluoride. Which energy change corresponds to the electron affinity of fluorine?
a) 2
b) 5
c) 4
d) 1
e) 6

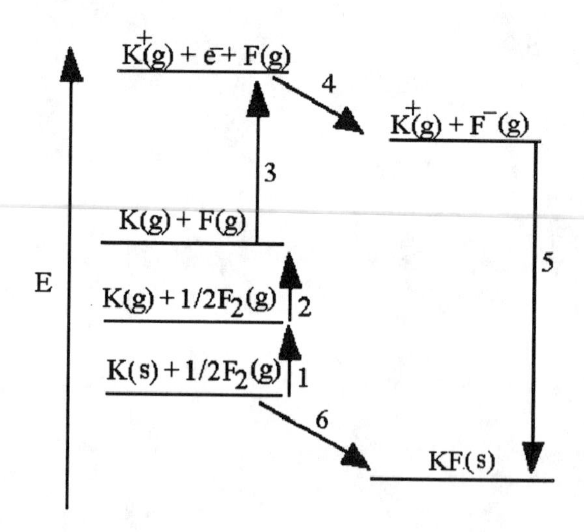

Answer: c Page: 260

22. The diagram below is the Born-Haber cycle for the formation of potassium fluoride. Which energy change corresponds to the first ionization energy of potassium?
 a) 2
 b) 5
 c) 4
 d) 3
 e) 6

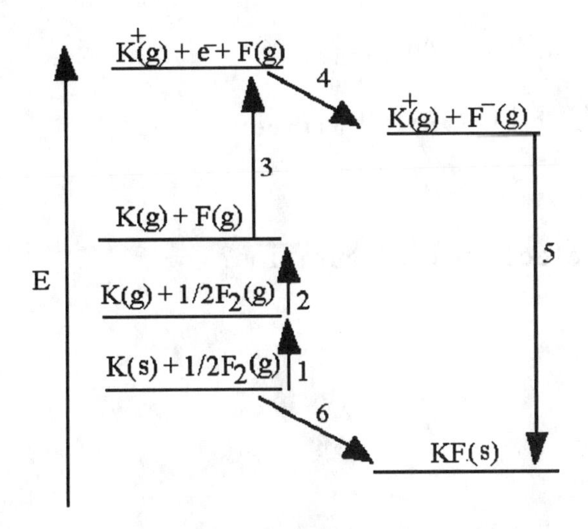

Answer: d Page: 260

23. A Born-Haber analysis shows that KF is more stable than KF_2 because
 a) of the very high heat of sublimation of K
 b) of the very high first ionization potential of F
 c) of the very high second ionization potential of K
 d) the lattice energy of KF_2 is much greater than that of KF
 e) the lattice energy of KF is much greater than that of KF_2

Answer: c Page: 260

24. A Born-Haber analysis shows CaF_2 preferred over CaF due to
 a) the relative magnitudes of lattice energies of CaF_2 and CaF
 b) the removal of valence, not core, electrons in both the first and second ionization potentials for Ca
 c) the low heat of sublimation of Ca
 d) <u>both</u> the relative magnitudes of lattice energies of CaF_2 and CaF <u>and</u> the removal of valence, not core, electrons in both the first and second ionization potentials for C
 e) <u>both</u> the removal of valence, not core, electrons in both the first and second ionization potentials for Ca <u>and</u> the low heat of sublimation of Ca

Answer: d Page: 260

25. According to the Born-Haber cycle, the ΔH_f° of KBr is equal to

a) $\Delta H_f^\circ[K_{(g)}] + \Delta H_f^\circ[Br_{(g)}] + I_1(K) + E(Br) + \Delta H_{lattice}$

b) $\Delta H_f^\circ[K_{(g)}] - \Delta H_f^\circ[Br_{(g)}] - I_1(K) - E(Br) - \Delta H_{lattice}$

c) $\Delta H_f^\circ[K_{(g)}] - \Delta H_f^\circ[Br_{(g)}] + I_1(K) - E(Br) + \Delta H_{lattice}$

d) $\Delta H_f^\circ[K_{(g)}] + \Delta H_f^\circ[Br_{(g)}] - I_1 - E(Br) + \Delta H_{lattice}$

e) $\Delta H_f^\circ[K_{(g)}] + \Delta H_f^\circ[Br_{(g)}] + I_1(K) + E(Br) - \Delta H_{lattice}$

Answer: e Page: 260

26. Which ion below has a noble gas electron configuration?
a) Li^{2+}
b) Be^{2+}
c) B^{2+}
d) C^{2+}
e) N^{2-}

Answer: b Page: 262

27. Which ion below has a noble gas electron configuration?
a) S^{3-}
b) O^{2+}
c) I^{+}
d) K^{-}
e) Cl^{-}

Answer: e Page: 262

28. Which one of the following electron configurations corresponds to a P^{3-} ion?
a) $[Ne]3s^2$
b) $[Ne]3s^23p^6$
c) $[Ne]3s^23p^3$
d) $[Ne]3p^2$

Answer: b Page: 262

29. Which one of the following is the electron configuration for the S^{2-} ion?
a) $[Ar]3s^23p^6$
b) $[Ar]3s^23p^2$
c) $[Ne]3s^23p^2$
d) $[Ne]3s^23p^6$

Answer: d Page: 262

ESSAY

30. Write the electron configuration for Cu^{2+}.

    Answer: $[Ar]3d^9$ Page: 262

MULTIPLE CHOICE

31. What is the principal quantum number of the electrons that are lost when tungsten forms a cation?
    a) 6
    b) 5
    c) 4
    d) 3
    e) 2
    f) 1

    Answer: a Page: 262

32. Which one of the following species has the electron configuration $[Ar]3d^4$?
    a) Mn^{2+}
    b) Cr^{2+}
    c) V^{3+}
    d) Fe^{3+}

    Answer: b Page: 262

33. Which one of the following is the electron configuration for the Co^{2+} ion?
    a) $1s^22s^22p^63s^23p^64s^13d^6$
    b) $1s^22s^22p^63s^23p^64s^03d^7$
    c) $1s^22s^22p^63s^23p^64s^03d^5$
    d) $1s^22s^22p^63s^23p^64s^23d^9$

    Answer: b Page: 262

34. Which one of the following is the electron configuration for the Fe^{2+} ion?
    a) $1s^22s^22p^63s^23p^64s^03d^6$
    b) $1s^22s^22p^63s^23p^64s^23d^4$
    c) $1s^22s^22p^63s^23p^64s^13d^5$
    d) $1s^22s^22p^63s^23p^64s^23d^8$

    Answer: a Page: 262

35. Of the following choices, which has the greatest diameter?
    a) Na^+
    b) Na
    c) Na^-

    Answer: c Page: 263

36. The halide ion with the smallest diameter is
    a) Br^-
    b) Cl^-
    c) I^-
    d) F^-

    Answer: d Page: 263

37. Of the following ions, which is the smallest?
    a) Y^{3+}
    b) Sr^{2+}
    c) Rb^+

    Answer: a Page: 263

38. Which ion in the isoelectronic series below has the largest radius?
    a) Al^{3+}
    b) Na^+
    c) O^{2-}
    d) F^-
    e) N^{3-}

    Answer: e Page: 263

39. Which ion in the isoelectronic series below has the smallest radius?
    a) Al^{3+}
    b) Na^+
    c) O^{2-}
    d) F^-
    e) N^{3-}

    Answer: a Page: 263

40. Which ion below has the smallest radius?
    a) Al^{3+}
    b) K^+
    c) S^{2-}
    d) F^-
    e) P^{3-}

    Answer: a Page: 263

41. Which ion below has the largest radius?
    a) Cl^-
    b) K^+
    c) Br^-
    d) F^-
    e) Na^+

    Answer: c Page: 263

42. Which one of the following sets contains species that are <u>all</u> isoelectronic?
    a) F, Ne, Na
    b) C^{4-}, N^{3-}, O^{2-}
    c) P^{3+}, S^{2-}, Ar
    d) Cl, Ar, K

    Answer: b Page: 263

43. Which one of the following sets contains species that are <u>all</u> isoelectronic?
    a) O, F, Ne
    b) C^{4+}, N^{3-}, O^{2-}
    c) P^{3-}, S^{2-}, Ar
    d) Na, Mg, Al

    Answer: c Page: 263

44. Which one of the following species is isoelectronic with argon?
    a) Kr
    b) P^{2-}
    c) Cl^{-}
    d) Si^{2+}

    Answer: c Page: 263

45. Which one of the following species has the largest radius?
    a) Rb^{+}
    b) Sr^{2+}
    c) Br^{-}
    d) Kr

    Answer: c Page: 263

46. Select the compound in which the cation and anion are closest together.
    a) KF
    b) K_2S
    c) RbCl
    d) $SrBr_2$

    Answer: a Page: 263

47. How many valence electrons do the halogens, the alkali metals, and the alkaline earth metals each have, respectively?
    a) 2, 4, 6
    b) 1, 5, 7
    c) 8, 2, 3
    d) 7, 1, 2
    e) 2, 7, 4

    Answer: d Page: 265

48. In general, the distance between bonded atoms _____ as the number of shared electron pairs increases.
a) increases
b) decreases
c) remains unchanged

Answer: b Page: 266

49. How many single covalent bonds must a silicon atom form to have a complete octet in its valence shell?
a) 3
b) 4
c) 1
d) 2

Answer: b Page: 266

50. What type of covalent bond is the longest?
a) single
b) double
c) triple
d) they are all the same length

Answer: a Page: 266

51. In which of the molecules below is the carbon-carbon distance shortest?
a) $H_2C{=}CH_2$
b) $H{-}C{\equiv}C{-}H$
c) $H_3C{-}CH_3$
d) $H_2C{=}C{=}CH_2$
e) $H_3C{-}CH_2{-}CH_3$

Answer: b Page: 266

52. How many hydrogen atoms must bond to nitrogen to give it an octet of valence electrons?
a) 1
b) 2
c) 3
d) 4
e) 5

Answer: c Page: 266

53. How many hydrogen atoms must bond to silicon to give it an octet of valence electrons?
    a) 1
    b) 2
    c) 3
    d) 4
    e) 5

    Answer: d Page: 266

54. In the following molecule, which atom will have the greatest build up of negative charge?

```
      Cl
      |
      C
     /|\
    F I Br
```

    a) Cl
    b) F
    c) Br
    d) I
    e) C

    Answer: b Page: 267

55. Which atom below has the highest electronegativity?
    a) Br
    b) O
    c) Cl
    d) N
    e) F

    Answer: e Page: 267

56. Which atom below has the highest electronegativity?
    a) Si
    b) Cl
    c) Rb
    d) Ca
    e) S

    Answer: b Page: 267

57. Which atom below has the lowest electronegativity?
    a) Rb
    b) F
    c) Si
    d) Cl
    e) Ca

    Answer: a Page: 267

58. The ability of an atom in a molecule to attract electrons to itself is termed
    a) paramagnetism
    b) diamagnetism
    c) electronegativity
    d) electron affinity
    e) first ionization potential

    Answer: c Page: 267

59. Which set of arrows corresponds to increasing electronegativity?

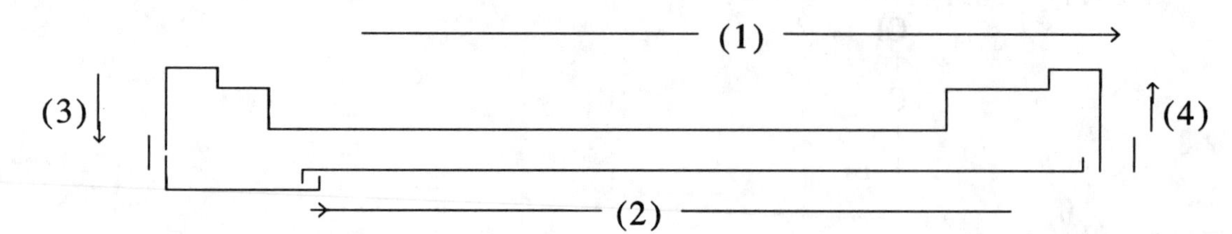

    a) 1,4
    b) 3,2
    c) 3,1
    d) 2,4

    Answer: a Page: 267

60. Which element from the following list has the greatest electronegativity?
    a) Si
    b) Mg
    c) P
    d) S

    Answer: d Page: 267

61. A gaseous element with a high electronegativity reacts with Na to form a compound with the general formula NaX. To which group does the element belong?
    a) 4A
    b) 5A
    c) 6A
    d) 7A

    Answer: d Page: 267

62. Given the electronegativities below, which of the following covalent single bonds is most polar?

Element:	H	C	N	O
Electronegativity:	2.1	2.5	3.0	3.5

a) C-H
b) N-H
c) O-H
d) O-C
e) O-N

Answer: c Page: 268

63. Of the molecules below, which is the most polar?
a) HBr
b) HI
c) HCl
d) HF

Answer: d Page: 268

64. Which one of the following bonds would be the least polar?
a) Na-S
b) P-S
c) C-F
d) Si-Cl

Answer: b Page: 268

65. ICl_4^- has how many total valence electrons?
a) 34
b) 35
c) 36
d) 28
e) 8

Answer: c Page: 269

66. NO^- has how many total valence electrons?
a) 15
b) 14
c) 16
d) 10
e) 12

Answer: e Page: 269

67. How many pairs of electrons not involved in bonds are located on the central atom of arsine, AsH_3?
a) 0
b) 1
c) 2
d) 3

Answer: b Page: 269

68. How many pairs of electrons not involved in bonds are located on the central atom of tribromide ion, Br_3^-?
a) 0
b) 1
c) 2
d) 3

Answer: d Page: 269

ESSAY

69. Draw the Lewis structure of ICl_2^+.

Answer:

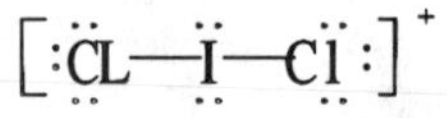

[:C̤̈L—Ï̤—C̤̈l:]$^+$

Page: 269

MULTIPLE CHOICE

70. The Lewis electron-dot structure of PF_3 gives the central P
a) 2 nonbonding pairs and 2 bonding pairs
b) 1 nonbonding pair and 3 bonding pairs
c) 3 nonbonding pairs and 1 bonding pair
d) 2 nonbonding pairs and 3 bonding pairs
e) 3 nonbonding pairs and 3 bonding pairs

Answer: b Page: 269

71. The Lewis electron dot structure of HCN (H bonded to C)
a) gives C 1 nonbonding pair
b) gives N 1 nonbonding pair
c) gives H 1 nonbonding pair
d) gives N 2 nonbonding pairs
e) gives C 2 nonbonding pairs

Answer: b Page: 269

72. The Lewis electron-dot structure of N_2H_2
    a) shows a nitrogen-nitrogen triple bond
    b) shows a nitrogen-nitrogen single bond
    c) gives each nitrogen 1 nonbonding pair
    d) gives each nitrogen 2 nonbonding pairs
    e) gives each hydrogen 1 nonbonding pair

    Answer: c Page: 269

73. When the Lewis electron-dot formula for SF_4 is drawn, how many nonbonding pairs (lone pairs) of electrons are on the sulfur atom?
    a) 0
    b) 1
    c) 2
    d) 3

    Answer: b Page: 269

74. Which one of the following is a correct Lewis electron-dot formula for SO_3?

    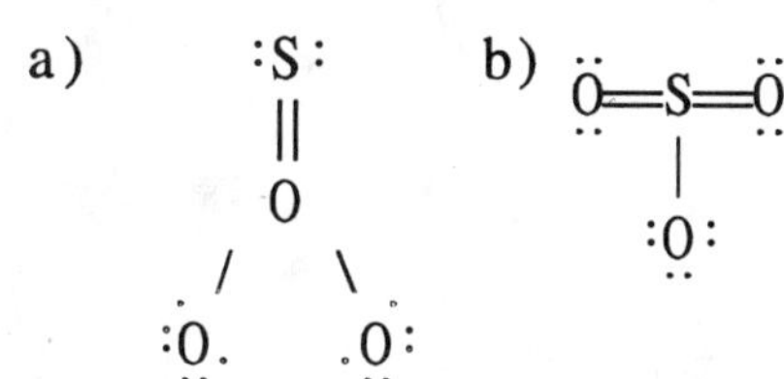

    c) 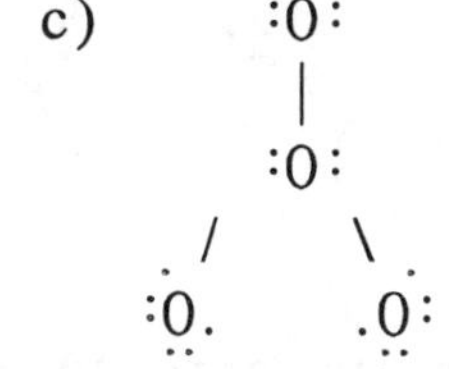

    d) 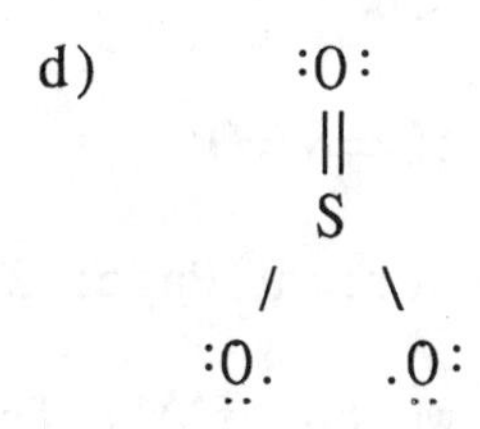

    Answer: d Page: 269

75. Which one of the following is a correct Lewis electron-dot formula for CO_3^{2-}?

    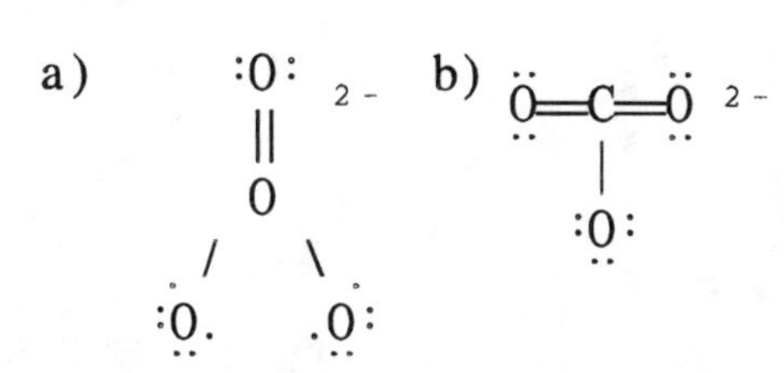

    c) 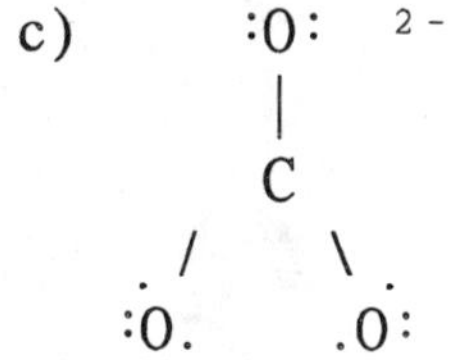

    d) 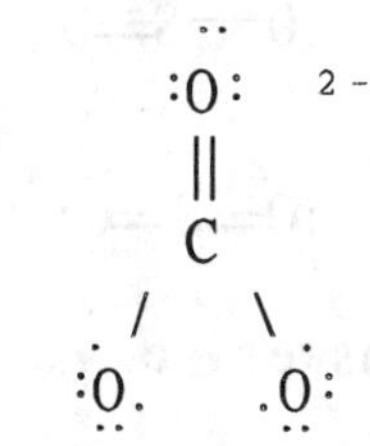

    Answer: a Page: 269

76. Which one of the following is the correct Lewis electron-dot formula for POCl?
    a) P=O—Cl: b) O=P—Cl: c) O=P=Cl: d. :P—Cl=O

    Answer: b Page: 269

77. Which one of the following structures is not correct according to the number of valence electrons on the central atom?

a)
```
  ..  ..  ..
 :O—S—O:
  ..      ..
```
b)
```
  ..  ..  ..
 :O—S=O:
  ..
```
c)
```
  ..  ..  ..
 :O=S=O:
```

Answer: a Page: 269

78. In which one of the following structures is the formal charge on the sulfur atom the greatest?

a)
```
  ..  ..  ..
 :O—S—O:
  ..      ..
```
b)
```
  ..  ..  ..
 :O—S=O:
  ..
```
c)
```
  ..  ..  ..
 :O=S=O:
```

Answer: a Page: 271

79. In which of the following structures is the formal charge zero on both oxygen atoms?

a)
```
  ..  ..  ..
 :O—S—O:
  ..      ..
```
b)
```
  ..  ..  ..
 :O—S=O:
  ..
```
c)
```
  ..  ..  ..
 :O=S=O:
```

Answer: c Page: 271

80. Which one of the following structures has the smallest formal charge overall?

a)
```
  ..  ..  ..
 :O—S—O:
  ..      ..
```
b)
```
  ..  ..  ..
 :O—S=O:
  ..
```
c)
```
  ..  ..  ..
 :O=S=O:
```

Answer: c Page: 271

81. What is the formal charge on carbon in the molecule shown below?

```
..      ..
O==C==O
..      ..
```

a) 0
b) 1
c) 2
d) 3

Answer: a Page: 271

82. What is the formal charge on nitrogen in NO_3^-?

```
┌     :O:     ┐ -1
│      ||     │
│      N      │
│    /   \    │
│  :O.   .O:  │
└   ..    ..  ┘
```

a) -1
b) 0
c) +1
d) +2

Answer: c Page: 271

83. What is the formal charge on sulfur in SO_4^{2-}?

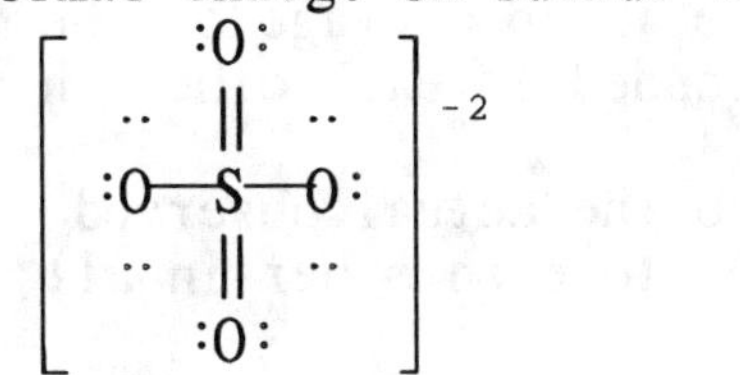

a) -2
b) 0
c) +2
d) +4

Answer: b Page: 271

84. In the resonance form of ozone shown, O = O - O:, the formal charge on the central oxygen atom is

a) 0
b) +1
c) -1
d) +2
e) -2

Answer: b Page: 271

ESSAY

85. Draw three equivalent resonance structures for the carbonate ion, $CO^{2-}{}_{3}$.

Answer:

```
     ..      2-         ..      2-        ..      2-
 [  :O:  ]         [   :O:  ]        [   :O:  ]
 [  / \\ ]         [   // \ ]        [   / \  ]
 [:O:  O:]         [ :O   :O:]       [ :O:  O:]
```

Page: 273

MULTIPLE CHOICE

86. In nitrogen dioxide,
    a) both bonds are single bonds
    b) both bonds are double bonds
    c) one bond is a double bond and the other is a single bond
    d) both bonds are the same, each being stronger and shorter than a single bond but longer and weaker than a double bond

    Answer: d Page: 273

87. For resonance forms of a molecule or ion
    a) one always corresponds to the actual observed structure
    b) all always correspond to the actual observed structure
    c) the actual observed structure is an average of the resonance forms
    d) the same atoms need not be bonded to each other in all resonance forms
    e) <u>both</u> all always correspond to the actual observed structure <u>and</u> the same atoms need not be bonded to each other in all resonance forms

    Answer: c Page: 273

88. How many resonance forms can be drawn for SO_2?
    a) 0
    b) 2
    c) 3
    d) 4

    Answer: b Page: 271

89. How many resonance forms can be drawn for CO_3^{2-}?
    a) 1
    b) 2
    c) 3
    d) 4

    Answer: c Page: 271

90. Of the following elements, which requires an octet?
    a) N
    b) B
    c) H
    d) Al
    e) Be

    Answer: a Page: 276

91. Of the following which cannot accommodate more than an octet?
    a) P
    b) As
    c) O
    d) S

    Answer: c Page: 276

92. The central atom in the triiodide ion, I_3^-, has ___ unbonded electron pairs and ___ bonded electron pairs in its valence shell.
    a) 2,2
    b) 3,1
    c) 1,3
    d) 3,2
    e) 3,3
    f) 0,2

    Answer: d Page: 276

93. The Lewis electron-dot structure of IF_5 gives the central I
    a) 1 nonbonding pair and 5 bonding pairs
    b) 5 bonding pairs only
    c) 5 nonbonding pairs and 1 bonding pair
    d) an octet
    e) 1 nonbonding pair and 4 bonding pairs

    Answer: a Page: 276

94. The Lewis electron-dot structure of XeF_4 gives the central Xe
    a) 1 bonding pair and 4 nonbonding pairs
    b) 2 bonding pairs and 4 nonbonding pairs
    c) 4 bonding pairs and 0 nonbonding pairs
    d) 4 bonding pairs and 1 nonbonding pair
    e) 4 bonding pairs and 2 nonbonding pairs

    Answer: e Page: 276

95. The species below which violates the octet rule is
    a) NF_3
    b) IF_3
    c) PF_3
    d) SbF_3
    e) AsF_3

    Answer: b Page: 276

96. The species below which violates the octet rule is
    a) SnF_4
    b) SiF_4
    c) CF_4
    d) SeF_4
    e) GeF_4

    Answer: d Page: 276

97. Which species below does not have an expanded octet on the central atom?
    a) SF_4
    b) KrF_2
    c) CF_4
    d) XeF_4
    e) IF_4^-

    Answer: c Page: 276

98. In which species below can the central atom be considered electron-deficient?
    a) NH_3
    b) XeF_2
    c) BF_3
    d) AsF_3
    e) CF_4

    Answer: c Page: 276

99. Select the species that violates the octet rule.
    a) ClF_3
    b) PCl_3
    c) SO_3
    d) CCl_4

    Answer: a Page: 276

100. Which one of the following species violates the octet rule?
    a) NI_3
    b) SO_2
    c) ICl_5
    d) SiF_4

    Answer: c Page: 276

101. Select the species that violates the octet rule.
   a) NF_3
   b) BeH_2
   c) SO_2
   d) CF_4

   Answer: b Page: 276

102. Bond enthalpy is
   a. always positive
   b. always negative
   c. sometimes positive, sometimes negative

   Answer: a Page: 279

103. Given that the average bond energies for C-H and C-Br bonds are 413 kJ/mol and 276 kJ/mol, respectively, calculate the heat of atomization of bromoform, $CHBr_3$.

   a) 1241 kJ/mol
   b) 689 kJ/mol
   c) -689 kJ/mol
   d) 1378 kJ/mol
   e) -1378 kJ/mol

   Answer: a Page: 279

ESSAY

104. Calculate the bond energy of C-F given that the heat of atomization of CHFClBr is 1502 kJ/mol and that the bond energy of C-H, C-Br, and C-Cl are 413 kJ/mol, 276 kJ/mol, and 328 kJ/mol, respectively.

   Answer:
   $\Delta H_{atomization}$ = (1 mol C-F)(BE_{C-F}) + (1 mol C-H)(BE_{C-H}) + (1 mol C-Br) + (1 mol C-Cl)(BE_{C-CL})
   1502 kJ/mol = (1 mol C-F)(BE_{C-F}) + (1 mol C-H)(413 kJ/mol) + (1 mol C-Br)(276 kJ/mol) + (1 mol C-Cl)(328 kJ/mol)
   BE_{C-F} = 485 kJ/mol
   Page: 279

105. From the given information given below, calculate the heat of combustion of methane, CH_4.

Bond	BE (kJ/mol)
C-H	413
O=O	495
C=O	799
O-H	463

Answer:
$CH_4 + 2O_2 \rightarrow CO_2 + 2H_2O$
$\Delta H_{combustion}$ = (4 mol C-H)(BE_{C-H}) + (2 mol O=O)($BE_{O=O}$) - (2 mol C=O)($BE_{C=O}$) - (4 mol O-H)(BE_{O-H})
$\Delta H_{combustion}$ = (4 mol C-H)(413 kJ/mol) + (2 mol O=O)(495 kJ/mol) - (2 mol C=O)(799 kJ/mol) - (4 mol O-H)(463 kJ/mol)
$\Delta H_{combustion}$ = -808 kJ
Page: 279

MULTIPLE CHOICE

106. Of the bonds C-N, C=N, and C≡N, the C-N bond is
a) strongest/shortest
b) strongest/longest
c) weakest/shortest
d) weakest/longest
e) intermediate in both strength and length

Answer: d Page: 279

107. Using the table of average bond energies (D in kJ/mol) below, the best estimate of ΔH in kJ for H-C≡C-H(g) + 2H-I(g) →

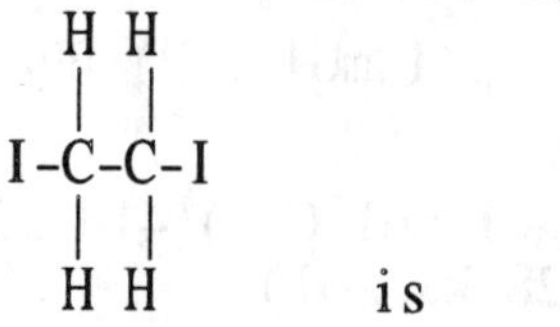

is

Bond:	C≡C	C-C	H-I	C-I	C-H
D:	835	346	246	216	411

a) +160
b) -160
c) -169
d) -63
e) +63

Answer: c Page: 279

108. Using the table of average bond energies (D in kJ/mol) below, the best estimate of ΔH in kJ for H-C≡C-H(g) + H-I(g) → H_2C=CHI(g) is

Bond:	C≡C	C=C	H-I	C-I	C-H
D:	835	602	295	213	411

a) +506
b) -931
c) -506
d) -96
e) +96

Answer: d Page: 279

109. Using the table of average bond energies (D in kJ/mol) below, the best estimate of ΔH in kJ for C≡O(g) + $2H_2$(g) → H_3C-O-H(g) is

Bond:	C-O	C=O	C≡O	C-H	H-H	O-H
D:	358	799	1072	411	432	459

a) +276
b) -276
c) +735
d) -735
e) -114

Answer: e Page: 279

110. As the number of covalent bonds between two atoms increases, the distance between the atoms ______ and the strength of the bond between them ______.
a) increases, increases
b) decreases, decreases
c) increases, decreases
d) decreases, increases

Answer: d Page: 279

111. The table shown below lists the bond dissociation energies for single covalent bonds formed between carbon atoms and atoms of elements A, D, Z, and E. Which element has the smallest atoms?

Bond	D (kJ/mol)
C-A	240
C-D	328
C-Z	276
C-E	485

a) A
b) D
c) Z
d) E

Answer: d Page: 279

112. The table shown below lists the bond dissociation energies for single covalent bonds formed between nitrogen atoms and atoms of elements A, D, Z, and E. Which element has the largest atoms?

Bond	D (kJ/mol)
N-A	240
N-D	328
N-Z	276
N-E	485

a) A
b) D
c) Z
d) E

Answer: a Page: 279

113. Use the table of bond dissociation energies to calculate ΔH (in kJ) for the following gas-phase reaction.

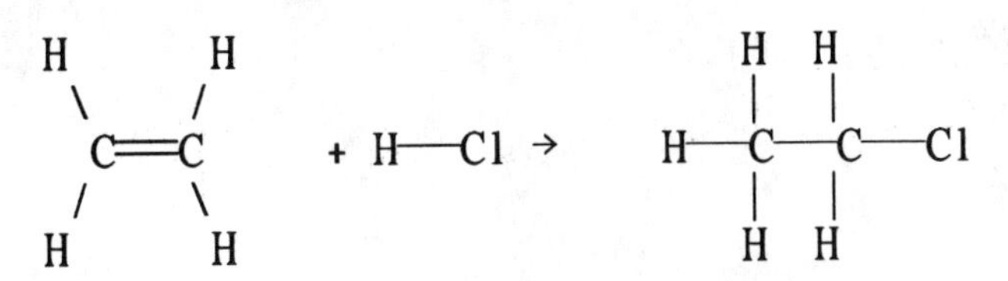

Bond	D (kJ/mol)
C-C	348
C=C	614
C-H	413
H-Cl	431
C-Cl	328

a) -44
b) 38
c) 304
d) 2134

Answer: a Page: 279

114. Use the table of bond dissociation energies to calculate ΔH (in kJ) for the following gas-phase reaction.

```
H       H                              H  H
 \     /                               |  |
  C═══C        + H───Br  →      H───C───C───Br
 /     \                               |  |
H       H                              H  H
```

Bond	D (kJ/mol)
C-C	348
C=C	614
C-H	413
H-Br	366
C-Br	276

a) 291
b) 2017
c) -57
d) -356

Answer: c Page: 279

115. Use the table of bond dissociation energies to determine the value of ΔH (in kJ) for the following reaction.

$$2HCl(g) + F_2(g) \rightarrow 2HF(g) + Cl_2(g)$$

Bond	D (kJ/mol)
H-Cl	431
F-F	155
H-F	567
Cl-Cl	242

a) -359
b) -223
c) 359
d) 223

Answer: c Page: 279

116. Most explosives are ____ compounds that decompose rapidly to produce ____ products and a great deal of _____.
a) ionic, gaseous, gases
b) gaseous, liquid, heat
c) dense, soluble, heat
d) metallic, solid, gas
e) molecular, gaseous, heat

Answer: e Page: 283

SHORT ANSWER

117. Write the formulas for nitroglycerine and trinitrotoluene (TNT).

Answer: $C_3H_5N_3O_9$ and $C_7H_5N_3O_6$ Page: 283

118. What is formed when nitroglycerine explodes? What is the physical state of each of these products?

Answer: $N_2(g)$, $CO_2(g)$, $H_2O(g)$, and $O_2(g)$ Page: 283

MULTIPLE CHOICE

119. Dynamite consists of nitroglycerine mixed with
a) potassium nitrate
b) damp KOH
c) TNT
d) diatomaceous earth
e) solid carbon

Answer: d Page: 283

120. Dynamite
    a) was invented by Alfred Nobel
    b) is made of nitroglycerine and an absorbent such as diatomaceous earth
    c) is a much safer explosive than pure nitroglycerine
    d) all of these

    Answer: d Page: 283

121. In which one of the following is the oxidation number of each atom zero?
    a) S_8
    b) PCl_5
    c) N_4O_6
    d) N_3^-

    Answer: a Page: 284

ESSAY

122. Assign oxidation numbers to all atoms in Na_3PO_4.

    Answer:
    Na +1
    P +5
    O -2
    Page: 284

123. Assign oxidation numbers to all atoms in CaS_4O_6.

    Answer:
    Ca +2

    S +5/2

    O -2
    Page: 284

MULTIPLE CHOICE

124. The oxidation number of manganese in $KMnO_4$ is
    a) 0
    b) +4
    c) -4
    d) -6
    e) +7

    Answer: e Page: 284

125. The oxidation number of nitrogen in NH_2F is
   a) +2
   b) -2
   c) +1
   d) -1
   e) +3

   Answer: d Page: 284

126. What is the oxidation number of Co in $CoCl_6^{3-}$?
   a) -3
   b) -6
   c) +8
   d) +3

   Answer: d Page: 284

127. What is the oxidation number of As in $NaAsO_3$?
   a) 0
   b) 2
   c) 4
   d) 5

   Answer: d Page: 284

128. What is the oxidation number of Br in $HBrO_2$?
   a) -1
   b) 2
   c) 3
   d) 5

   Answer: c Page: 284

129. With which one of the following does hydrogen react to form a compound in which the oxidation number of hydrogen is -1?
   a) O
   b) F
   c) Br
   d) S
   e) Mg

   Answer: e Page: 287

ESSAY

130. Write the formula for molybdenum (VI) sulfide.

   Answer: MoS_3 Page: 287

MULTIPLE CHOICE

131. The Stock nomenclature system uses Roman numerals to indicate oxidation numbers of the more electropositive element. Cr_2O_3 is called
    a) chromium(III) oxide
    b) chromium(II) oxide
    c) chromium(II) trioxide
    d) chromium(III) trioxide
    e) dichromium(III) trioxide

    Answer: a Page: 287

132. Palladium(IV) sulfide has the formula
    a) Pd_2S_4
    b) PdS_4
    c) Pd_4S
    d) PdS_2
    e) Pd_2S_2

    Answer: d Page: 287

Chapter 9: Molecular Geometry and Bonding Theories

MULTIPLE CHOICE

1. Which one of the models of molecular bonding listed below provides insight into the energetics of bond formation and into the electronic structures of molecules?
   a) the VSEPR model
   b) the valence-bond model
   c) the molecular orbital theory

   Answer: c Page: 295

2. Which one of the models of molecular bonding listed below allows description and prediction of the shapes of molecules?
   a) the VSEPR model
   b) the valence-bond model
   c) the molecular orbital theory

   Answer: a Page: 295

SHORT ANSWER

3. A molecule with the general formula AB_2 can take on one of two different geometries. Name these possible geometries.

   Answer: linear and bent Page: 295

4. A molecule with the general formula AB_3 can take on one of three different geometries. Name two of these possible geometries.

   Answer: trigonal planar, trigonal pyramidal, T-shaped Page: 295

MULTIPLE CHOICE

5. The basis of the VSEPR model of molecular bonding is
   a) regions of electron density on an atom will organize themselves so as to maximize *s*-character
   b) regions of electron density in the valence shell of an atom will arrange themselves so as to maximize overlap
   c) atomic orbitals of the bonding atoms must overlap for a bond to form
   d) electron pairs in the valence shell of an atom will arrange themselves so as to minimize repulsions
   e) hybrid orbitals will form as necessary to, as closely as possible, acheive spherical symmetry

   Answer: d Page: 296

6. According to VSEPR theory, if there are 3 pairs of electrons in the valence shell of an atom, they will be arranged in a(n) ________ geometry.
   a) octahedral
   b) linear
   c) tetrahedral
   d) trigonal planar
   e) trigonal bipyramidal

   Answer: d Page: 296

7. According to VSEPR theory, if there are 5 pairs of electrons in the valence shell of an atom, they will be arranged in a(n) ________ geometry.
   a) octahedral
   b) linear
   c) tetrahedral
   d) trigonal planar
   e) trigonal bipyramidal

   Answer: e Page: 296

8. According to VSEPR theory, if there are 4 pairs of electrons in the valence shell of an atom, they will be arranged in a(n) ________ geometry.
   a) octahedral
   b) linear
   c) tetrahedral
   d) trigonal planar
   e) trigonal bipyramidal

   Answer: c Page: 296

SHORT ANSWER

9. When are the electron-pair geometry and the molecular geometry of a molecule the same?

   Answer: when there are no lone pairs on the central atom Page: 298

MULTIPLE CHOICE

10. In counting regions of electron density around the central atom to predict the shape by VSEPR theory, which one of the following does not count as a single region?
    a) a lone pair of valence electrons
    b) a single covalent bond
    c) a sub-valence level electron pair
    d) a double covalent bond
    e) a triple covalent bond

    Answer: c Page: 298

11. The electron-pair geometry and molecular geometry of iodine trichloride are, respectively
    a) trigonal planar, trigonal planar
    b) tetrahedral, trigonal pyramidal
    c) trigonal bipyramidal, T-shaped
    d) octahedral, trigonal planar

    Answer: c Page: 298

12. Which one of the following has a perfect tetrahedron as its electron-pair geometry?
    a) CBr_4
    b) PH_3
    c) CCl_2Br_2
    d) XeF_4

    Answer: a Page: 298

13. Which one of the following has square planar molecular geometry?
    a) CCl_4
    b) XeF_4
    c) $AsH^+{}_4$
    d) PFl^5

    Answer: b Page: 298

14. What is the bond angle in tribromide, $Br^-{}_3$?
    a) 109.5°
    b) 120°
    c) 180°
    d) 90°

    Answer: c Page: 298

ESSAY

15. What is the molecular geometry of antimony pentafluoride?

    Answer: trigonal bipyramidal Page: 298

MULTIPLE CHOICE

16. What is the shape of the H_3O^+ ion?
    a) linear
    b) tetrahedral
    c) bent
    d) trigonal pyramidal

    Answer: d Page: 298

17. What is the shape of the CS_2 molecule?
    a) linear
    b) bent
    c) tetrahedral
    d) trigonal planar

    Answer: a Page: 298

18. What is the shape of the SiH_2Cl_2 molecule?
    a) trigonal planar
    b) tetrahedral
    c) trigonal pyramidal
    d) octahedral

    Answer: b Page: 298

19. Determine the shape of a $PHCl_2$ molecule.
    a) bent
    b) trigonal planar
    c) trigonal pyramidal
    d) tetrahedral

    Answer: c Page: 298

20. Determine the shape of a $CHCl_3$ molecule.
    a) bent
    b) trigonal planar
    c) trigonal pyramidal
    d) tetrahedral

    Answer: d Page: 298

21. What is the shape of an SF_2 molecule?
    a) linear
    b) bent
    c) trigonal planar
    d) tetrahedral

    Answer: b Page: 298

22. What is the shape of a PF_4^+ ion?
    a) octahedral
    b) tetrahedral
    c) trigonal pyramidal
    d) trigonal planar

    Answer: b Page: 298

23. What is the shape of a $BeCl^{3-}$ ion?
   a) trigonal planar
   b) bent
   c) tetrahedral
   d) trigonal pyramidal

   Answer: a Page: 298

24. The F-B-F bond angle in the BF_2^- ion is approximately
   a) 90°
   b) 109°
   c) 120°
   d) 180°

   Answer: c Page: 298

25. What is the approximate Cl-Si-Cl bond angle in $SiCl_2F_2$?
   a) 90°
   b) 109°
   c) 120°
   d) 180°

   Answer: b Page: 298

26. The approximate F-B-F bond angle in BF_3 is
   a) 90°
   b) 109°
   c) 120°
   d) 180°

   Answer: c Page: 298

27. If E symbolizes a lone pair, which one of the following has the smallest bond angle?
   a) AM_2E_2
   b) AM_3E
   c) AM_4
   d) they are all the same

   Answer: a Page: 300

28. In VSEPR theory, which type of electron-pair repulsions are largest?
   a) core/core
   b) valence nonbonding/valence bonding
   c) valence nonbonding/valence nonbonding
   d) core/valence bonding
   e) valence bonding/valence bonding

   Answer: c Page: 300

29. What is the approximate O-S-O bond angle in SO_2?
    a) 90°
    b) 109°
    c) 120°
    d) 180°

    Answer: c Page: 300

30. Which one of the following sets of molecules would have bond angles of 105°, 107°, and 109.5° respectively?
    a) CH_4, H_2O, NH_3
    b) H_2O, NH_3, CH_4
    c) NH_3, H_2O, CH_4
    d) H_2O, CH_4, NH_3

    Answer: b Page: 300

31. What is the approximate O-C-O bond angle in CO_3^{2-}?
    a) 90°
    b) 109°
    c) 120°
    d) 180°

    Answer: c Page: 300

32. The approximate F-N-F bond angle in NF_3 is
    a) 90°
    b) 109°
    c) 120°
    d) 180°

    Answer: b Page: 300

33. The approximate Cl-C-Cl bond angle in CCl_2O is
    a) 90°
    b) 109°
    c) 120°
    d) 180°

    Answer: c Page: 300

34. The approximate F-Xe-F bond angle in XeF_4 is
    a) 90°
    b) 109°
    c) 120°
    d) 180°

    Answer: a Page: 300

35. Which one of the following species would be expected to have bond angles of 120°?
a) PH_3
b) ClO_3
c) NCl_3
d) BCl_3

Answer: d Page: 300

36. In the trigonal bipyramidal geometry, lone pairs fill the ___ positions first.
a) axial
b) equatorial

Answer: b Page: 303

37. What is the shape of a BrO_3^- ion?
a) trigonal pyramidal
b) trigonal planar
c) bent
d) tetrahedral

Answer: a Page: 303

38. What is the geometry of the left most carbon atom in the molecule below?

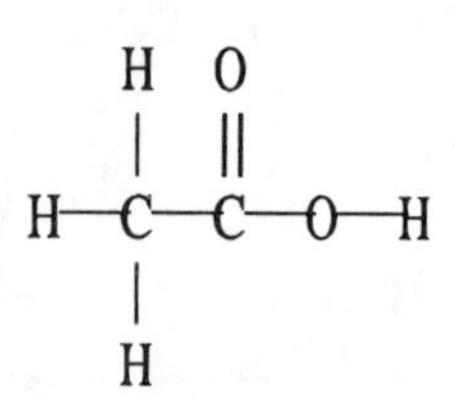

a) trigonal planar
b) trigonal bipyramidal
c) tetrahedral
d) octahedral

Answer: c Page: 304

39. Predict the molecular geometry of the right most carbon in the molecule below.

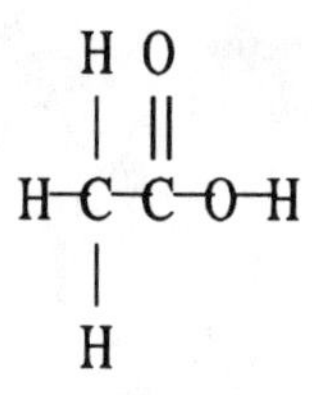

a) trigonal planar
b) trigonal bipyramidal
c) tetrahedral
d) octahedral

Answer: a Page: 304

40. The bond angles marked a, b, and c in the following molecule would be closest to
a) 90°, 90°, 90°
b) 120°, 120°, 90°
c) 120°, 120°, 109°
d) 109°, 120°, 109°

```
        :O: H :O:
         ||  |  ||
   ..                ..
H—N—C—C—C—O—H
                      ..
a  |   b   |  c
   H       H
```

Answer: d Page: 304

41. The bond angles a, b, and c in the molecule shown below would respectively be
a) 109.5°, 109.5°, 109.5°
b) 120°, 109.5°, 120°
c) 107°, 109.5°, 120°
d) 90°, 180°, 90°

```
   H     H   :O:
   |  a  |  b ||  c
                  ..
H—N——C——C—O—H
  ..              ..
         |
         H
```

Answer: c Page: 304

42. The bond angle marked "a" in the following molecule would be closest to
   a) 90°
   b) 109°
   c) 120°
   d) 180°

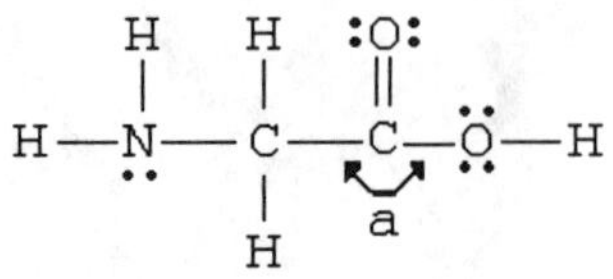

```
     H    H   :O:
     |    |    ||
H ── N ── C ── C ── O ── H
     ..   |     \_/  ..
          H      a
```

   Answer: c Page: 304

43. Which one of the molecules below is polar?
   a) SbF_5
   b) AsH_3
   c) I_2
   d) SF_6

   Answer: b Page: 305

44. Which of the following is nonpolar?
   a) OF_2
   b) OH_2
   c) SCl_2
   d) KrF_2
   e) $TeCl_2$

   Answer: d Page: 305

45. Which of the following is polar?
   a) CCl_4
   b) XeF_4
   c) SeF_4
   d) $SiCl_4$
   e) SiF_4

   Answer: c Page: 305

46. Which of the following is nonpolar?
   a) BF_3
   b) NF_3
   c) IF_3
   d) PBr_3
   e) $BrCl_3$

   Answer: a Page: 305

47. Three monosulfur fluorides exist: SF_2, SF_4, and SF_6. Which of these is/are polar?
   a) SF_2 only
   b) SF_2 and SF_4 only
   c) SF_4 only
   d) SF_6 only
   e) SF_4, SF_4, and SF_6

   Answer: b Page: 305

48. Determine the shape and polarity of the $BeCl_2$ molecule.
   a) linear, nonpolar
   b) linear, polar
   c) bent, nonpolar
   d) bent, polar

   Answer: a Page: 305

49. Determine the shape and polarity of the PF_3 molecule.
   a) trigonal planar, polar
   b) trigonal planar, nonpolar
   c) trigonal pyramidal, polar
   d) trigonal pyramidal, nonpolar

   Answer: c Page: 305

50. Which one of the following molecules is polar?
   a) $BeCl_2$
   b) BF_3
   c) CBr_4
   d) SiH_2Cl_2

   Answer: d Page: 305

51. Which one of the following molecules is polar?
   a) CCl_4
   b) BCl_3
   c) NCl_3
   d) $BeCl_2$

   Answer: c Page: 305

52. Determine the shape and polarity of a CHF_3 molecule.
   a) trigonal pyramidal, polar
   b) tetrahedral, nonpolar
   c) seesaw, nonpolar
   d) tetrahedral, polar

   Answer: d Page: 305

53. The BCl_3 molecule is ______ and ______.
a) trigonal pyramidal, polar
b) trigonal pyramidal, nonpolar
c) trigonal planar, polar
d) trigonal planar, nonpolar

Answer: d Page: 305

ESSAY

54. According to valence bond theory, what orbitals must overlap in order for hydrogen to bond to bromine to form HBr?

Answer: the 1s orbit of hydrogen with a 4p orbital of bromine

Page: 309

MULTIPLE CHOICE

55. In general, one can predict the hybridization of the central atom of a molecule by first determining the ______ geometry of the molecule using VSEPR theory.
a) electron-pair
b) molecular

Answer: a Page: 311

56. In general, in molecules with an electron-pair geometry of tetrahedral, the hybridization of the central atom is
a) sp
b) sp_2
c) sp_3
d) sp_3d
e) sp_3d_2

Answer: c Page: 311

57. In general, in molecules with an electron-pair geometry of trigonal bipyramidal, the hybridization of the central atom is
a) sp
b) sp_2
c) sp_3
d) sp_3d
e) sp_3d_2

Answer: d Page: 311

58. Generally, a molecule in which the central atom is sp hybridized will have ______ electron-pair geometry.
    a) octahedral
    b) linear
    c) trigonal planar
    d) trigonal bipyramidal
    e) tetrahedral

    Answer: b Page: 311

59. Generally, a molecule in which the central atom is sp_2 hybridized will have ______ electron-pair geometry.
    a) octahedral
    b) linear
    c) trigonal planar
    d) trigonal bipyramidal
    e) tetrahedral

    Answer: c Page: 311

60. What is the hybridization of the carbon atom in carbon dioxide?
    a) sp
    b) sp^2
    c) sp^3
    d) sp^3d
    e) sp^3d^2

    Answer: b Page: 311

61. What is the hybridization of the central atom in XeF_4?
    a) sp
    b) sp^2
    c) sp^3
    d) sp^3d
    e) sp^3d^2

    Answer: e Page: 311

62. Of the following choices, which one has sp^2 hybridization of the central atom?
    a) PH_3
    b) Co_3^{2-}
    c) ICl_3
    d) I_3^-

    Answer: b Page: 311

63. In which one of the following is the central atom sp^3d^2 hybridized?
    a) PCl_5
    b) XeF_4
    c) PH_3
    d) Br_3^-

    Answer: b Page: 311

64. The sp_3d_2 hybrid orbital set contains how many orbitals?
    a) 2
    b) 3
    c) 4
    d) 5
    e) 6

    Answer: e Page: 311

65. The sp_2 hybrid orbital set contains how many orbitals?
    a) 2
    b) 3
    c) 4
    d) 5
    e) 6

    Answer: b Page: 311

66. The respective hybridizations of nitrogen in NF_3 and NH_3 are
    a) sp^2 and sp^2
    b) sp and sp^3
    c) sp^3 and sp
    d) sp^3 and sp^3
    e) sp^2 and sp^3

    Answer: d Page: 311

67. The respective hybridizations of iodine in IF_3 and IF_5 are
    a) sp^3 and sp^3d
    b) sp^3d and sp^3d^2
    c) sp^3d and sp^3
    d) sp^3d^2 and sp^3d
    e) sp^3d^2 and sp^3d^2

    Answer: b Page: 311

68. The respective hybridizations of bromine in BrF_5 and arsenic in AsF_5 are
    a) sp^3 and sp^3d
    b) sp^3d and sp^3d^2
    c) sp^3d and sp^3
    d) sp^3d^2 and sp^3d
    e) sp^3d^2 and sp^3d^2

    Answer: d Page: 311

69. The hybrid orbitals used for bonding by the sulfur atom in SF_4 are
a) sp
b) sp^2
c) sp^3
d) sp^3d

Answer: d Page: 311

70. What type of hybrid orbitals is used for bonding by Xe in the XeF_2 molecule?
a) sp^2
b) sp^3
c) sp^3d
d) sp^3d^2

Answer: c Page: 311

71. What is the hybridization and H-O-C bond angle for the oxygen atom labeled y?
a) sp, 180°
b) sp^2, 109°
c) sp^3, 109°
d) sp^3d^2, 90°

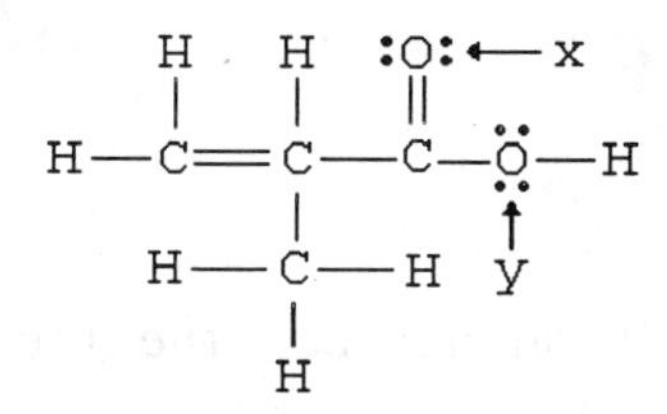

Answer: c Page: 311

72. The AsF_6^- ion is octahedral. The hybrid orbitals used by the As atom for bonding are
a) sp^2d^2
b) sp^3
c) sp^3d
d) sp^3d^2

Answer: d Page: 311

73. The AsF_5 molecule is trigonal bipyramidal. The hybrid orbitals used by the As atom for bonding are
a) sp^2d^2
b) sp^3
c) sp^3d^2
d) sp^2d

Answer: d Page: 311

74. What type of hybrid orbitals is used for bonding by Xe in the XeF_4 molecule?
    a) sp^2
    b) sp^3
    c) sp^3d
    d) sp^3d^2

    Answer: d Page: 311

75. Sideways overlap of two p-orbitals resulting in two regions of electron density in common to the two nuclei are known as
    a) a pi bond
    b) a sigma bond
    c) a delta bond
    d) a double bond

    Answer: a Page: 317

76. A typical triple bond consists of
    a) three sigma bonds
    b) three pi bonds
    c) one sigma and two pi bonds
    d) two sigma and one pi bond

    Answer: c Page: 317

ESSAY

77. What atomic orbitals overlap to form the double bond between the two carbon atoms in ethylene, C_2H_4?

    Answer:
    one sp^2 hybrid orbital on each carbon overlaps, end on, and one unhybridized 2p orbital on each carbon overlaps sideways
    Page: 317

MULTIPLE CHOICE

78. Which one of the following elements most readily forms pi bonds?
    a) P
    b) Si
    c) S
    d) As
    e) O

    Answer: e Page: 317

79. Free rotation can occur about
    a) single bonds
    b) double bonds
    c) triple bonds

    Answer: a Section: 32

80. There are __ σ and __ π bonds, respectively, in H-C≡C-H.
    a) 3 and 2
    b) 3 and 4
    c) 4 and 3
    d) 2 and 3
    e) 5 and 0

    Answer: a Page: 326

81. The N/N bonding in HNNH consists of
    a) one σ bond and one π bond
    b) one σ bond and two π bonds
    c) two σ bonds and one π bond
    d) two σ bonds and two π bonds
    e) one σ bond and no π bonds

    Answer: a Page: 326

82. There are __ σ and __ π bonds, respectively, in $H_2C{=}C{=}CH_2$.
    a) 4 and 2
    b) 2 and 4
    c) 2 and 2
    d) 2 and 6
    e) 6 and 2

    Answer: e Page: 326

83. The total number of π bonds in H-C≡C-C≡C-C≡N is
    a) 3
    b) 4
    c) 6
    d) 9
    e) 12

    Answer: c Page: 326

84. How many σ bonds are in the molecule shown?

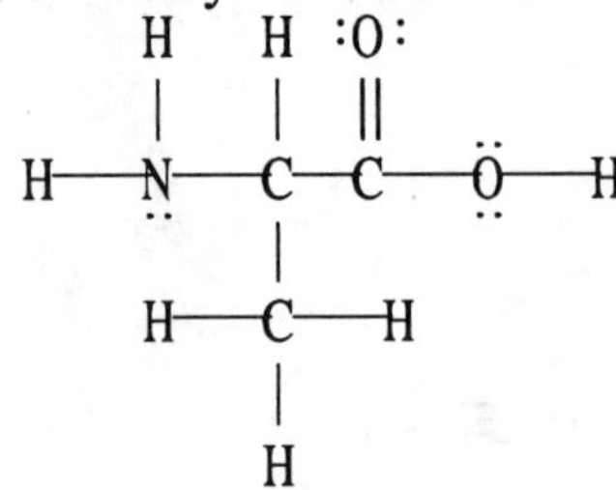

a) 1
b) 2
c) 12
d) 13

Answer: c Page: 326

85. How many π bonds are in the molecule shown below?

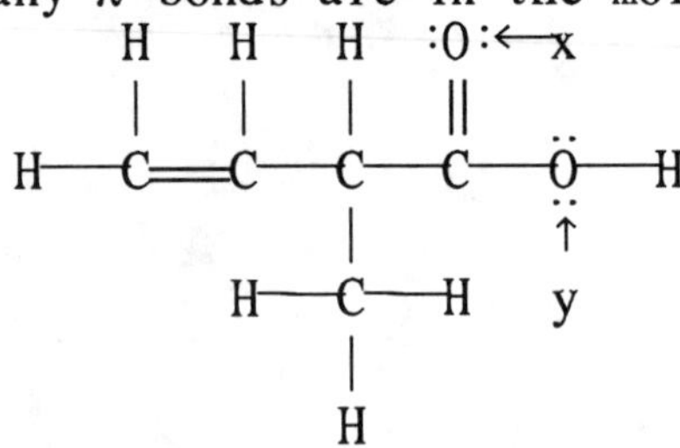

a) 0
b) 1
c) 2
d) 4

Answer: c Page: 326

86. How many π bonds are in this molecule?

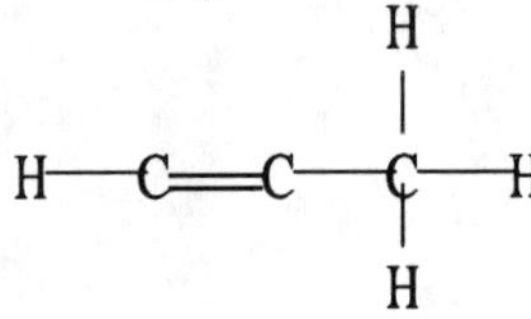

a) 7
b) 6
c) 2
d) 1

Answer: c Page: 326

87. The Lewis dot structure of carbon monoxide is $:C\equiv O:$. The respective hybridizations of carbon and oxygen are
    a) sp and sp^3
    b) sp^2 and sp^3
    c) sp^3 and sp^2
    d) sp and sp
    e) sp^2 and sp^2

    Answer: d Page: 327

88. The hybridization of the central carbon in $H_2C{=}C{=}CH_2$ is
    a) sp
    b) s^2p
    c) sp^2
    d) s^2p^2
    e) sp^3d

    Answer: a Page: 329

89. The hybridization of the terminal (non-central) carbons in $H_2C{=}C{=}CH_2$ is
    a) sp
    b) sp^2
    c) sp^3
    d) sp^3d
    e) sp^3d^2

    Answer: b Page: 332

90. The hybridization of the nitrogen in $H\text{-}C\equiv N:$ is
    a) sp
    b) s^2p
    c) s^3p
    d) sp^2
    e) sp^3

    Answer: a Page: 332

91. What is the hybridization of the carbon atom labeled 8?
    a) sp
    b) sp^2
    c) sp^3
    d) sp^3d

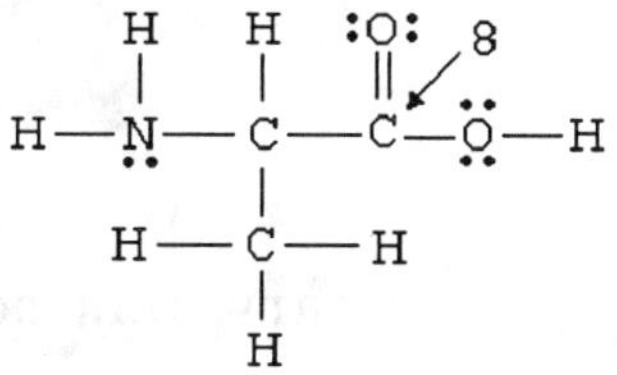

```
      H    H   :O:  8
      |    |    ||  ↙
  H — N̈ — C —— C — Ö — H
           |
      H —  C — H
           |
           H
```

    Answer: b Page: 332

92. How many unhybridized p-atomic orbitals are there on an sp hybridized carbon atom?
a) 0
b) 1
c) 2
d) 3

Answer: c Page: 334

93. What is the hybridization of the oxygen atom labeled x?

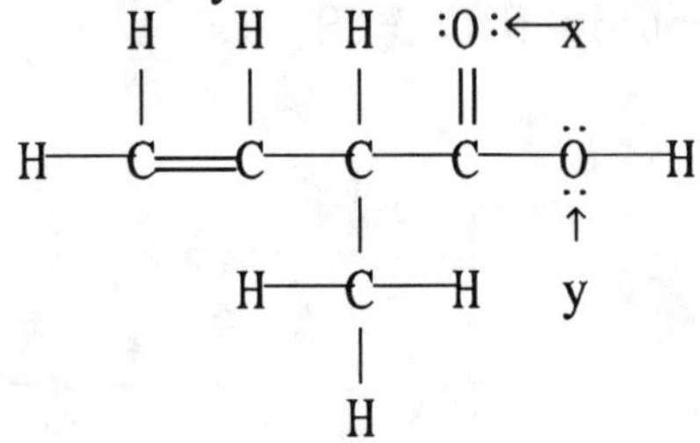

a) sp
b) sp^2
c) sp^3
d) sp^3d

Answer: b Page: 334

94. Describe the hybrid orbitals used for bonding by the carbon atom in the following molecule.

O═C═O

a) sp^3
b) sp^2
c) sp
d) sp^2d

Answer: b Page: 334

95. Structural changes around a double bond in the ____ portion of rhodopsin trigger the chemical reactions that result in vision.
a) protein
b) opsin
c) retinal

Answer: c Page: 334

ESSAY

96. Explain the reason that intense bright light causes temporary blindness.

Answer:
The intense bright light causes all of the retinal to separate from the opsin and the reattachment, which is necessary for further vision, is a slow reaction.

Page: 334

97. What is meant by delocalized electrons?

    Answer: electrons that are not associated with just one or two atoms

    Page: 334

MULTIPLE CHOICE

98. Electrons in ___ bonds remain localized between two atoms. Electrons in ___ bonds can become delocalized between more than two atoms.
    a) pi, sigma
    b) sigma, pi
    c) pi, pi
    d) sigma, sigma

    Answer: b

99. The combination of two atomic orbitals results in the formation of ___ molecular orbitals.
    a) 1
    b) 2
    c) 3
    d) 4

    Answer: b

100. The bond order of any molecule containing equal numbers of bonding and antibonding electrons is
    a) 0
    b) 1
    c) 2
    d) 3

    Answer: a

101. Molecular orbital theory describes bonding in H_2 as having
    a) both the σ_{1s} and σ^*_{1s} orbitals filled
    b) the σ_{1s} orbital filled and the σ^*_{1s} orbital empty
    c) the σ_{1s} orbital filled and the σ^*_{1s} orbital half-filled
    d) the σ_{1s} orbital half-filled and the σ^*_{1s} orbital filled
    e) the σ_{1s} orbital empty and the σ^*_{1s} orbital filled

    Answer: b

102. Which one of the following has unpaired electrons?
    a) C_2
    b) N_2
    c) F_2
    d) O_2

    Answer: d

103. Using Molecular Orbital Theory, determine the number of unpaired electrons in OF^+ (isoelectronic with O_2).
a) 0
b) 3
c) 1
d) 2

Answer: d

104. What type of molecular orbital always has electron density in common to two atoms?
a) bonding
b) antibonding
c) atomic
d) molecular

Answer: a

105. Molecular orbital theory describes the respective bond orders in H_2, H_2^+, and H_2^- as
a) 1, 0, and 0
b) 1, 1/2, and 0
c) 1, 0, and 1/2
d) 1, 1/2, and 1/2
e) 1, 2, and 0

Answer: d

106. Molecular orbital theory describes the bond order in He_2^+ as
a) 0
b) 0.5
c) 1
d) 1.5
e) 2

Answer: b

107. According to molecular orbital theory, what is the bond order of the bond between the two nitrogen atoms in N_2?
a) 0
b) 1
c) 2
d) 3
e) 4

Answer: d

108. Using Molecular Orbital Theory, determine the bond order of N_2^{2+}.
a) 0
b) 3
c) 1
d) 2

Answer: d

109. Using Molecular Orbital Theory, determine the bond order of the Be_2 molecule.
a) 0
b) 1
c) 2
d) 3

Answer: a

110. Using Molecular Orbital Theory, determine the bond order of the C_2 molecule.
a) 0
b) 1
c) 2
d) 3

Answer: c

111. The addition of one electron to the O_2 molecule will cause the bond order to
a) increase
b) decrease
c) remain the same

Answer: b

112. The addition of one electron to the N_2^+ ion will cause the bond order to
a) increase
b) remain the same
c) decrease

Answer: a

113. How many electrons can an antibonding pi molecular orbital hold at most?
a) 1
b) 2
c) 4
d) 6
e) 8

Answer: b

114. What type of molecular orbital has electron density along the internuclear axis but not in common to the two atoms?
a) σ
b) σ^*
c) π
d) π^*
e) sp

Answer: b

115. Which one of the following will appear to weigh more in a magnetic field than outside of it?
a) C_2
b) N_2
c) F_2
d) O_2

Answer: d

116. The general energy-level diagram for molecular orbitals of second-row diatomic molecules predicts which of the following to be paramagnetic?
a) O_2 only
b) N_2 only
c) N_2 and B_2
d) N_2 and O_2
e) B_2 and O_2

Answer: e

117. Which one of the following species is paramagnetic?
a) N_2
b) C_2^{2+}
c) F_2
d) B_2^+

Answer: d

ESSAY

118. What is meant by the terms HOMO and LUMO?

Answer:
HOMO is highest occupied molecular orbital, LUMO is lowest unoccupied molecular orbital

119. What can be said about the energy gap between HOMO and LUMO in white or colorless substances?

Answer: The energy gap between HOMO and LUMO is very large.

MULTIPLE CHOICE

120. In molecules containing alternating single and double bonds, the p bonds are said to be
    a) atomic
    b) occupied
    c) conjugated
    d) dyed
    e) hybridized

    Answer: c

121. What happens to the energy gap between HOMO and LUMO as conjugation increases?
    a) it decreases
    b) it increases
    c) it remains unchanged

    Answer: a

122. Which one of the following is false concerning β-carotene?
    a) it contains 11 conjugated double bonds
    b) it is the substance chiefly responsible for the orange color of carrots
    c) the human body converts it to vitamin-A
    d) it has a very large HOMO-LUMO gap
    e) its π electrons are extensively delocalized

    Answer: d

Chapter 10: Gases

MULTIPLE CHOICE

1. Which one of the following is known as a greenhouse gas?
   a) O_2
   b) CH_4
   c) Cl_2
   d) C_2H_2
   e) Xe

   Answer: b Page: 343

2. The main component of air is
   a) oxygen
   b) argon
   c) carbon dioxide
   d) nitrogen
   e) none of these

   Answer: d Page: 343

3. Which of the following is/are characteristic of gases?
   a) high compressibility
   b) relatively large distances between molecules
   c) formation of homogeneous mixtures regardless of the natures of non-reacting gas components
   d) all of the above
   e) none of the above

   Answer: d Page: 343

4. Which one of the following has a slight odor of bitter almonds and is toxic?
   a) NH_3
   b) N_2O
   c) CO
   d) CH_4
   e) HCN

   Answer: e Page: 344

5. Which one of the following has the odor of rotting eggs?
   a) NH_3
   b) H_2S
   c) CO
   d) NO_2

   Answer: b Page: 344

6. Gases consist mostly of
   a) electron clouds
   b) atomic nuclei
   c) empty space
   d) ions

   Answer: c Page: 344

7. How many Newtons of force does a gas at a pressure of 10.0 Pa exert on an area of 5.5 m^2?
   a) 55 N
   b) 0.55 N
   c) 5.5 N
   d) 1.8 N
   e) 18 N

   Answer: a Page: 345

8. How many Newtons of force does a gas at a pressure of 325 torr exert on an area of 5.5 m^2?
   a) 1.8×10^3 N
   b) 59 N
   c) 2.4×10^5 N
   d) 0.017 N
   e) 101 N

   Answer: c Page: 345

9. What is standard atmospheric pressure in inches of mercury?
   a) 1930 in Hg
   b) 101 in Hg
   c) 76.00 in Hg
   d) 29.92 in Hg
   e) 33.0 in Hg

   Answer: d Page: 345

10. Which one of the following is not true about a pascal?
    a) 1 Pa = $1N/m^2$
    b) it is the SI unit for pressure
    c) 1 atm = 101325 Pa
    d) 1 Pa = 100 torr

    Answer: d Page: 345

11. The National Weather Service routinely supplies atmospheric pressure data to pilots in order for them to set their altimeters. The units NWS uses for atmospheric pressure are inches of mercury. A barometric pressure of 30.51 inches of mercury corresponds to how many kPa?
    a) 77.50 kPa
    b) 775 kPa
    c) 1.020 kPa
    d) 103.3 kPa

    Answer: d Page: 345

12. 30 feet of water exert an atmosphere of pressure. Calculate the number of torr exerted on a diver at a depth of 100.0 feet on a standard day. Don't forget the pressure of the atmosphere above the water.
    a) 3.33 torr
    b) 2533 torr
    c) 763 torr
    d) 3293 torr

    Answer: d Page: 345

13. A closed-end manometer was attached to a vessel containing argon. If the difference in the mercury levels in the two arms of the manometer was 12.2 cm and the atmospheric pressure was 783 torr, what was the pressure of the argon in the container?
    a) 122 torr
    b) 661 torr
    c) 771 torr
    d) 795 torr

    Answer: a Page: 346

14. The left end of an open-end manometer was attached to a container of neon at a pressure of 683 torr. The right arm of the manometer was attached to a container of helium. Calculate the pressure of the helium if the mercury in the left arm of the manometer was 9.92 cm higher than the mercury in the right arm and atmospheric pressure was 788 torr.
    a) 673 torr
    b) 778 torr
    c) 782 torr
    d) 583 torr

    Answer: c Page: 346

15. A gas vessel is attached to an open-tube manometer filled with a nonvolatile liquid of density 0.791 g/mL as shown below. The difference in heights of the liquid in the two sides of the manometer is 43.4 cm when the atmospheric pressure is 755 mm Hg. Given that the density of mercury is 13.6 g/mL, what is the pressure in atm of the enclosed gas?
a) 1.03
b) 0.960
c) 0.993
d) 0.990
e) 0.987

Answer: b Page: 346

16. A gas vessel is attached to an open-tube manometer filled with a nonvolatile liquid of density 0.993 g/mL as shown below. The difference in heights of the liquid in the two sides of the manometer is 32.3 cm when the atmospheric pressure is 765 mm Hg. Given that the density of mercury is 13.6 g/mL, what is the pressure in atm of the enclosed gas?
a) 1.04
b) 1.01
c) 0.976
d) 0.993
e) 1.08

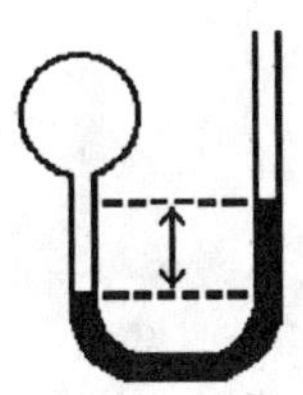

Answer: a Page: 346

17. A manometer filled with a liquid of which one of the following densities would exhibit the smallest height difference for any given pressure?
a) 13.6 g/mL
b) 2.29 g/mL
c) 18.2 g/mL
d) 0.00234 g/mL
e) 0.0918 g/mL

Answer: c Page: 347

18. If one was told that their blood pressure was 130/80, what would their systolic pressure be?
a) 130 Pa
b) 130 torr
c) 80 Pa
d) 80 torr
e) 80 psi

Answer: b Page: 348

ESSAY

19. What four variables are required to define the state of a gas?

Answer: pressure, volume, temperature, number of moles Page: 348

MULTIPLE CHOICE

20. The first person to investigate the relationship between the pressure of a gas and its volume was
a) Amadeo Avogadro
b) Lord Kelvin
c) Jacques Charles
d) Robert Boyle
e) Joseph Louis Gay-Lussac

Answer: d Page: 348

21. Which one of the following is a correct statement of Boyle's law?
a) PV = constant
b) $\frac{P}{V} =$ constant
c) $\frac{V}{P} =$ constant
d) $\frac{V}{T} =$ constant
e) $\frac{n}{P} =$ constant

Answer: a Page: 349

22. Boyle's law is valid under conditions of constant n and ______
a. pressure
b. volume
c. temperature

Answer: c Page: 349

23. What will the volume of a balloon be at a depth of 50 feet if its volume on the surface of the water was 2.84 L? Thirty feet of water equals one atmosphere. Assume constant temperature.
a) 1.70 L
b) 4.74 L
c) 1.06 L
d) 3.05 L

Answer: a Page: 349

24. 24.2 g of a gas initially at 4.00 atm is compressed from 8.00 L to 2.00 L at constant temperature. What is the resulting pressure in atm of the gas?
a) 4.00
b) 2.00
c) 1.00
d) 8.00
e) 16.0

Answer: e Page: 349

25. 5.0 moles of a gas at 1.0 atm is expanded at constant temperature from 10 L to 15 L. What is the final pressure in atm?
a) 1.5
b) 7.5
c) 0.67
d) 3.3

Answer: c Page: 349

26. Which one of the following is a valid statement of Charles' law?
a) $\frac{P}{T}$ = constant
b) $\frac{V}{T}$ = constant
c) PV = constant
d) $V \propto n$
e) $P_{total} = pi + pj + pk + \ldots$

Answer: b Page: 350

27. Which one of the following is a valid statement of Avogadro's law?
a) $\frac{P}{T}$ = constant
b) $\frac{V}{T}$ = constant
c) PV = constant
d) $V \propto n$
e) $P_{total} = pi + pj + pk + \ldots$

Answer: d Page: 350

28. At what temperature is the volume of an ideal gas zero?
   a) 0°C
   b) -45°F
   c) -273 K
   d) -363 K
   e) -273°C

   Answer: e Page: 350

29. A balloon originally had a volume of 4.39 L at 44°C and a pressure of 729 torr. To what temperature must the balloon be cooled to reduce its volume to 3.78 L if the pressure is constant?
   a) 38°C
   b) 0°C
   c) 72.9°C
   d) 273°C

   Answer: b Page: 350

30. If 3.21 mol of a gas occupies 56.2 L at 44°C and 793 torr, what volume will 5.29 mol of this gas occupy under these conditions?
   a) 14.7 L
   b) 61.7 L
   c) 30.9 L
   d) 92.6 L

   Answer: d Page: 350

31. Which of the following is impossible for an ideal gas?
   a) $\frac{V_1}{T_1} = \frac{V_2}{T_2}$

   b) $V_1T_1 = V_2T_2$

   c) $\frac{V_1}{V_2} = \frac{T_1}{T_2}$

   d) $V_2 = \frac{T_2}{T_1} V_1$

   Answer: b Page: 350

32. A gas originally at 27°C and 1.00 atm pressure in a 3.9 liter flask is cooled at constant pressure until the temperature is 11°C. What is the new volume of the gas (in liters)?
   a) 0.27
   b) 3.7
   c) 3.9
   d) 4.1

   Answer: b Page: 350

33. How many <u>additional</u> moles of gas would have to be added to a flask containing 2.00 moles of gas at 25°C and 1.00 atm pressure in order to increase the pressure to 1.60 atm under conditions of constant temperature and volume?
a) 0.800
b) 1.00
c) 1.20
d) 3.20

Answer: c Page: 350

34. If 50.75 g of a gas occupies 10.0 L at STP, what will be the volume in L occupied by 129.3 g of the gas at STP?
a) 3.92
b) 50.8
c) 12.9
d) 25.5
e) 5.08

Answer: d Page: 352

35. 2.35 mol He occupies 57.9 L at 300 K and 1.00 atm. What is its volume in L at 423 K and 1.00 atm?
a) 0.709 L
b) 41.1 L
c) 81.6 L
d) 1.41 L
e) 57.9 L

Answer: c Page: 352

36. 12.28 g H_2 occupies 100.0 L at 400 K and 2.00 atm. What volume in L would 9.49 g H_2 occupy at 353 K and 2.00 atm?
a) 109
b) 68.2
c) 54.7
d) 147
e) 77.3

Answer: b Page: 352

37. How many moles of gas occupy 60.82 L at 31°C and 367 mm Hg?
a) 1.18
b) 0.850
c) 894
d) 11.6
e) 0.120

Answer: a Page: 352

38. What is the pressure in atm of 6.022 g CH_4 in a 30.0 L vessel at 402 K?
    a) 2.42
    b) 6.62
    c) 0.413
    d) 12.4
    e) 22.4

    Answer: c Page: 352

39. At what temperature in °C does 0.444 mol of CO occupy 11.8 L at 889 mm Hg?
    a) 51
    b) 73
    c) 14
    d) 32
    e) 106

    Answer: e Page: 352

40. Determine the volume (in L) of 0.25 mol of gas at 545 mm Hg and 15°C.
    a) 0.011
    b) 0.43
    c) 4.2
    d) 8.2

    Answer: d Page: 352

41. What pressure (in atm) will be exerted by 1.3 moles of gas in a 13 liter flask at 22°C?
    a) 5.5
    b) 2.4
    c) 0.41
    d) 0.18

    Answer: b Page: 352

42. How many moles of gas are in a 0.325 L flask at 0.914 atm and 19°C?
    a) 1.24×10^{-2}
    b) 1.48×10^{-2}
    c) 9.42
    d) 12.4

    Answer: a Page: 352

43. A gas in a 325 milliliter container is found to have a pressure of 695 mm Hg at 19°C. How many moles of gas are in the flask?
    a) 1.24×10^{-2}
    b) 1.48×10^{-2}
    c) 9.42
    d) 12.4

    Answer: a Page: 352

44. 1.9 moles of gas are in a flask at 21°C and 697 mm Hg. The flask is opened and more gas is placed in the flask. The new pressure is 795 mm Hg and the temperature is now 26°C. How many moles of gas are now in the flask?
a) 1.6
b) 2.1
c) 2.9
d) 3.5

Answer: b Page: 352

45. What volume (in liters) will 1.3 moles of gas occupy at 22°C and 2.5 atm pressure?
a) 0.079
b) 0.94
c) 13
d) 31

Answer: c Page: 352

46. Calculate the volume (in liters) of 0.65 moles of an ideal gas at 365 mm Hg and 97°C.
a) 0.054
b) 9.5
c) 11
d) 41

Answer: d Page: 352

47. Determine the volume (in L) occupied by 1.5 mol of gas at 35°C and 2.0 atm pressure.
a) 38
b) 19
c) 2.2
d) 0.053

Answer: b Page: 352

48. 3.00 L of an ideal gas in a closed container at 25.0°C and 76.0 mm Hg is heated to 300°C. What is the pressure (in mm Hg) of the gas at this temperature?
a) 912
b) 146
c) 76.5
d) 39.5

Answer: b Page: 352

49. What mass of nitrogen dioxide would be contained in a 4.32 L vessel at 48°C and 1062 torr?
a) 5.35×10^4 g
b) 53.5 g
c) 10.5 g
d) 70.5 g

Answer: c Page: 352

50. Which one of the following has the correct numerical value, for the given units, of the gas constant?
a) 62.36 cal/mol-K
b) 0.0821 m^3-Pa/mol-K
c) 1.987 L-atm/mol-°C
d) 8.314 J/mol-K
e) 14.7 kg-mol/psi-K

Answer: d Page: 353

ESSAY

51. What temperature and pressure are specified by STP?

Answer: 0°C and 1atm Page: 353

MULTIPLE CHOICE

52. The molar volume of a gas at STP is
a) 0.08206 L
b) 62.36 L
c) 1 L
d) 22.4 L
e) 14.7 L

Answer: d Page: 353

53. 1.50 moles of a gas are contained in a 15.0 L cylinder. The temperature is increased from 100°C to 150°C. The ratio of final pressure to initial pressure, $\frac{P_2}{P_1}$ is
a) 1.50
b) 0.667
c) 0.882
d) 1.13

Answer: d Page: 356

54. A gas originally at 25°C and 1.00 atm pressure in a 2.5 liter container is allowed to expand until the pressure is 0.85 atm and the temperature is 15°C. What is the new volume of the gas?
a) 3.0 L
b) 2.8 L
c) 2.6 L
d) 2.1 L

Answer: b Page: 356

55. Which one of the following correctly relates pressure, temperature, and volume to molar mass of a gas?
a) $M = \frac{dRT}{PV}$

b) $M = \frac{gRT}{PV}$

c) $M = \frac{PT}{gRV}$

d) $M = \frac{gV}{RT}$

Answer: b Page: 357

56. Which one of the following correctly relates pressure, temperature, and volume to density of a gas?
a) $d = \frac{PM}{RT}$

b) $d = \frac{gRT}{PM}$

c) $d = \frac{PTM}{gRV}$

d) $d = \frac{gV}{RT}$

Answer: a Page: 357

57. Calculate the density of ammonia gas in a 4.32 L container at 837 torr and 45°C.
a) 3.86 g/L
b) 0.719 g/L
c) 0.432 g/L
d) 0.194 g/L

Answer: b Page: 357

58. 2.49 g of a gas was found to occupy a volume of 752 mL at 1.98 atm and 62°C. Which one of the following could be the gas?
   a) SO_2
   b) SO_3
   c) NH_3
   d) NO_2
   e) Ne

   Answer: d Page: 357

59. Which of the following gases has density of 0.900 g/L at STP?
   a) CH_4
   b) Ne
   c) CO
   d) N_2
   e) NO

   Answer: b Page: 357

60. Which of the following gases has density of 2.104 g/L at 303 K and 1.31 atm?
   a) He
   b) Ne
   c) Ar
   d) Kr
   e) Xe

   Answer: c Page: 357

61. What is the density in g/L of N_2O at 1.53 atm and 45.2°C?
   a) 18.2
   b) 1.76
   c) 0.388
   d) 9.99
   e) 2.58

   Answer: e Page: 357

62. Determine the molecular weight of a gas if 3.5 g of gas occupy 2.1 L at STP.
   a) 41
   b) 5.5×10^3
   c) 37
   d) 4.6×10^2

   Answer: c Page: 357

63. What is the molecular weight of a gas which has a density of 6.70 g/L at STP?
    a) 496
    b) 150
    c) 73.0
    d) 3.35

    Answer: b Page: 357

64. What is the molecular weight of a gas which has a density of 7.10 g/L at 25.0°C and 1.00 atm pressure?
    a) 174
    b) 14.6
    c) 28
    d) 5.75×10^{-3}

    Answer: a Page: 357

65. What is the molecular weight of a gas which has a density of 5.75 g/L at STP?
    a) 3.90
    b) 129
    c) 141
    d) 578

    Answer: b Page: 357

66. Determine the density (in g/L) of chlorine (Cl_2) gas at 25°C and a pressure of 450 mm Hg.
    a) 20
    b) 4.9
    c) 1.7
    d) 0.86

    Answer: c Page: 357

67. What volume of hydrogen gas at 38°C and 763 torr can be produced by reaction of 4.33 g of zinc with excess sulfuric acid?
    a) 1.68 L
    b) 2.71×10^{-4} L
    c) 3.69×10^{4} L
    d) 2.84 L

    Answer: a Page: 359

68. What volume of HCl gas is required to react with excess magnesium metal to produce 6.82 L of hydrogen gas at 2.19 atm and 35°C?
a) 6.82 L
b) 2.19 L
c) 13.6 L
d) 4.38 L

Answer: c Page: 359

69. What volume of fluorine gas is required to react with 2.67 g of calcium bromide to form calcium fluoride and bromine at 41°C and 4.31 atm?
a) 10.4 mL
b) 210 mL
c) 420 mL
d) 79.9 mL

Answer: d Page: 359

70. A 12.3 vessel was found to contain N_2, Ar, He, and Ne. The total pressure in the vessel was 987 torr and the partial pressures of nitrogen, argon, and helium were 44 torr, 486 torr, and 218 torr, respectively. What was the pressure of neon in the vessel?
a) 42.4 torr
b) 521 torr
c) 19.4 torr
d) 239 torr

Answer: d Page: 359

71. What is the pressure in a 12.2 L vessel that contains 2.34 g of carbon dioxide, 1.73 g of sulfur dioxide, and 3.33 g of argon at 42°C?
a) 263 torr
b) 134 torr
c) 395 torr
d) 116 torr

Answer: a Page: 359

72. 3.0 L of He gas at 5.6 atm pressure and 25°C and 4.5 L of Ne gas at 3.6 atm and 25°C are combined at constant temperature into a 9.0 L flask. What is the total pressure (in atm) in the 9.0 L flask?
a) 2.6
b) 9.2
c) 1.0
d) 3.7

Answer: d Page: 359

73. 2.0 L of H_2 gas at 3.5 atm pressure and 1.5 L of N_2 gas at 2.6 atm pressure are combined at a constant temperature of 25°C into a 7.0 L flask. What is the total pressure in the 7.0 L flask?
a) 0.56 atm
b) 2.8 atm
c) 1.0 atm
d) 1.6 atm

Answer: d Page: 359

74. What volume of sulfur dioxide can be produced by reaction of 3.82 g of calcium sulfite with excess HCl at 44°C and 827 torr?
a) 760 mL
b) 1.39×10^{-4} mL
c) 1.00×10^{-3} mL
d) 0.106 mL

Answer: a Page: 359

75. Automobile air bags use the decomposition of sodium azide as their source of gas for rapid inflation: $2NaN_3(s) \rightarrow 2Na(s) + 3N_2(g)$. How many grams of NaN_3 are required to provide 40.0 L of N_2 at 25°C and 763 mm Hg?
a) 1.64 g
b) 1.09 g
c) 160 g
d) 71.1 g
e) 107 g

Answer: d Page: 359

76. The Mond process produces pure nickel metal via the thermal decomposition of nickel tetracarbonyl: $Ni(CO)_4(l) \rightarrow Ni(s) + 4CO(g)$. How many liters of CO would be formed from 444 g of $Ni(CO)_4$ at 752 mm Hg and 22°C?
a) 0.356
b) 63.7
c) 255
d) 20.2
e) 11.0

Answer: c Page: 359

77. How many liters of $NH_3(g)$ at STP can be produced by the complete reaction of 7.5 g of H_2O according to the equation shown below?

$$Mg_3N_2(s) + 6H_2O(l) \rightarrow 3Mg(OH)_2(aq) + 2NH_3(g)$$

a) 3.1 L
b) 9.3 L
c) 19 L
d) 28 L

Answer: a Page: 359

78. How many liters of $H_2O(g)$ at STP would be required to produce 7.5 g of $NH_3(g)$ according to the equation shown below?

$$Mg_3N_2(s) + 6H_2O(g) \rightarrow 3Mg(OH)_2(aq) + 2NH_3(g)$$

a) 0.059
b) 30
c) 0.039
d) 44

Answer: b Page: 359

79. Ammonium nitrite undergoes decomposition to produce only gases as shown below.

$$NH_4NO_2(s) \rightarrow N_2(g) + 2H_2O(g)$$

How many liters of gas will be produced by the decomposition of 35.0 g of $NH_4NO_2(s)$ at 525°C and 1.5 atm?
a) 47
b) 160
c) 15
d) 72

Answer: d Page: 359

80. The decomposition of potassium chlorate is used to produce oxygen in the laboratory.

$$2KClO_3(s) \rightarrow 2KCl(s) + 3O_2(g)$$

How many liters of $O_2(g)$ at 25°C and 1.00 atm pressure can be produced by the decomposition of 7.5 g of $KClO_3(s)$?
a) 4.5
b) 7.5
c) 2.3
d) 3.7

Answer: c Page: 359

SHORT ANSWER

81. What is the partial pressure of neon in a 4.00 L vessel that contains 0.838 mol of chloroform,0.184 mol of ethane, and 0.755 mol of neon at a total pressure of 928 torr?

Answer:

$P_{Ne} = X_{Ne}P_t$

$$X\ P_{Ne} = \frac{0.755 \text{ mol Ne}}{0.838 \text{ mol chloroform} + 0.184 \text{ mol ethane} + 0.755 \text{ mole Ne}}$$

928 torr

$P_{Ne} = 394$ torr

Page: 361

MULTIPLE CHOICE

82. In a gas mixture of He, Ne, and Ar of total pressure 8.40 atm, what is the mole fraction of Ar if the respective partial pressures of He and Ne are 1.50 and 2.00 atm?
a) 0.179
b) 0.238
c) 0.357
d) 0.583
e) 0.417

Answer: d Page: 361

83. A gas mixture of total pressure 4.00 atm and 16.0 total moles contains gases X and Z. If the partial pressure of Z is 2.75 atm, how many moles of X are in the mixture?
a) 11.0
b) 5.00
c) 6.75
d) 9.25
e) 12.0

Answer: b Page: 361

84. A mixture of two gases, A and B, at a total pressure of 0.95 atm is found to contain 0.32 moles of gas A and 0.56 moles of gas B. What is the partial pressure (in atm) of gas B?
a) 1.7
b) 1.5
c) 0.60
d) 0.35

Answer: c Page: 361

85. A flask contains a mixture of two gases, A and B, at a total pressure of 2.6 atm. There are 2.0 moles of gas A and 5.0 moles of gas B in the flask. What is the partial pressure (in atm) of gas A?
a) 9.1
b) 6.5
c) 1.04
d) 0.74

Answer: d Page: 361

86. Sodium hydride was reacted with water and the hydrogen produced was collected over water. How much sodium hydride was reacted if 982 mL of hydrogen were collected at 28°C and a pressure of 765 torr? The vapor pressure of water at this temperature is 28 torr.

$$NaH + H_2O \rightarrow NaOH + H_2$$

a) 2.93 g
b) 0.960 g
c) 0.925 g
d) 0.0388 g

Answer: c Page: 362

87. 4.22 g of CuS were reacted with excess HCl and the resulting H_2S was collected over water. What volume of H_2S was collected at 32°C when the atmospheric pressure was 749 torr? The vapor pressure of water at this temperature is 36 torr.
a) 850 L
b) 0.124 L
c) 0.587 L
d) 1.18 L

Answer: d Page: 362

88. According to kinetic molecular theory,
a) gases consist of tiny particles in constant, random motion
b) the average kinetic energy of the particles of a gas is directly proportional to the centrigrade temperature
c) attractive and repulsive forces between gas particles are stronger than those between gas particles and container walls
d) the collisions between gas particles are inelastic

Answer: a Page: 364

89. The average kinetic energy of the particles of a gas is directly proportional to
a) the rms speed
b) the square of the rms speed
c) the square root of the rms speed
d) the square of the average particle mass

Answer: b Page: 364

90. The kinetic-molecular theory predicts pressure to rise as the temperature of a gas increases because
 a) the average kinetic energy of the gas molecules decreases
 b) the gas molecules collide more frequently with the wall
 c) the gas molecules collide less frequently with the wall
 d) the gas molecules collide more energetically with the wall
 e) <u>both</u> the gas molecules collide more frequently with the wall <u>and</u> the gas molecules collide more energetically with the wall

 Answer: e Page: 364

91. According to the kinetic-molecular theory, molecules of different gases at the same temperature always have the same
 a) molecular weight
 b) pressure
 c) average kinetic energy
 d) volume

 Answer: c Page: 364

ESSAY

92. Calculate the rms speed of methane molecules at 45°C.

 Answer:

$$\mu = \frac{\sqrt{3(8.314\ \text{kg}\cdot\text{m}^2/\text{s}^2\cdot\text{mol}\cdot\text{K})(318\ \text{K})}}{1.604\ \text{x}\ 10^{-2}\ \text{kg/mol}} = 703\ \text{m/s}$$

 Page: 366

MULTIPLE CHOICE

93. Which one of the following gases will diffuse the fastest at a given temperature?
 a) NH_3
 b) CH_4
 c) Ar
 d) HBr

 Answer: b Page: 367

94. A tank containing both HF and HBr gases developed a leak. Which gas will effuse faster and by what factor?
 a) HF,4
 b) HBr,4
 c) HF,2
 d) HBr,2

 Answer: c Page: 367

95. The root-mean-square speed in m/s of CO at 113°C is
   a) 317
   b) 58.3
   c) 586
   d) 993
   e) 31.5

   Answer: c Page: 367

96. At 333 K, which of the pairs of gases below would have the most nearly identical rates of effusion?
   a) N_2O and NO_2
   b) CO and N_2
   c) N_2 and O_2
   d) CO and CO_2
   e) NO_2 and N_2O_4

   Answer: b Page: 367

97. At STP, the root-mean-square speed of CO_2 is how many times that of SO_2?
   a) 2.001
   b) 2.119
   c) 1.000
   d) 1.206
   e) 1.456

   Answer: d Page: 367

98. Arrange the following gases in order of increasing average molecular speed at 25°C.

   He, O_2, CO_2, N_2

   a) He, N_2, O_2, CO_2
   b) He, O_2, N_2, CO_2
   c) CO_2, O_2, N_2, He
   d) CO_2, N_2, O_2, He

   Answer: c Page: 367

99. Arrange the following gases in order of increasing average molecular speed at 25°C.

   Cl_2, O_2, F_2, N_2

   a) Cl_2, F_2, O_2, N_2
   b) Cl_2, O_2, F_2, N_2
   c) N_2, F_2, Cl_2, O_2
   d) Cl_2, F_2, N_2, O_2

   Answer: a Page: 367

100. Which one of the following gases would have the highest average molecular speed at 25°C?
a) O_2
b) N_2
c) CO_2
d) CH_4

Answer: d Page: 367

101. A sample of oxygen gas was found to effuse at a rate equal to three times that of an unknown gas. What is the molecular weight of the unknown gas?
a) 288
b) 96
c) 55
d) 4

Answer: a Page: 367

102. A sample of oxygen gas was found to effuse at a rate equal to two times that of an unknown gas. What is the molecular weight of the unknown gas?
a) 64
b) 128
c) 8
d) 16

Answer: b Page: 367

103. N_2 gas effused through a pinhole in 5.5 seconds. How long will it take an equivalent amount of CH_4 to effuse under the same conditions?
a) 7.3
b) 5.5
c) 3.1
d) 4.2

Answer: d Page: 367

104. O_2 gas effused through a pinhole in 5.0 seconds. How long will it take an equivalent amount of CO_2 to effuse under the same conditions?
a) 4.3
b) 0.23
c) 3.6
d) 5.9

Answer: d Page: 367

105. Helium gas (He) effused through a pinhole in 53 seconds. An equivalent amount of an unknown gas, under the same conditions, effused through the hole in 248 seconds. What is the molecular weight of the unknown gas?
a) 0.18 g/mol
b) 5.5 g/mol
c) 88 g/mol
d) 18.7 g/mol

Answer: c Page: 367

106. In which one of the following gases at 67°C is the mean free path the shortest?
a) Xe
b) PH_3
c) NO_2
d) C_4H_{10}

Answer: a Page: 370

ESSAY

107. What two properties of real gases cause deviation from ideal behavior?

Answer: Gas particles themselves have volume and they do attract one another.

Page: 370

MULTIPLE CHOICE

108. Of the following molecules, which one should deviate the most from ideal behavior?
a) CF_4
b) CCl_4
c) CBr_4
d) CI_4

Answer: d Page: 370

109. Under which temperature/pressure conditions below does N_2O least resemble an ideal gas?
a) 415 K/10.0 atm
b) 307 K/2.50 atm
c) STP
d) 211 K/99.3 atm
e) 273 K/0.207 atm

Answer: c Page: 370

110. An ideal gas differs from a real gas in that the molecules of an ideal gas
   a) have no attraction for one another
   b) have appreciable molecular volumes
   c) have a molecular weight of zero
   d) have no kinetic energy

   Answer: a Page: 370

111. A real gas will behave most like an ideal gas under conditions of
   a) high temperature and high pressure
   b) high temperature and low pressure
   c) low temperature and high pressure
   d) low temperature and low pressure

   Answer: b Page: 370

112. Which one of the following gases would deviate the <u>least</u> from ideal gas behavior?
   a) He
   b) CH_4
   c) Kr
   d) CO_2

   Answer: a Page: 370

ESSAY

113. Explain how conversion of uranium to UF_6 allowed separation of ^{235}U and ^{238}U.

   Answer:
   UF_6 has a low boiling point rendering it easily gasified. The mass difference between the two isotopes of uranium are large enough to allow UF_6 to effuse faster than $^{238}UF_6$. Thus the two isotopes are separated by effusion of UF_6 gas.
   Page: 371

114. What two factors are being corrected for in the van der Waals equation?

   Answer: molecular volume and molecular attractions Page: 372

Chapter 10: Gases

MULTIPLE CHOICE

115. In the van der Waals equation, the factor a, has the units
   a. L-atm/mol-K
   b. mol/L-K
   c. L^2-atm/mol^2
   d. L/mol
   e. g/L

   Answer: d Page: 372

116. The van der Waals equation $[P + a(n/V)^2](V - bn) = nRT$ adjusts pressure and volume to account for deviations from Ideal Gas Law behavior. Which term in the equation above addresses the effect of intermolecular forces?
   a) n
   b) T
   c) V
   d) -bn
   e) $+a(n/V)^2$

   Answer: e Page: 372

117. The van der Waals equation $[P + a(n/V)^2](V - bn) = nRT$ adjusts pressure and volume to account for deviations from Ideal Gas Law behavior. Which term in the equation above addresses the effect of finite molecular volume?
   a) n
   b) T
   c) V
   d) -bn
   e) $+a(n/V)^2$

   Answer: d Page: 372

118. The two constants "a" and "b" in the van der Waals equation, $[P + a(n/V)^2](V - bn) = nRT$, are experimentally determined. Which statement below is true?
   a) Both "a" and "b" increase with an increase in molar mass and an increase in complexity of molecular structure.
   b) Both "a" and "b" decrease with an increase in molar mass and an increase in complexity of molecular structure.
   c) "a" and "b" respond oppositely to an increase in molar mass but similarly to an increase in complexity of molecular structure.
   d) "a" and "b" respond similarly to an increase in molar mass but oppositely to an increase in complexity of molecular structure.
   e) Both "a" and "b" appear to respond without clear pattern to an increase in molar mass and an increase in complexity of molecular structure.

   Answer: a Page: 372

Chapter 11: Intermolecular Forces, Liquids, and Solids

MULTIPLE CHOICE

1. Crystalline solids
   a) have their particles arranged randomly
   b) have highly ordered structures
   c) are usually very soft
   d) exist only at high temperatures

   Answer: b Page: 383

2. In liquids, the attractive intermolecular forces are
   a) very weak compared with kinetic energies of the molecules
   b) strong enough to hold molecules relatively close together
   c) strong enough to keep the molecules confined to vibrating about their fixed lattice points
   d) not strong enough to keep molecules from moving past each other
   e) strong enough to hold molecules relatively close together but not strong enough to keep molecules from moving past each other

   Answer: e Page: 383

3. Which one of the following is not a condensed phase?
   a) gas
   b) liquid
   c) solid

   Answer: a Page: 384

4. As a solid element melts, the atoms become ________ and they have _________ attraction for one another.
   a) more separated, more
   b) more separated, less
   c) closer together, more
   d) closer together, less

   Answer: b Page: 384

5. In which one of the following substances is the kinetic energy the greatest compared to the interparticle attractive forces?
   a) $H_2O(l)$
   b) $NaCl(s)$
   c) $CO_2(s)$
   d) $CO(g)$
   e) $CH_3OH(l)$

   Answer: d Page: 384

ESSAY

6. What effect does increasing the pressure on a substance have on the strength of intermolecular forces in that substance? Why?

Answer:
It increases the strength of intermolecular forces because the molecules are pushed closer together.
Page: 384

7. What types of molecules exhibit dipole-dipole attraction?

Answer: Neutral molecules with a permanent dipole. Page: 385

MULTIPLE CHOICE

8. Of the pairs of substances below, which pair involves ion-dipole attraction?
a) $C_6H_{11}O_6$, CH_3OH
b) RbI, $LiNO_3$
c) $C_{10}H_8$, C_6H_6
d) KBr, H_2O

Answer: d Page: 385

9. Which one of the following exhibits dipole-dipole attraction between molecules?
a) XeF_4
b) AsH_3
c) CO_2
d) $AlCl_3$

Answer: b Page: 385

10. What is the predominant intermolecular force in AsH_3?
a) London-dispersion forces
b) ion-dipole attraction
c) ionic bonding
d) dipole-dipole attraction
e) hydrogen-bonding

Answer: d Page: 385

11. Based on molecular mass and dipole moment of the five compounds in the table below, which should have the highest boiling point?

Compound	Molecular Mass (amu)	Dipole Moment (debye)
$CH_3CH_2CH_3$	44	0.0
CH_3OCH_3	46	1.3
CH_3Cl	50	2.0
CH_3CHO	44	2.7
CH_3CN	41	3.9

a) $CH_3CH_2CH_3$
b) CH_3OCH_3
c) CH_3Cl
d) CH_3CHO
e) CH_3CN

Answer: e Page: 385

12. The principle difference in respective normal boiling points of ICl (97°C; molecular mass 162 amu) and Br_2 (59°C; molecular mass 160 amu) is due to
a) London-dispersion forces
b) dipole-dipole interactions
c) hydrogen bonding
d) both hydrogen-bonding and dipole-dipole interactions
e) both dipole-dipole interactions and London dispersion forces

Answer: b Page: 385

13. When NaCl dissolves in water, the force of attraction that exists between Na^+ and H_2O is called
a) dipole-dipole
b) ion-ion
c) hydrogen bonding
d) ion-dipole

Answer: d Page: 385

SHORT ANSWER

14. London dispersion forces result from the attraction between

Answer: instantaneous and induced dipoles Page: 386

MULTIPLE CHOICE

15. For molecules of approximately equal mass and size, the strengths of intermolecular attractions increase with increasing
    a) polarity
    b) molecular mass
    c) molecular diameter
    d) temperature
    e) vapor pressure

    Answer: a Page: 386

SHORT ANSWER

16. What types of molecules exhibit London dispersion forces?

    Answer: All molecules exhibit London dispersion forces. Page: 386

MULTIPLE CHOICE

17. The strength of London dispersion forces depends on what two factors?
    a) molecular mass and polarizability
    b) polarizability and size
    c) molecular mass and volatility
    d) size and shape
    e) vapor pressure and size

    Answer: d Page: 386

18. The ease with which the charge distribution in a molecule can be distorted by an external electrical field is called
    a) electronegativity
    b) hydrogen bonding
    c) polarizability
    d) volatility
    e) viscosity

    Answer: c Page: 386

ESSAY

19. Explain why, at room temperature, iodine is a solid, bromine is a liquid, and chlorine is a gas.

    Answer:
    All of these atoms are neutral and non-polar. Iodine is the largest with very strong London dispersion forces. Bromine is smaller with weaker London dispersion forces. Chlorine is smaller still and thus has still weaker London dispersion forces. The London dispersion forces between iodine molecules are strong enough to keep them held rigidly in place at room temperature. Those between bromine molecules are strong enough to keep them very close together, but not strong enough to prevent them moving relative to each other. Those between chlorine molecules are too weak even to keep the molecules close together.

    Page: 386

MULTIPLE CHOICE

20. Which noble gas has the highest boiling point?
    a) Ne
    b) He
    c) Xe
    d) Ar
    e) Rn
    f) Kr

    Answer: e Page: 386

21. London-dispersion force is the attractive force between
    a) an ion and a permanent dipole
    b) an instantaneous dipole and an induced dipole
    c) two permanent dipoles
    d) two molecules with hydrogen bonded to an oxygen atom

    Answer: b Page: 386

22. Which one of the following derivatives of ethane has the highest boiling point?
    a) C_2Br_6
    b) C_2F_6
    c) C_2I_6
    d) C_2Cl_6

    Answer: c Page: 386

ESSAY

23. Explain why the boiling points of normal hydrocarbons are higher than those of branched hydrocarbons of similar molecular weight.

Answer:
Normal hydrocarbons can align to contact each other over their entire lengths and branched hydrocarbons cannot. This causes the London-dispersion forces between normal hydrocarbons to be greater than those between branched hydrocarbons.

Page: 386

MULTIPLE CHOICE

24. What is the predominant intermolecular force in CBr_4?
a) London-dispersion forces
b) ion-dipole attraction
c) ionic bonding
d) dipole-dipole attraction
e) hydrogen-bonding

Answer: a Page: 386

25. The intermolecular force(s) responsible for the fact that CH_4 has the lowest boiling point in the set CH_4, SiH_4, GeH_4, SnH_4 is/are
a) hydrogen bonding
b) dipole-dipole interactions
c) London-dispersion forces
d) mainly hydrogen bonding but also dipole-dipole interactions
e) mainly London-dispersion forces but also dipole-dipole interactions

Answer: c Page: 386

26. Iodine (I_2) is a solid at room temperature. What is the major attractive force that exists among different I_2 molecules in the solid?
a) dispersion
b) dipole
c) ionic
d) covalent

Answer: a Page: 386

27. Which one of the following substances has dispersion forces as its <u>only</u> intermolecular force?
a) CH_3OH
b) NH_3
c) H_2S
d) CH_4

Answer: d Page: 387

28. Which one of the following substances has dispersion forces as the <u>only</u> intermolecular force?
    a) CH_3OH
    b) NH_3
    c) H_2S
    d) Kr

    Answer: d Page: 387

ESSAY

29. Molecules with hydrogen bonded to ____, _____, or _____ can exhibit hydrogen bonding.

    Answer: fluorine, oxygen, nitrogen Page: 389

MULTIPLE CHOICE

30. Hydrogen bonding is a special case of
    a) London-dispersion forces
    b) ion-dipole attraction
    c) dipole-dipole attraction
    d) none of these

    Answer: c Page: 289

31. The intermolecular force(s) responsible for the fact that OH_2 has the highest boiling point in the set OH_2, SH_2, SeH_2, TeH_2 is/are
    a) hydrogen bonding
    b) dipole-dipole interactions
    c) London-dispersion forces
    d) mainly hydrogen bonding but also dipole-dipole interactions
    e) mainly London-dispersion forces but also dipole-dipole interactions

    Answer: d Page: 289

32. Which one of the following compounds will have hydrogen bonds as one of its intermolecular forces?
    a) H_2S
    b) SiH_4
    c) HCl
    d) NH_3

    Answer: d Page: 389

33. Which one of the following substances would have hydrogen bonding as one of its intermolecular forces?

a) 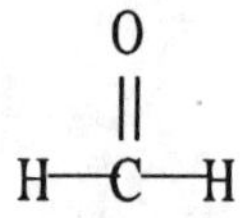
```
  0
  ||
H—C—H
```

b)
```
       0
       ||
H3C—C—CF3
```

c)
```
   H   0
   |  //
H—C—C
   |   \
   H    H
```

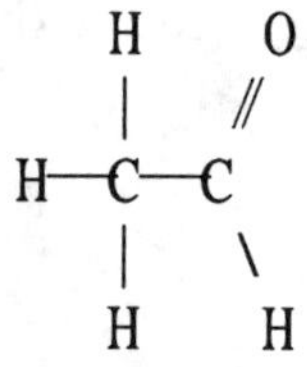

d) 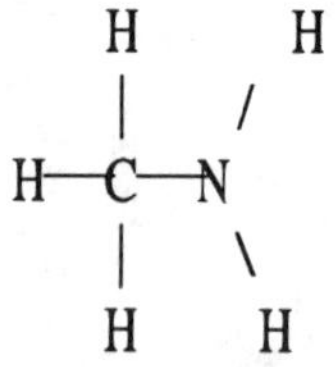
```
   H    H
   |   /
H—C—N
   |   \
   H    H
```

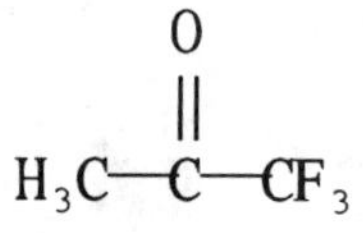

Answer: d Page: 389

34. Which one of the following substances would have hydrogen bonding as one of its intermolecular forces?

a) 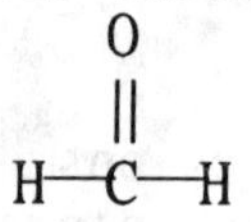
```
  0
  ||
H—C—H
```

b)
```
        0
        ||
CH3—C—CH3
```

c)
```
H       0
 \     //
  N—C
 /     \
H       H
```

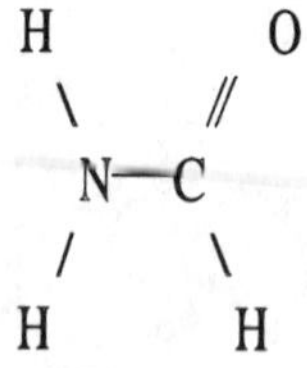

d) 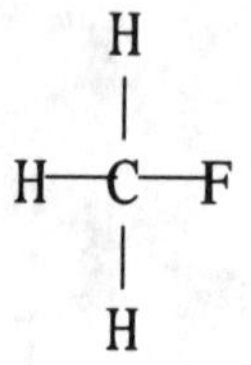
```
   H
   |
H—C—F
   |
   H
```

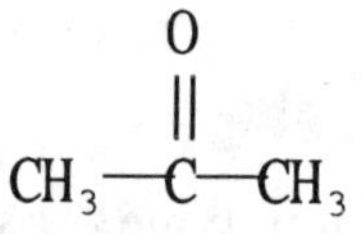

Answer: c Page: 389

35. Which one of the following substances would have hydrogen bonding as one of its intermolecular forces?

a) 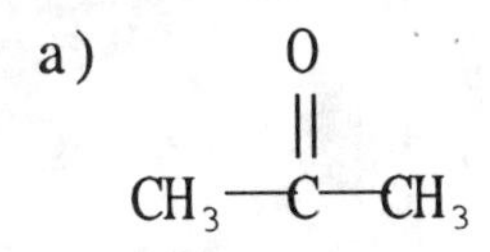

b) 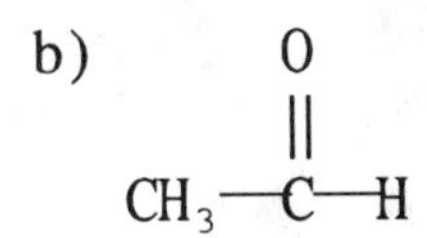

c) 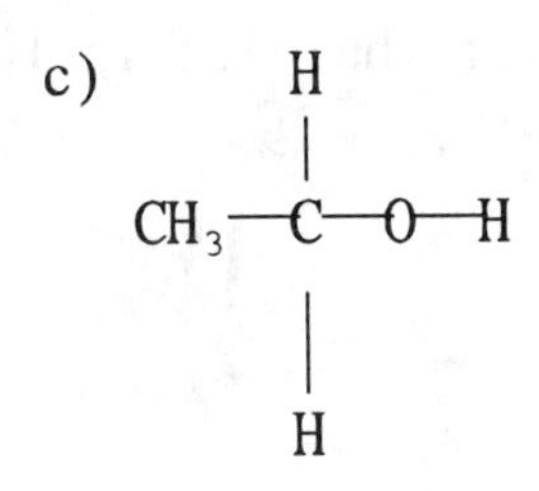

d) CH_3—N—CH_3
        |
       CH_3

Answer: a Page: 389

36. Rank the following in order of increasing strength assuming Y is the same in each case.

O-H•••Y, N-H•••Y, F-H•••Y

a) O-H•••Y < N-H•••Y < F-H•••Y
b) F-H•••Y < N-H•••Y < O-H•••Y
c) N-H•••Y < O-H•••Y < F-H•••Y
d) N-H•••Y < F-H•••Y < O-H•••Y
e) O-H•••Y < F-H•••Y < N-H•••Y

Answer: c Page: 391

37. Rank the following in order of increasing strength assuming X is the same in each case.

X-H•••F, X-H•••N, X-H•••O

a) X-H•••O < X-H•••N < X-H•••F
b) X-H•••F < X-H•••O < X-H•••N
c) X-H•••N < X-H•••O < X-H•••F
d) X-H•••N < X-H•••F < X-H•••O
e) X-H•••O < X-H•••F < X-H•••N

Answer: b Page: 391

38. Rank the following in order of increasing strength.

    F-H•••F, N-H•••N, O-H•••O

    a) O-H•••O < N-H•••N < F-H•••F
    b) F-H•••F < O-H•••O < N-H•••N
    c) N-H•••N < O-H•••O < F-H•••F
    d) N-H•••N < F-H•••F < O-H•••O
    e) O-H•••O < F-H•••F < N-H•••N

    Answer: c Page: 391

39. What intermolecular force is responsible for the fact that ice is less dense than liquid water?
    a) London dispersion
    b) dipole-dipole
    c) ion-dipole
    d) hydrogen bonding
    e) ionic bonding

    Answer: d Page: 392

40. Which type of intermolecular force tends to be the strongest?
    a) London dispersion
    b) dipole-dipole
    c) hydrogen bonding

    Answer: c Page: 392

41. Which one of the following should have the lowest boiling point?
    a) PH_3
    b) H_2S
    c) HCl
    d) SiH_4

    Answer: d Page: 392

ESSAY

42. Why is the boiling point of carbon tetrachloride, CCl_4, higher than that of chloroform, $CHCl_3$, even though chloroform is polar and carbon tetrachloride is not?

    Answer:
    Carbon tetrachloride is significantly larger than chloroform. Thus, London-dispersion forces between carbon tetrachloride molecules raises its boiling point above that of chloroform even though chloroform exhibits both London-dispersion and dipole-dipole attractions.

    Page: 392

MULTIPLE CHOICE

43. What is the predominant intermolecular force in $(CH_3)_2NH$?
    a) London-dispersion forces
    b) ion-dipole attraction
    c) ionic bonding
    d) dipole-dipole attraction
    e) hydrogen-bonding

    Answer: e Page: 392

44. Which one of the following substances would have the <u>highest</u> boiling point?
    a) H_2O
    b) CO_2
    c) CH_4
    d) Kr

    Answer: a Page: 392

45. Which molecular substance from the following list would have the highest boiling point?
    a) N_2
    b) Br_2
    c) H_2
    d) Cl_2

    Answer: b Page: 392

46. What is the relationship between the SAE number listed on motor oil and its viscosity at any given temperature?
    a) as the SAE number increases, viscosity increases
    b) as the SAE number decreases, viscosity increases
    c) as the SAE number decreases, viscosity decreases
    d) there is no relationship between the SAE number and the viscosity

    Answer: a Page: 394

SHORT ANSWER

47. Define viscosity.

    Answer: The resistance of a liquid to flow. Page: 394

Chapter 11: Intermolecular Forces, Liquids, and Solids

MULTIPLE CHOICE

48. The energy required to expand the surface area of a liquid by a unit amount is called
    a) viscosity
    b) surface tension
    c) volatility
    d) meniscus
    e) capillary action

    Answer: b Page: 394

49. The curvature of the surface of a liquid in a container is called the
    a) viscosity
    b) surface tension
    c) volatility
    d) meniscus
    e) capillary action

    Answer: d Page: 394

50. Of the following, which one should have the greatest viscosity?

a)
```
  H H H H H H
  | | | | | |
H-C-C-C-C-C-C-H
  | | | | | |
  H H H H H H
```

b)
```
  H H H H
  | | | |
H-C-C-C-C-H
  | | | |
  H H H H
```

c)
```
  H H H H H H
  | | | | | |
H-C-C-C-C-C-C-H
  | | | | | |
  H H C H H H
```

d)
```
  H H H H H H
  | | | | | |
H-C-C-C-C-C-N-H
  | | | | |
  H H H H H
```

Answer: d Page: 394

51. What will be the shape of the surface of water in a polyethylene tube? Polyethylene has the formula shown below.

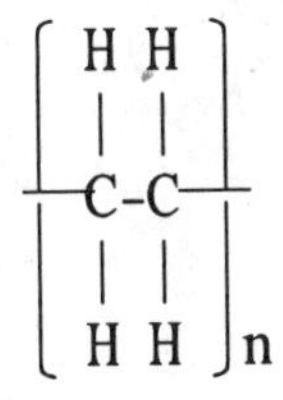

a) u-shaped
b) inverted-u shaped
c) flat

Answer: b Page: 394

52. Water will not rise in a capillary made of
a) polyethylene
b) glass
c) quartz

Answer: a Page: 394

53. Based on a knowledge of intermolecular forces, for which tube/liquid combination(s) would the meniscus be curved downward (upside-down U)?
a) glass/H_2O
b) glass/CH_3OH
c) glass/$H_3CCH_2CH_2CH_2CH_2CH_2CH_3$
d) polyethylene/$H_3CCH_2CH_2CH_2CH_2CH_2CH_3$
e) both glass/$H_3CCH_2CH_2CH_2CH_2CH_2CH_3$ and polyethylene/$H_3CCH_2CH_2CH_2CH_2CH_2$ CH_3

Answer: c Page: 394

54. Based on a knowledge of intermolecular forces, for which liquid(s) would the meniscus in a glass tube be curved downward (upside-down U)?
a) $H_3CCH_2CH_2CH_2CH_2CH_2CH_3$
b) C_6H_6
c) CH_3OH
d) $HOCH_2CH_2OH$
e) both $H_3CCH_2CH_2CH_2CH_2CH_2CH_3$ and C_6H_6

Answer: e Page: 394

55. Which one of the following substances would have the greatest surface tension at 25°C?
a) CH_4
b) CH_3Cl
c) CH_3OH
d) CO_2

Answer: c Page: 394

56. The direct conversion of a solid to a gas is called
    a) fusion
    b) vaporization
    c) condensation
    d) boiling
    e) sublimation

    Answer: e Page: 395

57. The substance with the largest enthalpy of vaporization is
    a) I_2
    b) Br_2
    c) Cl_2
    d) F_2

    Answer: a Page: 395

58. Which one of the following is an exothermic process?
    a) melting
    b) subliming
    c) freezing
    d) boiling

    Answer: c Page: 395

59. For a given substance, which is generally larger?
    a) ΔH_{fusion}
    b) $\Delta H_{vaporization}$

    Answer: b Page: 395

60. The enthalpy of fusion of water is 6.0 kJ/mol and the heat capacity is 75 J/mol•°C. How many kJ of heat would it take to convert 50 g of ice at 0°C to liquid water at 22°C?
    a) 3.8×10^2
    b) 21
    c) 17
    d) 0.46

    Answer: b Page: 395

61. The enthalpy of sublimation of a solid is always _______ than the enthalpy of fusion, and the enthalpy of vaporization of a liquid is always _______ than the enthalpy of fusion.
    a) greater, greater
    b) less, less
    c) less, greater
    d) greater, less

    Answer: a Page: 395

62. The curve below was generated by measuring the heat flow and temperature of a solid as it was heated. The slope of which portion of this curve corresponds to the heat capacity of the liquid of that substance?
a) A
b) B
c) C
d) D
e) E

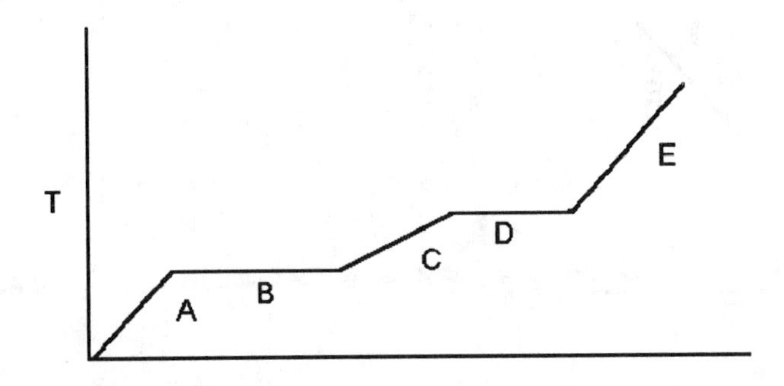

Answer: c Page: 396

63. The curve below was generated by measuring the heat flow and temperature of a solid as it was heated. The slope of which portion of this curve corresponds to the melting of that substance?
a) A
b) B
c) C
d) D
e) E

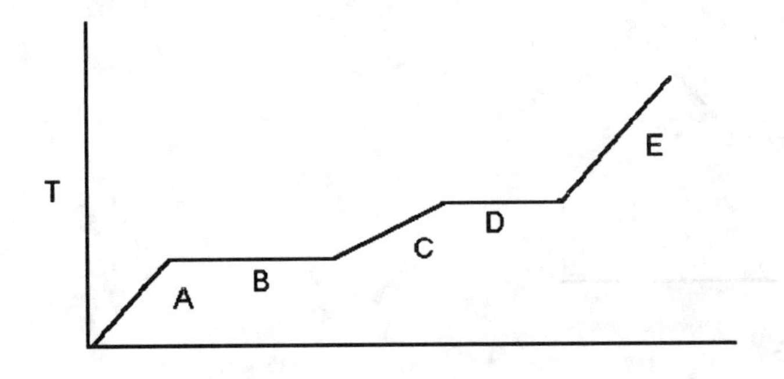

Answer: b Page: 396

64. The curve below was generated by measuring the heat flow and temperature of a solid as it was heated. Which physical state of this substance has the greatest heat capacity?
a) gas
b) liquid
c) solid

T

A B C D E

HEAT FLOW INTO THE SAMPLE

Answer: b Page: 396

65. The curve below was generated by measuring the heat flow and temperature of a solid as it was heated. The heat flow into the sample under which part of the curve corresponds to $\Delta H_{vaporization}$ of this substance?
a) A
b) B
c) C
d) D
e) E

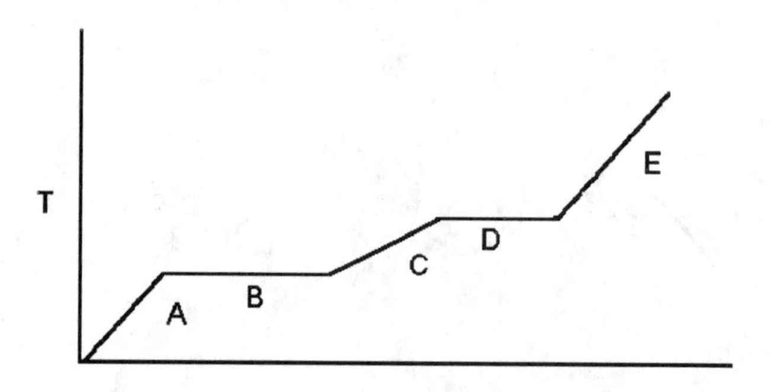

HEAT FLOW INTO THE SAMPLE

Answer: d Page: 396

66. A substance that will expand to fill its container yet has a density approaching that of a liquid and can behave as solvents is called a(n)
a) plasma
b) gas
c) liquid
d) amorphous solid
e) supercritical fluid

Answer: e Page: 399

67. Which one of the following should have the highest critical temperature?
    a) CBr_4
    b) CCl_4
    c) CF_4
    d) CH_4

    Answer: a Page: 398

68. The vapor pressure of a liquid
    a) increases linearly with increasing temperature
    b) increases nonlinearly with increasing temperature
    c) decreases linearly with increasing temperature
    d) decreases nonlinearly with increasing temperature
    e) is totally unrelated to its molecular structure

    Answer: b Page: 398

69. The critical temperature and pressure of CS_2 are 279°C and 78 atm respectively. At temperatures above 279°C, CS_2 can only occur as a
    a) solid
    b) liquid
    c) liquid and gas
    d) gas

    Answer: d Page: 398

70. What effect does molecular weight have on the vapor pressure of straight chain hydrocarbons, $C_nH_{(2n+2)}$?
    a) vapor pressure increases as molecular weight increases
    b) vapor pressure increases as molecular weight decreases
    c) molecular weight has no effect on vapor pressure

    Answer: b Page: 398

71. Increasing the amount of liquid in a closed container will cause the vapor pressure of the liquid to
    a) increase
    b) decrease
    c) remain the same
    d) depends on the liquid

    Answer: c Page: 398

72. Increasing the total pressure above a liquid will cause the boiling point of the liquid to
    a) increase
    b) decrease
    c) remain the same
    d) depends on the liquid

    Answer: a Page: 398

73. A substance that is volatile is one that is
a) highly flammable
b) highly viscous
c) highly hydrogen-bonded
d) highly cohesive
e) easily vaporized

Answer: e Page: 400

74. Of the following, which is the most volatile?
a) CBr_4
b) CCl_4
c) CF_4
d) CH_4

Answer: d Page: 400

75. What is the slope of a plot of the natural log of the vapor pressure of a substance as a function of 1/T, where T is absolute temperature?
a) $\Delta H_{vaporization}$

b) $-\Delta H_{vaporization}$

c) $\frac{1}{\Delta H_{vaporization}}$

d) $\frac{-\Delta H_{vaporization}}{R}$

e) none of these

Answer: d Page: 402

76. Which one of the following properties of a liquid is <u>not</u> affected by an increase in intermolecular forces?
a) viscosity
b) molecular weight
c) heat of vaporization
d) boiling point

Answer: b Page: 402

ESSAY

77. What is the vapor pressure of a substance at its normal boiling point?

Answer: one atmosphere or 760 torr Page: 402

MULTIPLE CHOICE

78. As vapor pressure increases, boiling point ____ and volatility ____.
    a) decreases, increases
    b) increases, decreases
    c) increases, increases
    d) decreases, decreases
    e) decreases, remains constant

    Answer: a Page: 402

79. On the diagram below, which curve corresponds to the conditions of temperature and pressure under which the solid and the gas of the substance are in equilibrium?
    a) A
    b) B
    c) C
    d) D
    e) E
    f) F

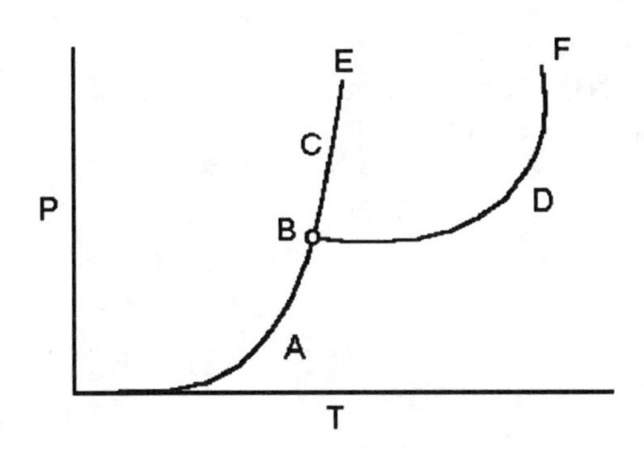

    Answer: a Page: 402

80. On the diagram below, the coordinates of point ___ correspond to the critical temperature and pressure.
    a) A
    b) B
    c) C
    d) D
    e) E
    f) F

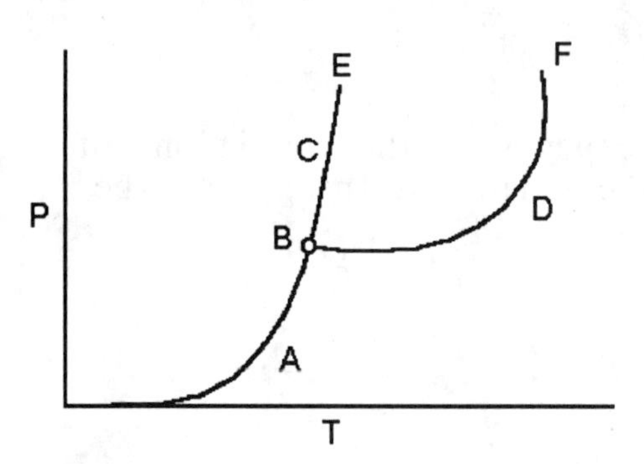

Answer: f Page: 402

81. The diagram below is the phase diagram for the substance X. Which physical state of this substance is the most dense?
    a) gas
    b) liquid
    c) solid

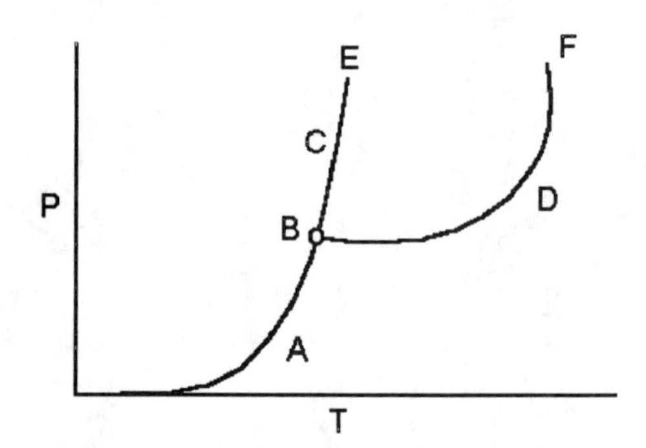

Answer: c Page: 402

82. On a phase diagram (P vs. T), the
    a) critical point is that beyond which gas and solid are indistinguishable
    b) triple point is that at which solid, liquid, and gas are in equilibrium
    c) solid is generally found at high T and low P
    d) liquid is generally found at high T and low P
    e) critical point is that beyond which gas and solid are indistinguishable <u>and</u> the triple point is that at which solid, liquid, and gas are in equilibrium

Answer: b Page: 402

83. A substance whose triple point occurs at 222 K and 3.93 atm
    a) will melt rather than sublime under normal ambient conditions
    b) will have a critical point of 211 K and 2.93 atm
    c) will have a critical point of 233 K and 2.93 atm
    d) will sublime rather than melt under normal ambient conditions
    e) will not have a critical point

    Answer: d Page: 402

84. Using the phase diagram shown below, identify the region that corresponds to the solid phase.
    a) w
    b) x
    c) y
    d) z

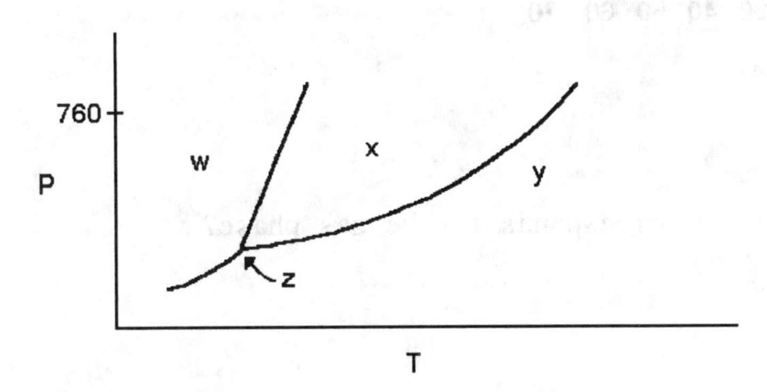

Answer: a Page: 402

85. In which phase does this substance exist at room temperature and pressure?
    a) w
    b) x
    c) y
    d) z

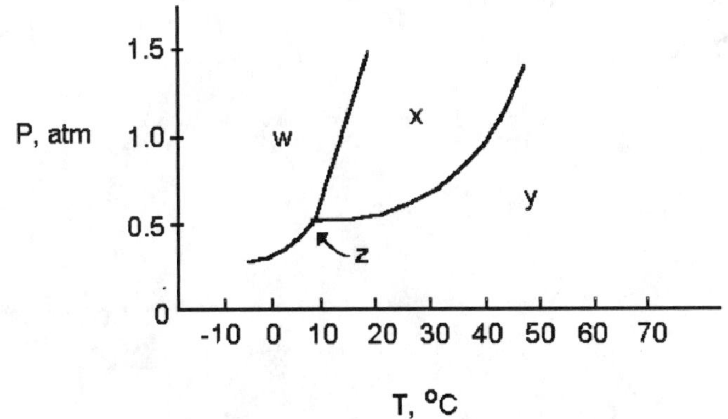

Answer: b Page: 402

86. What is the normal boiling point of this substance?
    a) 10°C
    b) 20°C
    c) 30°C
    d) 40°C

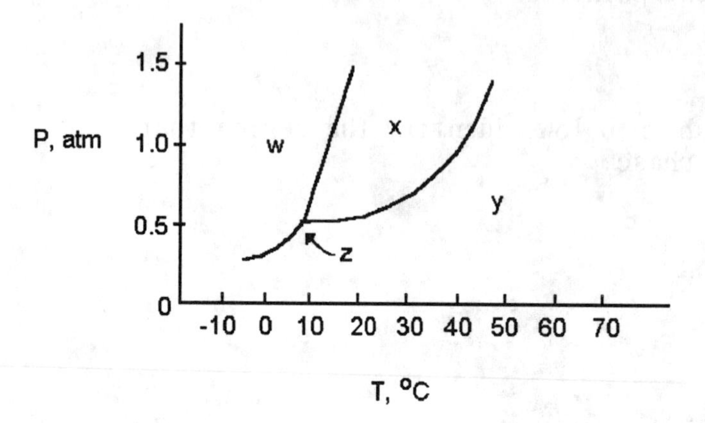

Answer: d Page: 402

87. Which portion of the diagram corresponds to the gas phase?
    a) w
    b) x
    c) y
    d) z

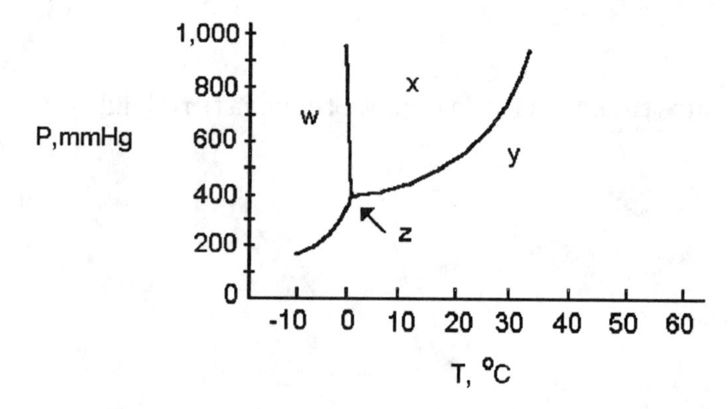

Answer: c Page: 402

88. What is the normal boiling point of this substance?
    a) -3
    b) 10
    c) 25
    d) 38

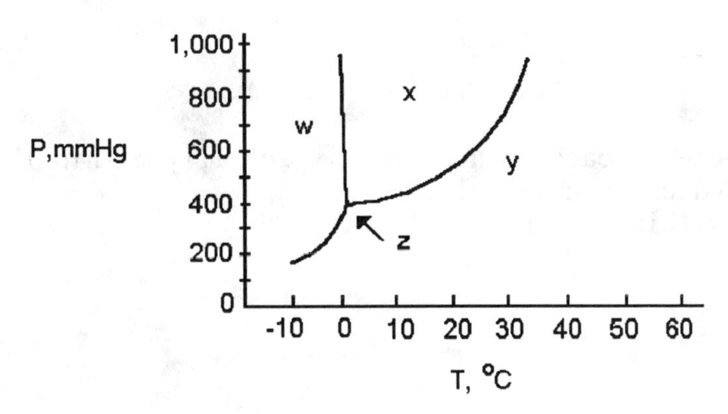

Answer: c Page: 402

ESSAY

89. Explain the difference between an amorphous and a crystalline solid on the microscopic level.

    Answer:
    Amorphous solids lack long-range order that is found in crystalline solids.

    Page: 404

MULTIPLE CHOICE

90. A solid was found to slowly soften and eventually become liquid upon heating. What type of solid was it?
    a) crystalline
    b) amorphous

    Answer: b Page: 404

91. Crystalline solids differ from amorphous solids in that crystalline solids have
    a) appreciable intermolecular attractive forces
    b) a long-range repeating pattern of atoms, molecules, or ions
    c) atoms, molecules, or ions that are close together
    d) much larger atoms, molecules, or ions

    Answer: b Page: 404

92. The unit cell with all sides the same length and all angles equal to 90° that has lattice points only at the corners is called
a) monoclinic
b) body-centered cubic
c) primitive cubic
d) face-centered cubic

Answer: c Page: 405

93. What portion of the volume of each corner atom is actually within the volume of a face-centered cubic unit cell?
a) all of each atom is within the unit cell
b) $\frac{1}{2}$
c) $\frac{1}{4}$
d) $\frac{1}{8}$
e) $\frac{1}{16}$

Answer: d Page: 405

94. How many atoms are actually contained within a face-centered cubic unit cell?
a) 1
b) 1.5
c) 3
d) 4
e) 2
f) 5

Answer: d Page: 405

95. Which one of the following cannot form a solid with a lattice based on the sodium chloride structure?
a) NaBr
b) LiF
c) RbI
d) CuO
e) $CuCl_2$

Answer: e Page: 406

ESSAY

96. Calculate the density, in g/cm^3, of chromium given that it crystallizes in a solid based on a body-centered cubic unit cell and has an atomic radius of 0.134 nm.

Answer:
the length of the internal diagonal, c = 4 x 0.134 nm = 0.536 nm
$c^2 = b^2 + a^2$
$b^2 = a^2 + a^2$. thus, $b^2 = 2a^2$
$c^2 = 2a^2 + a^2$
$(4 \times 0.134\ nm)^2 = 3a^2$
$a = 0.309\ nm = 3.09 \times 10^{-8}\ cm$

$$density = \frac{2\ atoms}{(3.09\times10^{-8} cm)^3} \times \frac{1\ mol}{6.02\times10^{23} atoms} \times \frac{52.00\ g}{1\ mol} = 5.86\ g/cm^3$$

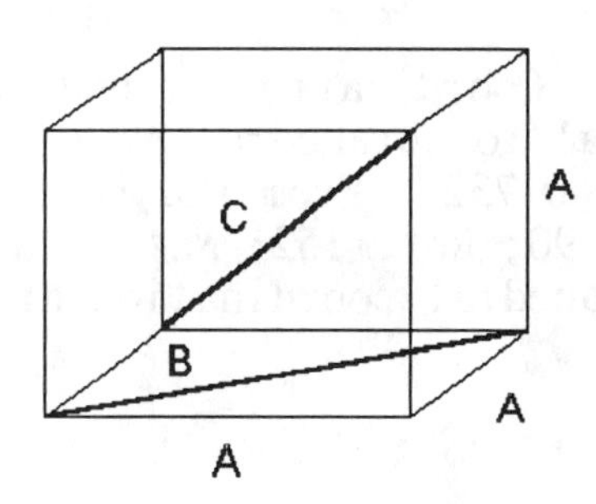

Page: 407

MULTIPLE CHOICE

97. Chromium crystallizes to afford a body-centered cubic unit cell, which has atoms at the center and the corners of a cube. Summing up the chromium atoms partitioned between the adjoining unit cells shows how many chromium atoms per unit cell?
a) 1
b) 2
c) 4
d) 6
e) 8

Answer: b Page: 407

98. CsCl crystallizes in a unit cell which contains the Cs^+ at the center of a cube having a Cl^- at each corner. Each unit cell contains __ Cs^+ and __ Cl^-, respectively.
a) 1 and 2
b) 2 and 1
c) 1 and 1
d) 2 and 2
e) 2 and 4

Answer: c Page: 407

99. Which cubic crystal structure(s) is/are the most efficient in filling the space inside the unit cell?
a) simple cubic
b) face-centered cubic
c) body-centered cubic
d) face-centered cubic and body-centered cubic

Answer: b Page: 407

100. The radius of I^- can be considered as 206 pm. Coordination around metal cations theoretically switches from tetrahedral to octahedral at $r^+/r^- = 0.414$ and from octahedral to cubic at $r_+/r^- = 0.732$. From the following data in pm for cation radii (Ag^+, 129; Li^+, 90; Rb^+, 152; Na^+, 116) predict which salts below will exhibit tetrahedral coordination around their respective cations?
a) LiI only
b) RbI only
c) LiI and NaI
d) NaI, AgI, and RbI
e) none of the above

Answer: e Page: 407

101. The element gallium crystallizes in a simple cubic crystal structure. The length of the unit cell edge is 3.7 Å. The atoms in a simple cubic unit cell touch in the center of each edge. What is the radius of a Ga atom (in Angstrom)?
a) 7.44
b) 3.72
c) 1.86
d) 0.93

Answer: c Page: 407

102. Potassium metal crystallizes in a body-centered cubic structure with a unit cell edge length of 5.31 Å. What is the radius of a potassium atom (in Angstrom)?
a) 1.33
b) 1.88
c) 2.30
d) 2.66

Answer: c Page: 407

103. Consider a face-centered cubic array of I^- ions (r = 2.16 Angstrom). What is the maximum radius (in Angstrom) that a cation could have and still fit in the holes on the edges of the FCC unit cell?
a) 0.90
b) 1.1
c) 1.8
d) 2.2

Answer: a Page: 407

104. Which type of close packing pattern results in a lattice that is based on the face-centered cubic unit cell?
a) AAAA
b) BBBB
c) ABAB
d) ABCABC

Answer: d Page: 408

105. What is the predominant intermolecular force in CaBr?
a) London-dispersion forces
b) ion-dipole attraction
c) ionic bonding
d) dipole-dipole attraction
e) hydrogen-bonding

Answer: c Page: 409

106. The type(s) of solid generally characterized by low melting point, softness and brittleness, and extremely low electrical conductivity is/are
a) ionic
b) molecular
c) metallic
d) network covalent
e) both ionic and molecular

Answer: b Page: 409

107. The type(s) of solid generally characterized by very high melting point, great hardness, and extremely low electrical conductivity is/are
    a) ionic
    b) molecular
    c) metallic
    d) network covalent
    e) both metallic and network covalent

    Answer: d Page: 409

108. Which choice below is not characteristic of a metallic solid?
    a) excellent thermal conductivity
    b) excellent electrical conductivity
    c) variable hardness (function of identity of metal)
    d) extreme brittleness
    e) variable melting point (function of identity of metal)

    Answer: d Page: 409

109. The scattering of light waves upon passing through a narrow slit is called
    a) diffusion
    b) grating
    c) diffraction
    d) adhesion
    e) incidence

    Answer: c Page: 410

ESSAY

110. Why are x-rays commonly used in the technique of x-ray crystallography instead of some other type of radiation?

    Answer:
    X-rays are commonly used in x-ray crystallography because the spacing between atoms in a crystalline solid is about the same as the wavelength of x-rays, making diffraction most efficient.

    Page: 410

MULTIPLE CHOICE

111. The solid of which one of the following has the highest melting point?
    a) CF_4
    b) CCl_4
    c) CBr_4
    d) CH_4

    Answer: c Page: 411

112. The crystal structure of a crystalline solid was found to be held together by hydrogen bonding. What type of solid is this?
a) covalent network
b) metallic
c) molecular
d) amorphous
e) ionic

Answer: c Page: 412

113. What type of forces hold the crystal structure of substances such as silicon carbide, boron nitride, and diamond together?
a) ionic bonds
b) hydrogen bonding
c) ion-dipole attraction
d) London dispersion forces
e) covalent bonds

Answer: e Page: 412

ESSAY

114. Why is silicon carbide so hard?

Answer:
It is a covalent-network solid that has covalent bonds running in 3 dimensions throughout the solid. Therefore, in order to distort the shape of the solid, a multitude of covalent bonds must be broken. (Thus, distortion of the solid takes a great deal of energy resulting in a very hard solid.)

Page: 412

MULTIPLE CHOICE

115. Copper(I) chloride solid has the zinc blend structure. In this structure, the chloride ions take on the
a) body-centered cubic structure
b) face-centered cubic structure
c) primitive cubic structure

Answer: b Page: 413

ESSAY

116. What are the three allotropic forms of elemental carbon?

Answer:
diamond, graphite, and fullerenes (or buckminsterfullerenes, or bucky balls)

Page: 414

117. What is located at each lattice point in a metallic solid? What holds a metallic solid together?

Answer:
Positively charged core atoms. It is held together by the electrostatic attraction between the positively charged core atoms at the lattice points and the negatively charged electron cloud that contains the valence electrons and extends throughout the crystal.

Page: 414

Chapter 12: Modern Materials

MULTIPLE CHOICE

1. In what year was the first systematic work involving liquid crystals reported?
   a) 1888
   b) 1943
   c) 1776
   d) 1978
   e) 1954

   Answer: a Page: 423

2. Which type of liquid crystal has the least order and is the most liquid-like?
   a) nematic
   b) smectic
   c) cholesteric

   Answer: a Page: 423

3. Which type of liquid crystal is colored and changes color with temperature?
   a) nematic
   b) smectic
   c) cholesteric

   Answer: c Page: 423

ESSAY

4. Explain why molecules containing only single bonds do not exhibit liquid crystal behavior.

   Answer:
   Free rotation can occur around single bonds so these molecules are flexible and coil instead of aligning.

   Page: 423

Chapter 12: Modern Materials

MULTIPLE CHOICE

5. Which of the following is most likely to exhibit liquid-crystalline behavior?
   a) CH_3CH_2-$C(CH_3)_2$-CH_2CH_3
   b) $CH_3CH_2CH_2CH_2CH_2CH_2CH_2CH_3$
   c) $CH_3CH_2CH_2CH_2CO_2^-Na^+$
   d) H_3CO-⟨benzene ring⟩-CO_2^- Na+
   e) H_3CO-⟨benzene ring⟩-N=N-⟨benzene ring⟩-OCH_3

   Answer: e Page: 423

6. In the smectic A liquid-crystalline phase
   a) the molecules are aligned along their long axes, with no ordering with respect to the ends of the molecules
   b) the molecules are arranged in sheets, with their long axes parallel and their ends aligned as well
   c) the molecules are aligned with their long axes tilted with respect to a line perpendicular to the plane in which the molecules are stacked
   d) disk-shaped molecules are aligned through a stacking of the disks in layers
   e) the molecules are oriented in a totally random fashion

   Answer: b Page: 423

7. Why are cholesteric liquid crystals colored?
   a) because each molecule is a chromophore
   b) because of the slight twist between layers
   c) because of the large spacing between layers
   d) because of the large number of conjugated bonds
   e) because all of the molecules contain multiple benzene rings

   Answer: b Page: 423

8. Which one of the following is not a polymer?
   a) cellulose
   b) nylon
   c) starch
   d) protein
   e) stainless steel

   Answer: e Page: 428

9. The empirical formula of an addition polymer
   a) is the same as the monomer from which it is formed except that 2 H and 1 O have been added
   b) is the same as the monomer from which it is formed except that 2 H and 1 O have been subtracted
   c) is the same as the monomer from which it is formed
   d) is the same as the monomer from which it is formed except that 2 H and 1 C have been added
   e) is the same as the monomer from which it is formed except that 2 H and 1 C have been subtracted

   Answer: c Page: 428

ESSAY

10. Write the chemical formulas for both polyethylene and the monomer from which it is formed.

    Answer: polyethylene is $(\text{-}CH_2\text{-}CH_2\text{-})_n$ and ethylene is $H_2C{=}CH_2$

    Page: 430

MULTIPLE CHOICE

11. Which one of the following is an addition polymer with the same structure as polyethylene except that one hydrogen on every other carbon is replaced by a benzene ring?
    a) polyvinyl chloride
    b) polypropylene
    c) polystyrene
    d) polyurethane
    e) nylon 6,6

    Answer: c Page: 430

ESSAY

12. Nylon is formed by the reaction of a ________ with a ________.

    Answer: diamine, diacid Page: 432

MULTIPLE CHOICE

13. What type of polymer can be reshaped?
    a) thermoplastic
    b) thermoset

    Answer: a Page: 432

14. An elastomer will fail to regain its original dimensions following a distortion beyond its
    a) glass transition
    b) phase boundary
    c) London forces
    d) crystallinity
    e) elastic limit

    Answer: e Page: 432

15. As the degree of crystallinity of a polymer increases
    a) hardness, density, and heat resistance decrease while solubility increases
    b) hardness, density, and heat resistance increase and solubility decreases
    c) hardness and density increase, heat resistance and solubility decrease
    d) hardness and density decrease, hcat resistance and solubility increase

    Answer: b Page: 432

16. What type of polyethylene has a lot of chain branching and an average molecular weight of 10^4 amu?
    a) high density
    b) low density
    c) cross linked

    Answer: b Page: 432

ESSAY

17. The dash board of automobiles is covered with plasticized polyvinyl chloride. Explain why this covering eventually cracks. Does this relate in any way to the "fog" that forms on the insides of new car windows?

    Answer:
    Over time, the plasticizer migrates out of the PVC making it brittle. The loss of plasticizer also causes a change of volume that cracks the brittle polymer. The fog forming on the inside of automobile windows is the plasticizer condensing.

    Page: 432

MULTIPLE CHOICE

18. A plastic container with what number designation will generally be the most easily recycled?
    a) 1
    b) 2
    c) 3
    d) 4
    e) 7

    Answer: a Page: 431

19. A plastic container with the letters LDPE stamped on it is made of
    a) polypropylene
    b) polystyrene
    c) polyvinyl chloride
    d) low density polyethylene
    e) polyethylene terephthalate

    Answer: d Page: 431

20. Polymers are largely ______.
    a) crystalline
    b) amorphous

    Answer: b Page: 432

21. The low density polyethylene used in forming films and sheets has an average molecular mass of _____ and substantial chain branching.
    a) 10^6 amu
    b) 100 amu
    c) 10^4 amu
    d) 500 amu
    e) 10^9 amu

    Answer: c Page: 433

22. What type of polyethylene is used to make bottles and pipes?
    a) low density with substantial branching
    b) low density with little branching
    c) high density with substantial branching
    d) high density with little branching
    e) crosslinked

    Answer: d Page: 433

23. Branching in polymer chains ________the degree of crystallinity.
    a) causes an increase in
    b) causes a decrease in
    c) has no effect on

    Answer: b Page: 433

24. What force causes the polymer chains in Kevlar to align to form a sheet-like structure?
    a) London dispersion forces
    b) dipole-dipole attraction
    c) ion-dipole attraction
    d) hydrogen bonding
    e) ionic bonding

    Answer: d Page: 434

25. What polymer is used to make bulletproof vests and protective clothing worn by fire fighters?
    a) polystyrene
    b) Kevlar
    c) polyethylene terephthalate
    d) nylon 3,6
    e) polyisobutylene

    Answer: b Page: 434

26. A highly crosslinked polymer is a
    a) thermoplastic
    b) thermoset

    Answer: b Page: 435

27. What is the monomer that is polymerized to make natural rubber?
    a) melamine
    b) formaldehyde
    c) ethylene
    d) isoprene
    e) adipic acid

    Answer: d Page: 435

28. A crosslinked polymer is a
    a) thermoset
    b) thermoplastic

    Answer: a Page: 435

29. Which one of the following is not true about the vulcanization of rubber?
    a) Goodyear discovered it by accident
    b) it involves heating rubber with sulfur dioxide
    c) it results in crosslinking the polymer chains
    d) it converts rubber from a soft and sticky substance to flexible, resilient one

    Answer: b Page: 435

30. Vulcanization of rubber entails
    a) conversion of an addition polymer to a condensation polymer
    b) conversion of a condensation polymer to an addition polymer
    c) increasing the average molecular weight of a condensation polymer
    d) decreasing the average molecular weight of an addition polymer
    e) crosslinking reactive polymer chains with sulfur atoms

    Answer: e Page: 435

31. Assume that vulcanization of polyisoprene with sulfur entails numerous couplings of two isoprene units (C_5H_8, each with 1 C=C) on separate polyisoprene chains and two sulfur atoms via formation of two new C-S-C crosslinks. What percent of the C=C units will be crosslinked if 4.8 g sulfur is completely consumed when mixed with 200 g polyisoprene?
    a) 7.6%
    b) 5.1%
    c) 2.5%
    d) 9.4%
    e) 3.7%

    Answer: b Page: 435

32. Which one of the following is an example of an amorphous ceramic?
    a) silicon carbide
    b) alumina
    c) glass
    d) zirconia
    e) tungsten

    Answer: c Page: 437

33. Which one of the following is not one of the chemical forms commonly found in ceramics?
    a) silicates
    b) oxides
    c) nitrates
    d) carbides
    e) aluminates

    Answer: c Page: 437

ESSAY

34. Replacing metals with ceramics for high temperature applications is desirable but also has its drawbacks. Explain.

    Answer:
    Ceramics are significantly lighter than high temperature metals but they are brittle and very difficult to manufacture without defects.

    Page: 438

Chapter 12: Modern Materials

MULTIPLE CHOICE

35. Sintering is
    a) placing in the middle
    b) finely dividing
    c) sieving to achieve uniform particle size
    d) heating to high temperature under pressure

    Answer: d Page: 438

36. In the sol-gel process, a metal is reacted with an alcohol to form a metal alkoxide. The metal alkoxide is then reacted with water to form the metal hydroxide. Why is the metal hydroxide not formed directly by reaction of a salt of the metal with base?
    a) because by forming the metal hydroxide by reaction of the metal salt with a base, finer particles are obtained
    b) because the metal hydroxide formed in this way is soluble and is more easily utilized
    c) the alcohol stabilizes the metal hydroxide making it less susceptible to attack by the base added later
    d) this method prevents oxidation of the metal to an unstable oxidation state

    Answer: a Page: 438

37. Why is it difficult to form objects from ceramics by pouring a gel in a casting and then heating?
    a) gels do not flow well to fill the casting
    b) considerable shrinking occurs when water is removed from the gel and voids result, weakening the object
    c) gels do not release well from the casting material
    d) the temperatures needed to remove the water from the gel distorts the shape of the casting material

    Answer: b Page: 438

38. Which one of the following is an example of a composite?
    a) salt water
    b) plaster of Paris
    c) polyethylene
    d) concrete with stones mixed into it

    Answer: d Page: 439

ESSAY

39. What two materials are formed into fibers and used to manufacture the space shuttle tiles?

    Answer: silica and aluminum borosilicate Page: 440

MULTIPLE CHOICE

40. The most widely used abrasive is
    a) corrundum
    b) graphite
    c) carborundum
    d) tungsten

    Answer: c Page: 440

ESSAY

41. What special property does a piezoelectric material possess?

    Answer: It generates an electrical potential when mechanically stressed.

    Page: 440

MULTIPLE CHOICE

42. What kind of materials exhibit the Meissner effect?
    a) abrasives
    b) refractories
    c) superconductors
    d) thermistors

    Answer: c Page: 440

43. What is the purpose of placing a thin film of tungsten carbide on the surface of a drill bit?
    a) to increase thermal conductivity
    b) to increase hardness
    c) to decrease corrosion
    d) to make a smooth surface that is less susceptible to binding in wood-based materials

    Answer: b Page: 440

ESSAY

44. List five properties a thin film should possess in order to be practically useful.

    Answer:
    chemical stability, good adhesion to substrate, uniform thickness, be chemically pure, include very few imperfections

    Page: 442

MULTIPLE CHOICE

45. In order for a substance to be coated onto a substrate as a thin film by vacuum deposition, that substance must
    a) be able to withstand very low pressures
    b) be readily entrained in a supersonic argon flow
    c) be a gas at room temperature
    d) be able to vaporize without losing its chemical identity

    Answer: d Page: 444

ESSAY

46. Why do sputtered coatings generally exhibit good adhesion to the substrate?

    Answer:
    Because the first sputtered atoms striking the surface of the substrate generally have enough energy to penetrate the substrate surface several atoms deep.

    Page: 444

47. Explain the process of chemical vapor deposition.

    Answer:
    The surface of the substrate is coated with a stable, volatile compound that is then converted chemically to a stable and adherent coating.

    Page: 444

MULTIPLE CHOICE

48. Considering types of film/substrate interaction and method of deposition, which thin film below should be most stably attached to its substrate?
    a) silver atoms on glass via sputtering
    b) silver atoms on aluminum oxide via sputtering
    c) silver atoms on glass via vacuum deposition
    d) silicon dioxide on steel via chemical vapor deposition
    e) silicon dioxide on aluminum oxide via chemical vapor deposition

    Answer: e Page: 444

49. What is the purpose of the hydrogen gas used in production of diamond thin films from methane and microwaves?
    a) to reduce the surface of the substrate to improve adhesion
    b) it disoldges surface atoms making a rougher surface to which the diamond will adhere
    c) its combustion produces the high temperatures necessary for the process
    d) it dilutes the methane gas to prevent formation of a thick layer of diamond
    e) to impede formation of graphite

    Answer: e Page: 446

Chapter 13: Properties of Solutions

MULTIPLE CHOICE

1. A solution contains 10% ethanol, 25% butanol, 40% propanol, and 25% methanol. What is the solvent?
   a) ethanol
   b) methanol
   c) butanol
   d) propanol

   Answer: d Page: 453

ESSAY

2. What type of solution does not involve a condensed phase?

   Answer: a mixture of gases Page: 453

MULTIPLE CHOICE

3. Which process occurring during solution formation is exothermic?
   a) separation of solute particles from each other
   b) separation of solvent particles from each other
   c) interaction of solvent with solute
   d) none of these

   Answer: c Page: 454

4. The process of solute particles being surrounded by solvent particles is known as
   a) salutation
   b) agglomeration
   c) solvation
   d) agglutination
   e) passivation

   Answer: c Page: 454

5. The dissolution of water in octane, C_8H_{18}, is prevented by
   a) London dispersion forces between octane molecules
   b) hydrogen bonding between water molecules
   c) dipole-dipole attraction between octane molecules
   d) ion-dipole attraction between water and octane molecules
   e) repulsion between like-charged water and octane molecules

   Answer: b Page: 456

6. When argon is placed in a container of neon, the argon spontaneously disperses throughout the neon. Why?
   a) large attractive forces between argon and neon atoms
   b) hydrogen bonding
   c) a decrease in energy occurs when the two mix
   d) the dispersion of argon atoms produces an increase in disorder
   e) solvent-solute interactions

   Answer: d Page: 456

7. Why is potassium bromide insoluble in carbon tetrachloride?
   a) solute-solute interactions are too large
   b) solvent-solvent interactions are too large
   c) solute-solvent interactions are too large
   d) none of these

   Answer: a Page: 456

ESSAY

8. Why does ammonium nitrate dissolve in water even though the process is highly endothermic?

   Answer: It is accompanied by a large increase in entropy. Page: 456

9. In what type of compound does one find waters of hydration? Where are these waters of hydration located within these compounds?

   Answer:
   Hydrates. The water molecules are found either surrounding ions or occupying lattice sites not specifically associated with either cation or anion.

   Page: 457

MULTIPLE CHOICE

10. A solution is said to contain 28% phosphoric acid by mass. What does this mean?
    a) 1 mL of this solution contains 28 g of phosphoric acid
    b) 1 L of this solution has a mass of 28 g
    c) 100 g of this solution contains 28 g of phosphoric acid
    d) 1 L of this solution contains 28 mL of phosphoric acid
    e) the density of this solution is 2.8 g/mL

    Answer: c Page: 458

11. What is the concentration of chloride ion, in percent, in a solution that contains 35.0 ppm chloride?
a) 3.50×10^{-3} %
b) 3.50×10^{2} %
c) 3.50×10^{-2} %
d) 3.50×10^{-6} %

Answer: a Page: 458

12. What mass of aluminum nitrate is required to make 500.0 mL of a solution that contains 23.3 ppm nitrate?
a) 9.90 mg
b) 13.3 mg
c) 11.6 mg
d) 3.88 mg

Answer: b Page: 458

13. A solution was made by dissolving calcium chloride in water and diluting to 500.0 mL. If this solution contained 44 ppm chloride ions, what was the concentration of calcium ions?
a) 44 ppm
b) 88 ppm
c) 22 ppm
d) 11 ppm

Answer: c Page: 458

14. What is the acetone concentration in ppm of a solution made by mixing 23.2 mg acetone with 2.000 L water?
a) 8.62
b) 11.6
c) 0.862
d) 0.0862
e) 1.16

Answer: b Page: 458

15. A solution is prepared by dissolving 23.7 g of $CaCl_2$ in 375 g of water. The density of the resulting solution is 1.05 g/mL. Calculate the % by weight of $CaCl_2$ in the solution described above.
a) 5.94%
b) 6.32%
c) 0.0632%
d) 0.0594%

Answer: a Page: 458

16. Calculate the % by weight of urea (MW = 60 g/mol) in a solution prepared by dissolving 16 g of urea in 39 g of H_2O.
    a) 29
    b) 41
    c) 0.29
    d) 0.41

    Answer: a Page: 358

17. What is the concentration of nitrate ions in a solution that contains 0.900 *M* aluminum nitrate?
    a) 0.900 *M*
    b) 0.450 *M*
    c) 0.300 *M*
    d) 2.70 *M*
    e) 1.80 *M*

    Answer: d Page: 459

18. What is the molality of KBr in a solution made by dissolving 2.21 g of KBr in 897 g of water?
    a) 2.46 m
    b) 0.0167 m
    c) 0.0207 m
    d) 2.07×10^{-5} m

    Answer: c Page: 459

ESSAY

19. Calculate the molarity of phosphoric acid in a solution that is 84 % phosphoric acid and has a density of 1.87 g/mL.

    Answer:

$$\frac{1.87 \text{ g solution}}{\text{mL solution}} \times \frac{0.84 \text{ g } H_3PO_4}{\text{g solution}} \quad \frac{1000 \text{ mL}}{1 \text{ L}} \times \frac{1 \text{ mol } H_3PO_4}{97.99 \text{ g } H_3PO_4} =$$

    16.0 M

    Page: 459

MULTIPLE CHOICE

20. Molality is
    a) moles solute/moles solvent
    b) moles solute/Liters solution
    c) moles solute/kg solution
    d) moles solute/kg solvent
    e) none (dimensionless)

    Answer: d Page: 459

21. The molality of lead nitrate in 0.726 M $Pb(NO_3)_2$ (density 1.202 g/mL) is
    a) 0.476 m
    b) 1.928 m
    c) 0.755 m
    d) 0.819 m
    e) 0.650 m

    Answer: c Page: 459

22. The molality in mol/kg of a benzene solution formed by mixing 12.0 g C_6H_6 with 38.0 g CCl_4 is
    a) 4.04
    b) 0.240
    c) 0.622
    d) 0.316
    e) 0.508

    Answer: a Page: 459

23. A solution is prepared by dissolving 15.0 g of NH_3 in 250 g of water. The density of the resulting solution is 0.974 g/mL. Calculate the <u>mole fraction</u> of NH_3 in the solution described above.
    a) 0.064
    b) 0.060
    c) 0.94
    d) 0.92

    Answer: b Page: 459

24. A solution is prepared by dissolving 15.0 g of NH_3 in 250 g of water. The density of the resulting solution is 0.974 g/mL. Calculate the <u>molarity</u> of NH_3 in the solution described above.
    a) 0.00353
    b) 0.882
    c) 60.0
    d) 3.53

    Answer: d Page: 459

25. A solution is prepared by dissolving 23.7 g of $CaCl_2$ in 375 g of water. The density of the resulting solution is 1.05 g/mL. Calculate the molarity of Cl^- in the solution described above.
a) 0.214 M
b) 0.562 M
c) 1.12 M
d) 1.14 M

Answer: c Page: 459

26. A solution is prepared by dissolving 23.7 g of $CaCl_2$ in 375 g of water. The density of the resulting solution is 1.05 g/mL. Calculate the molality of $CaCl_2$ in the solution described above.
a) 0.214 m
b) 0.570 m
c) 5.70 m
d) 63.2 m

Answer: b Page: 459

27. What is the molality of HCl in a solution prepared by dissolving 5.5 g of HCl in 200 g of C_2H_6O?
a) 27.5 m
b) 7.5×10^{-4} m
c) 3.3×10^{-2} m
d) 0.75 m

Answer: d Page: 459

28. What is the molarity of HCl in a solution prepared by dissolving 5.5 g of HCl in 200 g of C_2H_6O if the density of the solution is 0.79 g/mL?
a) 21 M
b) 0.93 M
c) 0.58 M
d) 6.0×10^{-4} M

Answer: c Page: 459

29. What is the mole fraction of He in a gaseous solution containing 4.0 g of He, 6.5 g of Ar, and 10.0 g of Ne?
a) 0.60
b) 1.5
c) 0.20
d) 0.11

Answer: a Page: 459

30. Calculate the mole fraction of urea (MW = 60 g/mol) in a solution prepared by dissolving 16 g of urea in 39 g of H_2O.
a) 0.58
b) 0.37
c) 0.13
d) 0.11

Answer: d Page: 459

31. Calculate the molality of urea (MW = 60 g/mol) in a solution prepared by dissolving 16 g of urea in 39 g of H_2O.
a) 96 m
b) 6.8 m
c) 0.68 m
d) 0.41 m

Answer: b Page: 459

32. Determine the molarity of a solution prepared by dissolving 16 g of urea (MW = 60) in 39 g of H_2O if the density of the solution is 1.3 g/mL.
a) 0.068 M
b) 3.7 M
c) 4.8 M
d) 6.3 M

Answer: d Page: 459

33. Which one of the following varies with temperature?
a) molarity
b) mass percent
c) mole fraction
d) molality

Answer: a Page: 476

34. The compound X has a solubility of 4.22 g per 100 mL of water. A solution containing 2.49 g of X per 100 mL of water is
a) unsaturated
b) saturated
c) supersaturated

Answer: a Page: 462

35. Which one of the following solutions is unstable?
a) unsaturated
b) saturated
c) supersaturated

Answer: c Page: 462

36. For most salts, the crystalization of excess solute from a supersaturated solution is
    a) endothermic
    b) exothermic

    Answer: b Page: 462

37. A saturated solution
    a) contains as much solvent as it can hold
    b) contains no double bonds
    c) contains dissolved solute in equilibrium with undissolved solid
    d) will rapidly precipitate if a seed crystal is added

    Answer: c Page: 462

38. In a saturated solution of a salt in water
    a) the rate of crystallization > the rate of solution
    b) the rate of solution > the rate of crystallization
    c) seed crystal addition may cause massive crystallization
    d) the rate of crystallization = the rate of solution
    e) addition of more water causes massive crystallization

    Answer: d Page: 462

ESSAY

39. Pairs of liquids that will mix in all proportions are called

    Answer: miscible Page: 463

MULTIPLE CHOICE

40. Which one of the following should be immiscible with carbon tetrachloride, CCl_4?
    a) C_6H_{14}
    b) Br_2
    c) CH_3CH_2OH
    d) C_3H_8

    Answer: c Page: 463

41. The principal reason for extremely low solubility of NaCl in benzene, C_6H_6, listed below is
    a) the great strength of solvent-solvent interactions
    b) the great strength of solute-solvent interactions
    c) the great strength of solute-solute interactions
    d) the great weakness of solute-solvent interactions
    e) the nonspontaneity of the increased disorder due to mixing of solute and solvent

    Answer: d Page: 463

42. Potassium hydroxide dissolves readily in water due to
    a) strong solute-solute interactions
    b) strong solvent-solvent interactions
    c) strong solute-solvent interactions
    d) weak solvent-solvent interactions

    Answer: c Page: 463

43. Which one of the following substances would be the most soluble in water?
    a) Ar
    b) NH_3
    c) NaCl
    d) CH_4

    Answer: c Page: 463

44. Which one of the following substances would be the most soluble in CCl_4?
    a) CH_3CH_2OH
    b) H_2O
    c) NH_3
    d) $C_{10}H_{22}$

    Answer: d Page: 463

45. The pairs shown below represent solutions in which the first member of the pair is the solute and the second member is the solvent. Which solution would have only dispersion forces as the attractive force between solute and solvent particles?
    a) HF/H_2O
    b) NH_3/CH_3OH
    c) C_6H_6/C_5H_{12}
    d) CH_2Cl_2/CH_3OH

    Answer: c Page: 463

46. The pairs shown below represent solutions in which the first member of the pair is the solute and the second member is the solvent. Which solution would have hydrogen bonds as one of the attractive forces between solute and solvent particles?
    a) HF/H_2O
    b) CH_4/CH_3OH
    c) C_6H_6/C_5H_{12}
    d) CH_2Cl_2/CH_3OH

    Answer: a Page: 463

47. Which of the following should be most miscible with water at the same temperature and pressure?
    a) $HOCH_2CH_2OH$
    b) $CHCl_3$
    c) $CH_3(CH_2)_9CHO$ (structure drawn with C=O double bond)
    d) $CH_3(CH_2)_8CH_2OH$
    e) CCl_4

    Answer: a Page: 463

48. Which one of the following substances would be the most soluble in CH_3OH?
    a) CCl_4
    b) Kr
    c) HCl
    d) CH_3CH_2OH

    Answer: d Page: 463

49. Which one of the following substances would be the most soluble in CCl_4?
    a) CI_4
    b) Kr
    c) HCl
    d) CH_3CH_2OH

    Answer: a Page: 463

50. Which one of the following substances would be the most soluble in benzene (C_6H_6)?
    a) CH_3CH_2OH
    b) NH_3
    c) NaCl
    d) CCl_4

    Answer: d Page: 463

51. Which one of the following is most soluble in water?
    a) CH_3OH
    b) $CH_3CH_2CH_2OH$
    c) CH_3CH_2OH
    d) $CH_3CH_2CH_2CH_2OH$
    e) $CH_3CH_2CH_2CH_2CH_2OH$

    Answer: a Page: 464

52. Which one of the following is most soluble in hexane, C_6H_{14}?
a) CH_3OH
b) $CH_3CH_2CH_2OH$
c) CH_3CH_2OH
d) $CH_3CH_2CH_2CH_2OH$
e) $CH_3CH_2CH_2CH_2CH_2OH$

Answer: e Page: 464

53. If all other factors are the same, what is the relationship between the number of OH groups in a molecule and its solubilty in water?
a) solubility decreases as the number of OH groups increases
b) solubility increases as the number of OH groups increases
c) there is no relationship between the solubility and the number of OH groups

Answer: b Page: 464

54. Calculate the concentration of nitrogen gas in water with a nitrogen gas at a partial pressure of 0.826 atm above it. Henry's Law constant for this system is 6.8×10^{-4} mol/L•atm.
a) 5.6×10^{-4} M
b) 1.2×10^{3} M
c) 8.2×10^{-3} M
d) 0.43 M

Answer: a Page: 465

55. For solubility of methane gas (CH_4), which solvent/temperature combination should afford the lowest value of the Henry's Law constant (k_H)?
a) C_6H_6/301 K
b) C_6H_6/322 K
c) C_6H_6/349 K
d) H_2O/301 K
e) H_2O/349 K

Answer: e Page: 465

56. Which gas/temperature set gives the largest Henry's Law constant (k_H) for the liquid solvent H_2O?
a) C_2H_4/45°C
b) HF/11°C
c) HCl/49°C
d) CO_2/32°C
e) N_2/15°C

Answer: b Page: 465

57. Which line on the graph shown below approximates the relationship between pressure and solubility for CO_2 gas in water?
   a) w
   b) x
   c) y

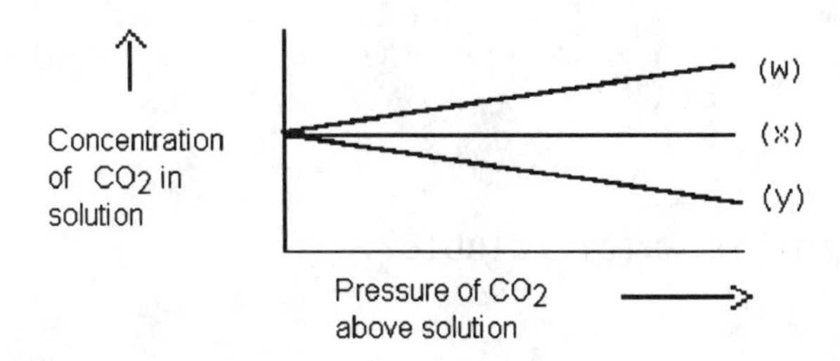

Answer: a Page: 465

58. Pressure has an appreciable effect only on the solubility of ____________ in liquids.
   a) gases
   b) solids
   c) liquids
   d) all of the above

Answer: a Page: 465

59. The solubility of oxygen gas in water at 25°C and 1.0 atm pressure of oxygen is 0.041 g/L. What is the solubility (in g/L) of oxygen in water at 3.0 atm and 25°C?
   a) 0.041
   b) 0.014
   c) 0.31
   d) 0.12

Answer: d Page: 465

60. The solubility of nitrogen gas in water at a nitrogen pressure of 1.0 atm is 6.9×10^{-4} M. What is the solubility (in moles/L) of nitrogen in water at a nitrogen pressure of 0.80 atm?
   a) 5.5×10^{-4}
   b) 8.6×10^{-4}
   c) 1.2×10^{3}
   d) 3.7×10^{-3}

Answer: a Page: 465

61. The solubility of Ar in water at 25°C is 1.6×10^{-3} mol/L when the pressure of the Ar above the solution is 1.0 atm. What is the solubility of Ar (in mol/L) at a pressure of 2.5 atm?
a) 1.6×10^{3}
b) 6.4×10^{-4}
c) 4.0×10^{-3}
d) 7.5×10^{-2}

Answer: c Page: 465

62. Which one of the following vitamins is water soluble?
a) D
b) E
c) A
d) B
e) K

Answer: d Page: 466

ESSAY

63. Illness caused by an excessive amount of vitamins is called

Answer: hypervitaminosis Page: 466

MULTIPLE CHOICE

64. True hypervitaminosis is observed solely for what type of vitamins?
a) water soluble
b) fat soluble
c) both water and fat soluble
d) neither water nor fat soluble

Answer: b Page: 466

65. The new Procter & Gamble product called olestra is formed by combining a sugar molecule with
a) alcohols
b) vitamin A
c) fatty acids
d) protein
e) cholesterol

Answer: c Page: 466

ESSAY

66. What is the potential danger involved with the consumption of the new Procter & Gamble product called olestra?

Answer:
it absorbs fat soluble vitamins and other nutrients and carries them out of the body

Page: 466

67. How can a slight increase in the temperature of the water in a lake result in the death of fish?

    Answer: the increased temperature reduces the solubilty of oxygen in the water

    Page: 467

MULTIPLE CHOICE

68. Which component of air is the primary problem in the disease known as the bends?
    a) O_2
    b) CO_2
    c) He
    d) N_2
    e) CO

    Answer: d Page: 467

ESSAY

69. Why does substitution of helium for nitrogen reduce the possibility of getting the bends?

    Answer: the solubility of He in biological fluids is far lower than that of N_2

    Page: 467

MULTIPLE CHOICE

70. If the partial pressure of oxygen in the air a diver breathes is too great, what problem results?
    a) respiratory tissue is damaged by oxidation
    b) hyperventilation
    c) the urge to breathe is increased and excessive CO_2 is removed from the body
    d) the urge to breathe is reduced and not enough CO_2 is removed from the body
    e) no problems result from this situation

    Answer: d Page: 469

71. Which line corresponds to the way molality of a gas dissolved in a liquid varies with temperature?
 a) w
 b) x
 c) y

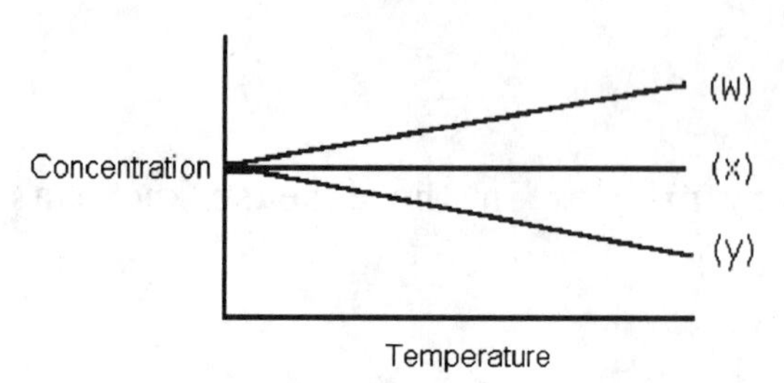

Answer: b Page: 467

72. Increasing the temperature of an aqueous solution of a gas will cause the _________ of the solution to ________.
 a) molality, increase
 b) molarity, decrease
 c) mole fraction, increase
 d) % by weight, increase

Answer: b Page: 467

73. In general, the solubility of ___ in water decreases as temperature increases.
 a) liquids
 b) gases
 c) solids

Answer: b Page: 467

74. Which line corresponds to the way molarity of a gas dissolved in a liquid varies with temperature?
 a) w
 b) x
 c) y

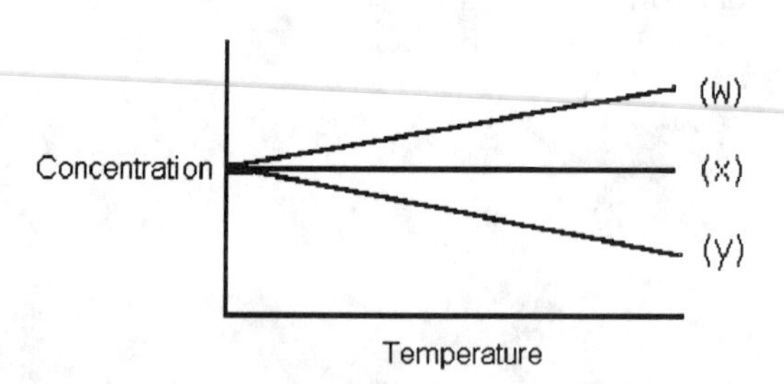

Answer: c Page: 467

75. A 0.100 m solution of which one of the following solutes will have the lowest vapor pressures?
    a) $KClO_4$
    b) $Ca(ClO_4)_2$
    c) $Al(ClO_4)_3$
    d) CH_3OH

    Answer: c Page: 469

76. A solution was made up of equal moles of liquid A (vapor pressure = 15.3 torr), liquid B (vapor pressure = 65.3 torr), liquid C (vapor pressure = 2.39 torr), and liquid D (vapor pressure = 78.3 torr). The vapor of which liquid will be in the highest concentration above the solution?
    a) A
    b) B
    c) C
    d) D

    Answer: d Page: 469

77. Addition of a non-volatile solute to a solvent causes which one of the following to change by the greatest amount?
    a) boiling point
    b) freezing point
    c) vapor pressure
    d) osmotic pressure

    Answer: d Page: 469

78. The magnitude of K_f and of K_b depends on the
    a) solute
    b) solvent
    c) solution
    d) temperature

    Answer: b Page: 469

79. Adding solute to a solution increases each of the following except
    a) molality
    b) osmotic pressure
    c) boiling point
    d) vapor pressure

    Answer: d Page: 469

80. The vapor pressure of pure ethanol at 60°C is 349 mm Hg. Raoult's Law predicts what vapor pressure in mm Hg at 60°C for a solution prepared by dissolving 10.0 mmol naphthalene (nonvolatile) in 90.0 mmol ethanol?
a) 34.9
b) 314
c) 600
d) 279
e) 69.8

Answer: b Page: 469

81. The vapor pressure of pure water at 25°C is 23.8 mm Hg. What is the vapor pressure of water above a solution prepared by dissolving 18 g of glucose (a nonelectrolyte, MW = 180 g/mol) in 95 g of water?
a) 24.3
b) 23.4
c) 0.451
d) 0.443

Answer: b Page: 469

82. The vapor pressure of pure water at 25°C is 23.8 mm Hg. Determine the vapor pressure of water at 25°C above a solution containing 35 g of urea (a nonvolatile, non-electrolyte, MW = 60 g/mol) dissolved in 75 g of water.
a) 2.9
b) 3.3
c) 21
d) 27

Answer: c Page: 469

83. As the concentration of a solute in a solution increases, the freezing point of the solution ________ and the vapor pressure of the solution ________.
a) increases, increases
b) increases, decreases
c) decreases, increases
d) decreases, decreases

Answer: d Page: 469

84. What conditions will result in a negative deviation from Raoult's law?
a) solute-solute and solvent-solvent interactions being stronger than solute-solvent interactions
b) solute-solute and solvent-solvent interactions being weaker than solute-solvent interactions
c) solute-solute and solvent-solvent interactions having the same strength as solute-solvent interactions
d) none of these

Answer: b Page: 470

85. Which liquid will have the <u>lowest</u> freezing point?
   a) pure H_2O
   b) aq. 0.60 m glucose
   c) aq. 0.60 m sucrose
   d) aq. 0.24 m FeI_3
   e) aq. 0.50 m KF

   Answer: e Page: 473

86. Which liquid will have the <u>lowest</u> freezing point?
   a) pure H_2O
   b) aq. 0.050 m glucose
   c) aq. 0.030 m CoI_2
   d) aq. 0.030 m AlI_3
   e) aq. 0.030 m NaI

   Answer: d Page: 473

87. The freezing point of ethanol (C_2H_5OH) is -114.6°C. The molal freezing point depression constant for ethanol is 2.00 °C/m. What is the freezing point (in °C) of a solution prepared by dissolving 50.0 g of glycerin ($C_3H_8O_3$, a nonelectrolyte) in 200 g of ethanol?
   a) -115
   b) -5.4
   c) -132
   d) -120

   Answer: d Page: 473

88. What is the freezing point (in °C) of a solution prepared by dissolving 11.3 g of $Ca(NO_3)_2$ (formula weight = 164 g/mol) in 115 g of water? The molal freezing point depression constant for water is 1.86 °C/m.
   a) -3.34
   b) -1.11
   c) 3.34
   d) 1.11

   Answer: b Page: 473

89. After swimming in the ocean for several hours, the swimmers noticed that their fingers appeared to be very wrinkled or shriveled up. This is an indication that seawater is ___ relative to the fluid in cells.
   a) isotonic
   b) hypertonic
   c) hypotonic
   d) none of these

   Answer: b Page: 475

90. A 1.00 m aqueous solution of compound X had a boiling point of 101.4°C. Which one of the following could be compound X? The boiling point elevation constant for water is 0.52 °C/m.
a) CH_3CH_2OH
b) $C_6H_{12}O_6$
c) Na_3PO_4
d) KCl

Answer: d Page: 476

91. How are freezing point depressions and boiling point elevations caused by a solute related to the molecular mass of the solute?
a) directly proportional
b) inversely proportional
c) not related at all

Answer: b Page: 476

92. A solution containing 100 g unknown liquid and 900 g water has a freezing point of -3.33°C. Given K_f = 1.86°C/m for water, the molecular weight in amu of the unknown liquid is
a) 69.0
b) 333
c) 619
d) 161
e) 62.1

Answer: e Page: 476

93. A solution prepared by dissolving 0.60 g of nicotine (a nonelectrolyte) in water to make 12 mL of solution has an osmotic pressure of 7.55 atm at 25°C. What is the molecular weight of nicotine? (R = 0.0821 L•atm/K mol)
a) 28 g/mol
b) 43 g/mol
c) 50 g/mol
d) 160 g/mol

Answer: d Page: 476

94. A solution is prepared by dissolving 6.00 g of an unknown nonelectrolyte in enough water to make 1.00 L of solution. The osmotic pressure of this solution is 0.750 atm at 25.0°C. What is the molecular weight of the unknown solute?
(R = 0.0821 L•atm/K•mol)
a) 16.4 g/mol
b) 196 g/mol
c) 110 g/mol
d) 30.6 g/mol

Answer: b Page: 476

95. The most likely van't Hoff factor for an 0.01 m CaI_2 solution is
    a) 1.00
    b) 3.00
    c) 1.27
    d) 2.69
    e) 3.29

    Answer: d Page: 477

96. Which produces the greatest number of ions when one mole dissolves in water?
    a) NaCl
    b) NH_4NO_3
    c) NH_4Cl
    d) Na_2SO_4

    Answer: d Page: 477

97. Which one of the following solutes has a limiting van't Hoff factor (i) of 3 when dissolved in water?
    a) KNO_3
    b) CH_3OH
    c) CCl_4
    d) Na_2SO_4

    Answer: d Page: 477

98. Determine the maximum value of i (van't Hoff factor) for $(NH_4)_3PO_4$.
    a) 1
    b) 2
    c) 3
    d) 4

    Answer: d Page: 477

99. Which one of the following 0.1 M aqueous solutions would have the lowest freezing point?
    a) NaCl
    b) $Al(NO_3)_3$
    c) K_2CrO_4
    d) Na_2SO_4

    Answer: b Page: 477

100. Determine the fraction of ionization of HX (a weak electrolyte) if a solution prepared by dissolving 0.020 moles of HX in 115 g of water freezes at -.47°C (K_f = 1.86 °C/m).
a) 0.044
b) 0.30
c) 0.45
d) 1.45

Answer: c Page: 477

101. Determine the freezing point (in °C) of a 0.015 molal solution of $MgSO_4$ (K_f of H_2O = 1.86 °C/m). Assume i = 2.0 for $MgSO_4$.
a) -0.056
b) -0.028
c) -0.17
d) -0.084

Answer: a Page: 477

102. A solution is prepared by dissolving 2.60 g of a strong electrolyte (formula weight = 101 g/mol) in enough water to make 1.00 L of solution. The osmotic pressure of the solution is 1.25 atm at 25.0°C. What is the van't Hoff factor (i) for the unknown solute?
(R = 0.0821 L•atm/K•mol)
a) 0
b) 1
c) 2
d) 3

Answer: c Page: 477

103. What is the phase of the dispersed substance in a sol?
a) gas
b) liquid
c) solid

Answer: c Page: 479

104. A colloid cannot be formed by mixing two substances in the ___ phase.
a) gas
b) liquid
c) solid

Answer: a Page: 479

105. What type of colloid is mayonnaise?
   a) sol
   b) aerosol
   c) foam
   d) solid foam
   e) emulsion
   f) solid sol

   Answer: e Page: 479

106. The phenomenon used to differentiate colloids and true solutions is called the ____________ effect.
   a) van't Hoff
   b) Tyndall
   c) Raoult
   d) Osmotic
   e) Henry

   Answer: b Page: 479

107. The process of a substance sticking to the surface of another is called
   a) absorption
   b) diffusion
   c) effusion
   d) adsorption

   Answer: d Page: 481

ESSAY

108. Why do colloidal clay particles coagulate when river water mixes with seawater?

   Answer:
   The ions in the seawater neutralize the charges on the colloidal particle surfaces allowing them to coagulate.
   Page: 481

MULTIPLE CHOICE

109. In addition to adding ions to a colloid, what can one do to cause a colloid to coagulate?
   a) stir it rapidly
   b) centrifuge it
   c) focus ultraviolet radiation on it
   d) heat it
   e) none of these

   Answer: d Page: 481

110. The process in which colloidal particles combine into larger particles is termed
    a) dialysis
    b) hydrophobicity
    c) coagulation
    d) hydrophilicity
    e) light scattering

    Answer: c Page: 481

Chapter 14: Chemical Kinetics

MULTIPLE CHOICE

1. Which one of the following is not valid for a reaction rate?
   a) mol/L
   b) *M*/s
   c) mol/hr
   d) g/day
   e) mol/L/hr

   Answer: a Page: 495

2. In the reaction $2NO_2 \rightarrow 2NO + O_2$ at 300°C, $[NO_2]$ drops from 0.0100 to 0.00650 M in 100 s. What is the average rate of disappearance of NO_2 for this period in M/s?
   a) 0.35
   b) 0.0035
   c) 0.000035
   d) 0.0070
   e) 0.0018

   Answer: c Page: 509

3. In the reaction $2NO_2 \rightarrow 2NO + O_2$ at 300°C, $[NO_2]$ drops from 0.0100 to 0.00650 M in 100 s. What is the average rate of appearance of 0 for this period in M/s?
   a) 0.000018
   b) 0.000035
   c) 0.000070
   d) 0.0035
   e) 0.0070

   Answer: a Page: 509

4. Use the table of data shown below to calculate the average rate of the reaction between 10 s and 30 s.

   $A + B \rightarrow C$

time (seconds)	[A] mol/L
0	0.124
10	0.110
20	0.088
30	0.073
40	0.054

   a) 0.0012
   b) -0.0019
   c) 0.0019
   d) -0.0012

   Answer: b Page: 495

5. Use the table of data shown below to calculate the average rate of the reaction between 3 min and 9 min.

A → 2C

time (seconds)	[A] mol/L
0	0.124
10	0.110
20	0.088
30	0.073
40	0.054

a) 0.12
b) 0.048
c) 0.14
d) 0.072

Answer: d Page: 495

6. Use the table of data shown below to calculate the average rate of the reaction between 10 s and 20 s.

A → B

time (seconds)	[A] mol/L
0	0.20
5	0.14
10	0.10
15	0.071
20	0.050

a) 6×10^{-3}
b) 8×10^{-3}
c) 5×10^{-3}
d) 200

Answer: c Page: 495

7. Which one of the following is not a valid expression for the rate of the reaction below?

$$4NH_3 + 7O_2 \rightarrow 4NO_2 + 6H_2O$$

a) $-\frac{1}{7}\frac{\Delta[O_2]}{\Delta t}$

b) $\frac{1}{4}\frac{\Delta[NO_2]}{\Delta t}$

c) $-\frac{1}{6}\frac{\Delta[H_2O]}{\Delta t}$

d) $-\frac{1}{4}\frac{\Delta[NH_3]}{\Delta t}$

Answer: c Page: 512

8. Which substance in the reaction below either appears or disappears the fastest?

$$4NH_3 + 7O_2 \rightarrow 4NO_2 + 6H_2O$$

a) NH_3
b) O_2
c) NO_2
d) H_2O

Answer: b Page: 512

9. Consider the following reaction.

$$A \rightarrow 2C$$

The average rate of appearance of C is given by [C]/t. How is the average rate of appearance of C related to the average rate of disappearance of A?
a) -2[A]/t
b) [A]/t
c) -[A]/t
d) -[A]/2t

Answer: a Page: 496

10. Consider the following reaction.

$$3A \rightarrow 2B$$

The average rate of appearance of B is given by [B]/t. How is the average rate of appearance of B related to the average rate of disappearance of A?
a) 2[A]/3t
b) -2[A]/3t
c) -3[A]/2t
d) -[A]/t

Answer: b Page: 496

11. A reaction was found to be second order in carbon monoxide concentration. What happens to the rate of the reaction if the concentration of carbon monoxide is doubled with everything else held constant?
a) it doubles
b) it remains unchanged
c) it triples
d) it increases by a factor of 4

Answer: d Page: 498

12. Which one of the following rate laws is for a reaction that is overall third order?

a) rate = $k[NO]^3[O_2]$

b) rate = $k[C_6H_8]^2[H_2]^2$

c) rate = $k\frac{[NH_3]^3[O_2]^3}{[OsO_2]^3}$

d) rate = $k\frac{[H_2O_2]^3}{[H_2]}$

Answer: c Page: 498

13. If the reaction 2A + 3D → products is first-order in A and second order in D, then the rate law will have the form, rate =
a) $k[A][D]$
b) $k[A]^2[D]^3$
c) $k[A][D]^2$
d) $k[A]^2[D]$
e) $k[A]^2[D]^2$

Answer: c Page: 498

14. A reaction was found to have the rate law, rate = $k[A]^x$. What are the units of k if the reaction is second order in A?
    a) M/s
    b) $M^{-1}s^{-1}$
    c) $1/s$
    d) $1/M$
    e) s/M^2

    Answer: b Page: 499

15. The kinetics of the reaction below were studied and it was determined that the reaction rate increased by a factor of 9 when the concentration of B was tripled. The reaction is _____ order in B.

    A + B → P

    a) zero
    b) first
    c) second
    d) third
    e) one-half

    Answer: c Page: 499

16. The kinetics of the reaction below were studied and it was determined that the reaction rate did not change when the concentration of B was tripled. The reaction is _____ order in B.

    A + B → P

    a) zero
    b) first
    c) second
    d) third
    e) one-half

    Answer: a Page: 499

17. The kinetics of the reaction below were studied and it was determined that the reaction rate decreased by a factor of 9 when the concentration of B was tripled. The reaction is _____ order in B.

    A + B → P

    a) zero
    b) first
    c) second
    d) third
    e) one-half

    Answer: e Page: 499

18. A reaction was found to be third order in A. What effect will tripling the concentration of A have on the reaction rate? It will cause the reaction rate to
a) remain constant
b) increase by a factor of 27
c) increase by a factor of 9
d) triple
e) decrease by a factor of the cube root of 3

Answer: b Page: 499

19. A reaction was found to be zero order in A. What effect will tripling the concentration of A have on the reaction rate? It will cause the reaction rate to
a) remain constant
b) increase by a factor of 27
c) increase by a factor of 9
d) triple
e) decrease by a factor of the cube root of 3

Answer: a Page: 499

20. The correct unit for the rate constant in the rate law having rate = k[D][X] is
a) $mol\ L^{-1}\ s^{-1}$
b) $L\ mol^{-1}\ s^{-1}$
c) $mol^{2}\ L^{-2}\ s^{-1}$
d) $mol\ L^{-1}\ s^{-2}$
e) $L^{2}\ mol^{-2}\ s^{-1}$

Answer: b Page: 499

21. Which one of the following does not affect the value of the rate constant?
a) temperature
b) catalyst
c) concentration

Answer: c Page: 500

22. Use the information below to determine the order of the reaction in reactant A.

$A + B \rightarrow P$

Trial	[A],M	[B],M	Rate
1	0.273	0.763	2.83
2	0.273	1.526	2.83
3	0.819	0.763	25.47

a) 1
b) 2
c) 3
d) 4
e) 0

Answer: b Page: 500

23. Use the information below to determine the order of the reaction in reactant B.

$A + B \rightarrow P$

Trial	[A],M	[B],M	Rate
1	0.273	0.763	2.83
2	0.273	1.526	2.83
3	0.819	0.763	25.47

a) 1
b) 2
c) 3
d) 4
e) 0

Answer: e Page: 500

24. Use the information below to determine the overall order of the reaction.

$A + B \rightarrow P$

Trial	[A],M	[B],M	Rate
1	0.273	0.763	2.83
2	0.273	1.526	2.83
3	0.819	0.763	25.47

a) 1
b) 2
c) 3
d) 4
e) 0

Answer: b Page: 500

25. Use the information below to determine the value of the rate constant for the following reaction.

$A + B \rightarrow P$

Trial	[A],M	[B],M	Rate
1	0.273	0.763	2.83
2	0.273	1.526	2.83
3	0.819	0.763	25.47

a) 38.0
b) 0.278
c) 13.2
d) 42.0
e) 2.21

Answer: a Page: 500

26. Given the initial-rate data below for the reaction, $mM + zZ \rightarrow$ products, the correct rate law is rate =

Initial Conc. (M) Reactants

Expt.	[M]	[Z]	Rate (mol^2/L^2 s)
1	0.100	0.100	4.0×10^{-5}
2	0.200	0.100	1.6×10^{-4}
3	0.100	0.200	8.0×10^{-5}

a) $k[M][Z]$
b) $k[M]^2[Z]$
c) $k[M]^2[Z]^2$
d) $k[M][Z]^2$
e) $k[M]^4[Z]^2$

Answer: b Page: 500

27. Given the initial-rate data below for the reaction $mM + zZ \rightarrow$ products, the correct rate constant in L^2/mol^2 s is

Initial Conc. (M) Reactants

Expt.	[M]	[Z]	Rate (mol/L s)
1	0.100	0.100	4.0×10^{-5}
2	0.200	0.100	1.6×10^{-4}
3	0.100	0.200	8.0×10^{-5}

a) 4.0×10^{-3}
b) 2.5×10^{2}
c) 4.0×10^{-2}
d) 2.5×10^{-2}
e) 1.6×10^{-4}

Answer: c Page: 500

28. The table shown below contains concentration and rate data for this reaction.

    A + 2B → C

    Determine the rate law for this reaction.

Experiment	Initial [A]	Initial [B]	Initial Rate
1	0.23	0.17	0.33
2	0.46	0.17	0.64
3	0.23	0.51	0.33

a) $R = k[A]^4[B]$
b) $R = k[A]^4$
c) $R = k[A]^3$
d) $R = k[A]^3[B]$

Answer: c Page: 500

29. The table shown below contains concentration and rate data for this reaction.

    A + 2B → C

Experiment	Initial [A]	Initial [B]	Initial Rate
1	0.23	0.17	0.33
2	0.46	0.17	0.64
3	0.23	0.51	0.33

Assume that the reaction described above is first order in both reactants A and B. Calculate the value of the reaction rate constant using data for Experiment 1.

a) 0.12
b) 19
c) 27
d) 8.4

Answer: d Page: 500

30. Select the rate law that corresponds to the data shown for the following reaction.

$2A + 3B \rightarrow 2C$

Experiment	Initial [A]	Initial [B]	Initial Rate
1	0.15	0.12	0.10
2	0.15	0.24	0.04
3	0.45	0.24	1.80

a) $R = k[A]^3[B]$
b) $R = k[A]^3$
c) $R = k[A]^2[B]^2$
d) $R = k[A]^2[B]$

Answer: d Page: 500

31. $2A + 3B \rightarrow 2C$

Experiment	Initial [A]	Initial [B]	Initial Rate
1	0.23	0.17	0.33
2	0.46	0.17	0.64
3	0.23	0.51	0.33

Assume that the reaction described above is first order in both reactants A and B. Calculate the value of the reaction rate constant using data for Experiment 1.

a) 37
b) 5.6
c) 0.67
d) 0.18

Answer: b Page: 500

32. Select the rate law that corresponds to the data shown for the following reaction.

$2A + B \rightarrow C$

Exp.	Initial [A]	Initial [B]	Initial Rate
1	0.015	0.022	0.125
2	0.030	0.044	0.500
3	0.060	0.044	0.500
4	0.060	0.066	1.125

a) Rate = $k[B]^2$
b) Rate = $k[A][B]^2$
c) Rate = $k[A][B]$
d) Rate = $k[A]^2[B]$

Answer: a Page: 500

33. Select the rate law that corresponds to the data shown for the following reaction.

$A + B \rightarrow C$

Exp.	Initial [A]	Initial [B]	Initial Rate
1	0.012	0.035	0.10
2	0.024	0.070	0.80
3	0.024	0.035	0.10
4	0.012	0.070	0.80

a) Rate = $k[B]^4$
b) Rate = $k[A][B]^3$
c) Rate = $k[A]^2[B]^2$
d) Rate = $k[B]^3$

Answer: d Page: 500

34. For a first order reaction, a plot of ____ versus ____ is linear.

a) $\ln [A]_t$, $\frac{1}{t}$

b) $\ln [A]_t$, t

c) $\frac{1}{[A]}$, t

d) [A], t

Answer: b Page: 502

ESSAY

35. Calculate the rate constant of a first order reaction if the initial concentration of reactant is 0.373 M and the concentration of reactant after 122 s is 0.0974 M.

Answer:

$$\ln \frac{[A]_t}{[A]_0} = -kt$$

$$\ln \frac{0.0974 \text{ M}}{0.0373 \text{ M}} = -k(122 \text{ s})$$

$$k = 0.0110 \text{s}^{-1}$$

Page: 502

MULTIPLE CHOICE

36. $2NO_2 \rightarrow 2NO + O_2$ follows second-order kinetics. At 300°C, $[NO_2]$ drops from 0.0100 to 0.00650 M in 100 s. Use of the integrated form of the proper rate equation affords a value of _______ L/mol•s for the rate constant k.
a) 0.096
b) 0.65
c) 0.81
d) 1.2
e) 0.54

Answer: e Page: 502

37. $CH_3\text{-}N{\equiv}C \rightarrow CH_3\text{-}C{\equiv}N$ is a first-order reaction. At 230.3°C, $k = 6.30 \times 10^{-}$ s^{-1}. If $[CH_3\text{-}N{\equiv}C]_0$ is 0.00100 M, $[CH_3\text{-}N{\equiv}C]$ in M after 1000 s is
a) 0.000533
b) 0.000234
c) 0.00188
d) 0.00427
e) 0.00000100

Answer: a Page: 502

38. Which of the following graphs is linear for aA $\rightarrow$ products?
a) ln [A] vs. t if 1st-order in A
b) ln [A] vs. t if 2nd-order in A
c) 1/[A] vs. t if 1st-order in A
d) $[A]^2$ vs. t if 2nd-order in A
e) $1/[A]^2$ vs. t if 2nd-order in A

Answer: a Page: 502

39. The reaction rate constant for a particular second order reaction is 0.47 L/mol•s. If the initial concentration of reactant is 0.25 mol/L, how many seconds will it take for the concentration to decrease to 0.13 mol/L?
a) 7.9
b) 1.4
c) 3.7
d) 1.7

Answer: a Page: 502

40. Which one of the following graphs shows the correct relationship between concentration and time for a <u>second</u> order reaction?

a)

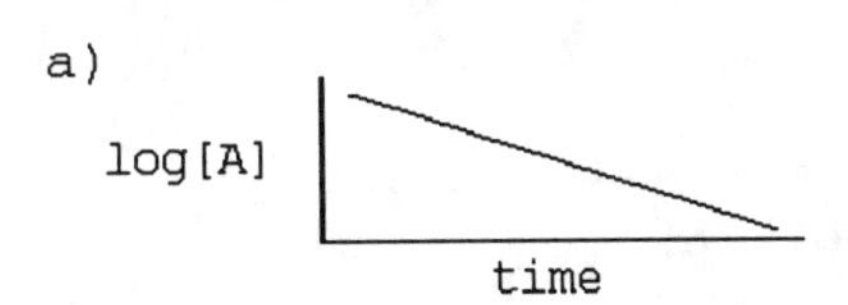

b)

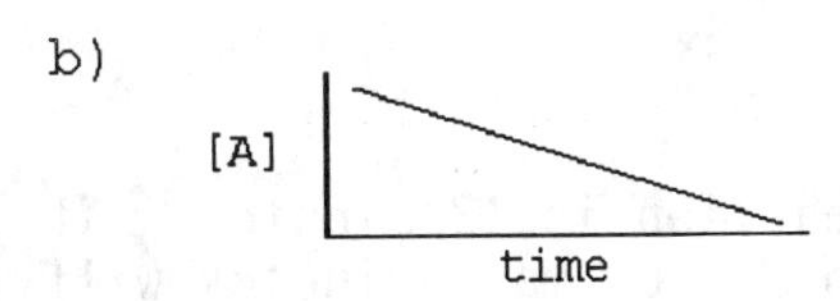

c)

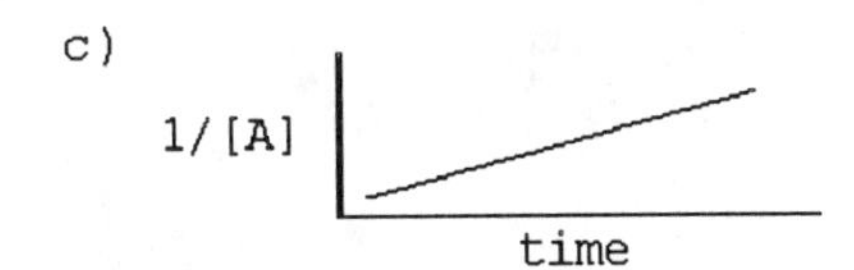

d)

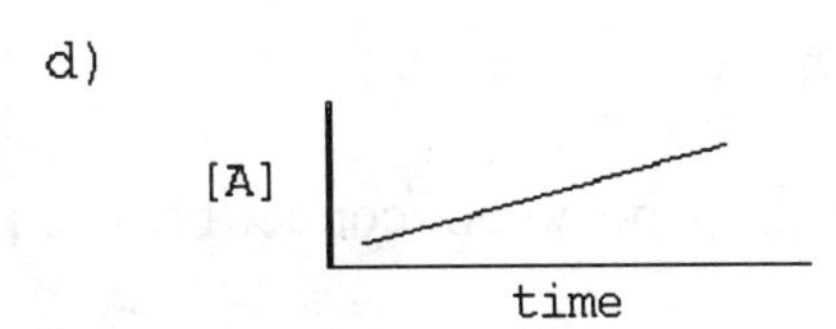

Answer: c Page: 502

41. A particular first order reaction has a rate constant of 0.33 min^{-1}. How many minutes will it take for a reactant concentration of 0.13 M to decrease to 0.088 M?
a) 1.2
b) 1.4
c) 0.51
d) 0.13

Answer: a Page: 502

42. The initial concentration of reactant in a first order reaction is 0.27 M. The rate constant for the reaction is 0.75 s^{-1}. What is the concentration (in mol/L) of reactant after 1.5 seconds?
a) 3.8
b) 1.7
c) 0.088
d) 0.020

Answer: c Page: 502

43. The reaction rate constant for a particular second order reaction is 0.13 L/mol•s. If the initial concentration of reactant is 0.26 mol/L, how many seconds will it take for the concentration to decrease to 0.13 mol/L?
a) 0.017
b) 0.50
c) 1.0
d) 30

Answer: d Page: 502

44. The half-life for a certain first order reaction is 13 minutes. If the initial concentration of reactant is 0.085 M, how many minutes will it take for it to decrease to 0.055 M?
a) 8.2
b) 11
c) 3.6
d) 0.048

Answer: a Page: 502

45. The graph shown below depicts the relationship between concentration and time for the following chemical reaction.

The slope of this line is equal to
a) k
b) -1/k
c) $\ln[A]_0$
d) -k

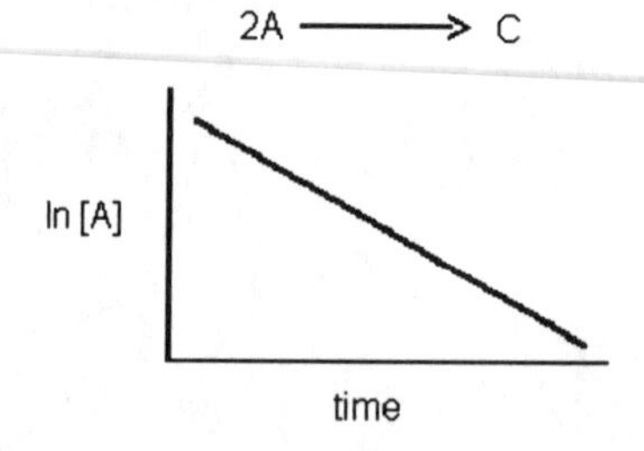

Answer: d Page: 502

46. The following reaction is second order and the rate constant is 0.039 L/mol•s.

    A → B

    If it took 23 seconds for the concentration of A to decrease to 0.30 M, what was the starting concentration of A?
    a) 2.4
    b) 0.27
    c) 0.41
    d) 3.7

    Answer: c Page: 502

47. A → B (first order)

time (sec)	[A]
0.0	1.60
5.0	0.80
10.0	0.40
15.0	0.20
20.0	0.10

    What is the reaction rate constant for this reaction?
    a) 0.013
    b) 0.030
    c) 0.14
    d) 3.0

    Answer: c Page: 502

48. A → B (first order)

time (sec)	[A]
0.0	1.60
5.0	0.80
10.0	0.40
15.0	0.20
20.0	0.10

    A plot of which of the following would produce a straight line for this reaction?
    a) [A] vs. time
    b) log[A] vs. time
    c) 1/log[A] vs. time
    d) 1/[A] vs. time

    Answer: b Page: 502

49. A → B (first order)

time (s)	[A] mol/L
0	0.20
5	0.14
10	0.10
15	0.071
20	0.050

What is the reaction rate constant (in s^{-1}) for this reaction?
a) 0.069
b) 0.030
c) 14
d) 0.46

Answer: a Page: 502

50. A → B (first order)

time (s)	[A] mol/L
0	0.20
5	0.14
10	0.10
15	0.071
20	0.050

What would the concentration of A be (in mol/L) after 40 seconds?
a) 0.013
b) 1.2
c) 0.17
d) 3.5×10^{-4}

Answer: a Page: 502

ESSAY

51. Derive an equation for the half life of a reaction that has the integrated rate equation below.

$$\frac{4\,[A]^2_0 - 3[A]_t}{[A]_0} = kt$$

Answer:
When $t - t_{(1/2)}$, $[A] = (1/2)[A]_0$

$$\frac{4\,[A]^2_0 - (3/2)[A]_0}{[A]_0} = kt_{(1/2)}$$

$$4[A]_0 - \frac{3}{2} = kt_{(1/2)}$$

Page: 504

MULTIPLE CHOICE

52. Calculate the rate constant of a first order process that has a half-life of 225 s.

    a) 0.693 s^{-1}
    b) 3.08×10^{-3} s^{-1}
    c) 1.25 s^{-1}

    Answer: b Page: 504

53. A process was found to have a half-life that depended on the initial concentration of reactant. For this process, which one of the following plots will be linear?
    a) ln [A] vs t
    b) $\frac{1}{[A]}$ vs t

    c) both of these are linear
    d) neither of these is linear

    Answer: b Page: 504

54. Half-life for the reaction xX → products
    a) is independent of rate constant k for both first- and second-order reactions
    b) is independent of $[X]_0$ for second-order but not first-order reactions
    c) is independent of $[X]_0$ for first-order but not second-order reactions
    d) is dependent upon $[X]_0$ for both first- and second-order reactions
    e) is independent of $[X]_0$ for both first- and second-order reactions

    Answer: c Page: 504

55. A → B (first order)

time (sec)	[A]
0	1.22
3	0.86
6	0.61
9	0.43
12	0.31
15	0.22
18	0.15

What is the half-life (in sec) for the reaction shown above?

a) 3
b) 6
c) 0.7
d) 0.1

Answer: b Page: 504

56. A → B (first order)

time (sec)	[A]
0	1.22
3	0.86
6	0.61
9	0.43
12	0.31
15	0.22
18	0.15

What is the value of the reaction rate constant (in sec^{-1}) for the reaction shown above?
a) 0.23
b) 1.0
c) 0.17
d) 0.12

Answer: d Page: 504

57. The reaction shown below is first order in H_2O_2.
$2H_2O_2(l) \rightarrow 2H_2O(l) + O_2(g)$

A solution originally at 0.600 M H_2O_2 is found to be 0.075 M after 54 minutes. What is the half-life for this reaction?
a) 6.8 min
b) 18 min
c) 14 min
d) 28 min

Answer: b Page: 504

58. A → B (first order)

time (sec)	[A]
0.0	1.60
5.0	0.80
10.0	0.40
15.0	0.20
20.0	0.10

What is the half-life (in seconds) for this reaction?
a) 23
b) 10
c) 5.0
d) 0.20

Answer: c Page: 504

59. A certain second order reaction has a half-life of 18 seconds when the initial concentration of reactant is 0.71 M. What is the reaction rate constant (in L/mol•s) for this reaction?
a) 0.078
b) 0.038
c) 0.020
d) 1.3

Answer: a Page: 505

60. As the temperature of a reaction is increased, the rate of the reaction increases because the
a) reactant molecules collide less frequently
b) reactant molecules collide with greater energy
c) activation energy is lowered
d) reactant molecules collide less frequently and with greater energy

Answer: b Page: 507

61. Reaction rate depends on
a) collision frequency
b) collision energy
c) collision orientation
d) all of these

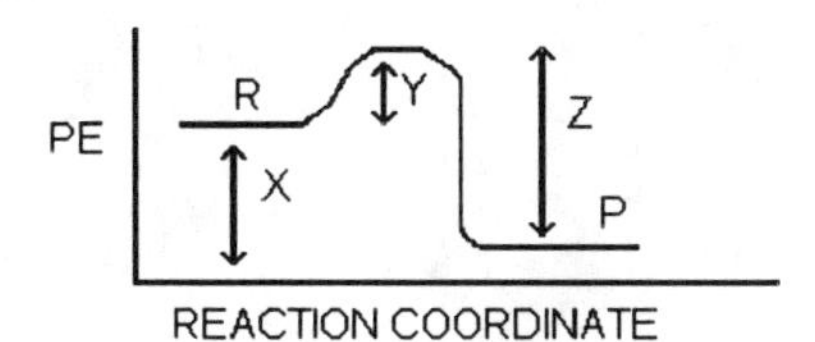

Answer: d Page: 507

62. In the diagram below, which measurement corresponds to the activation energy for the forward reaction?
a) X
b) Y
c) Z

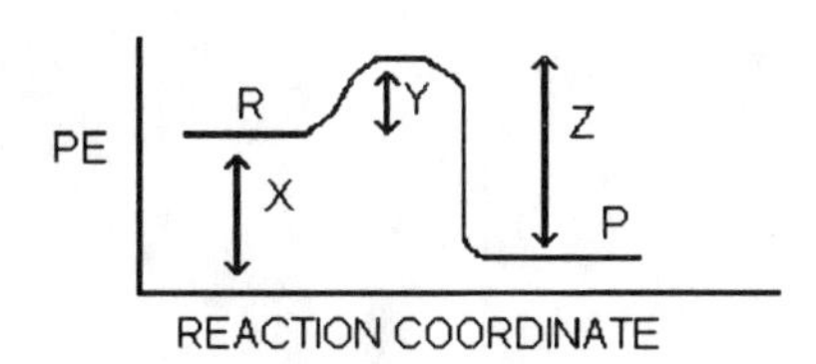

Answer: b Page: 507

63. In the diagram below, which measurement corresponds to the heat of reaction?
   a) X
   b) Y
   c) Z

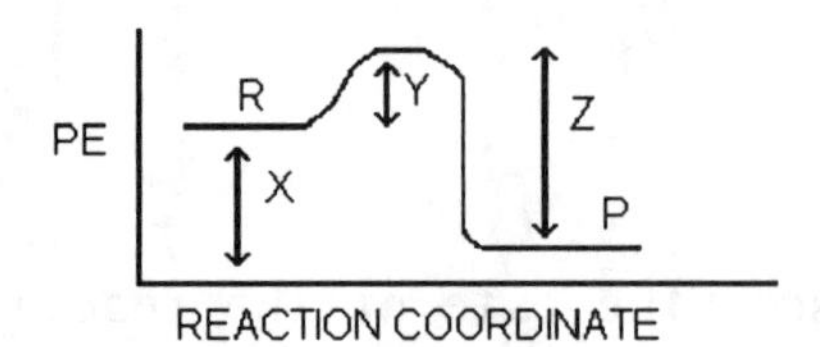

Answer: a Page: 507

64. The reaction diagrammed below is
   a) endothermic
   b) exothermic

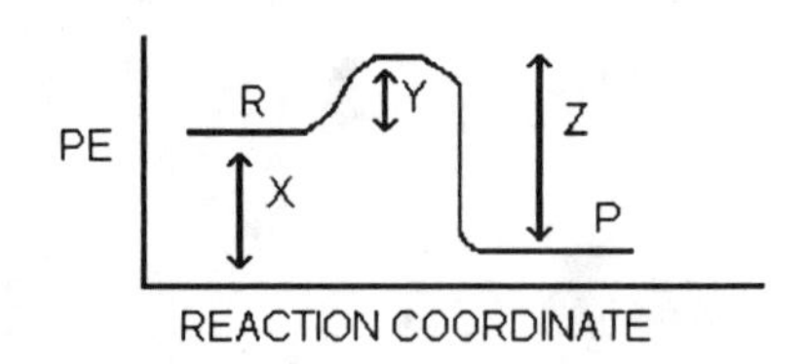

Answer: b Page: 507

ESSAY

65. Define activation energy.

   Answer: the minimum energy required to initiate a chemical reaction

   Page: 508

MULTIPLE CHOICE

66. Which line in the reaction profile corresponds to the activation energy for the forward reaction?
   a) w
   b) x
   c) y
   d) z

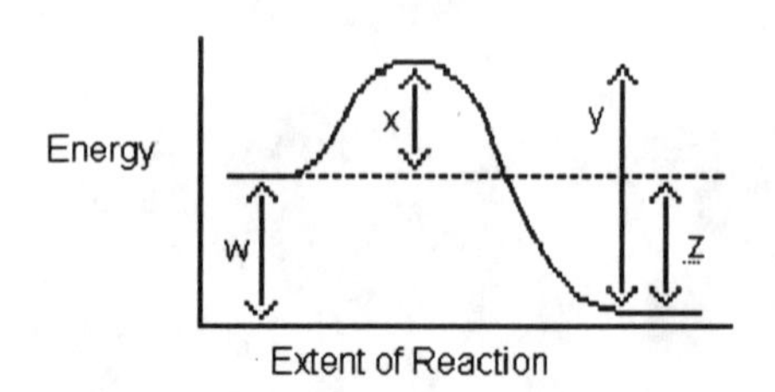

Answer: b Page: 508

67. In the potential energy profile of a reaction, the species that exists at the maximum on the curve is called the
   a) product
   b) transition state
   c) activation energy
   d) enthalpy of reaction
   e) atomic state

   Answer: b Page: 509

68. In the Arrhenius equation, ____ is the frequency factor.
   a) k
   b) A
   c) e
   d) E_a
   e) R
   f) T

   Answer: b Page: 511

69. As E_a increases, k
   a) increases
   b) decreases
   c) remains unchanged

   Answer: b Page: 511

ESSAY

70. Draw the curve one would expect for a plot of ln k versus (1/T). Be sure to indicate the meaning of the slope and the y-intercept.

   Answer:

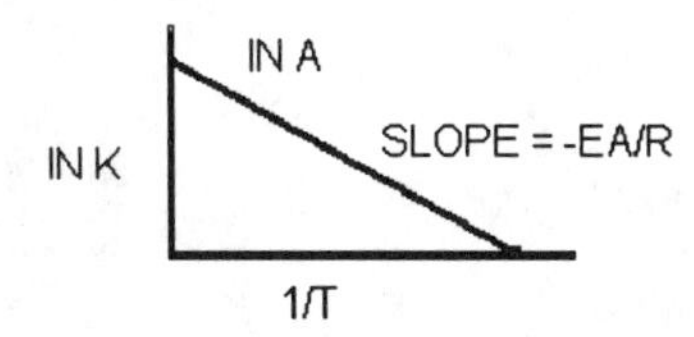

   Page: 511

MULTIPLE CHOICE

71. Calculate the activation energy of a reaction that has a rate constant of 4.41 x $10^{-3}s^{-1}$ at 78°C and rate constant of 9.79 x $10^{-2}s^{-1}$ at 315 K.
   a) 2.67 kJ/mol
   b) 2.90 kJ/mol
   c) 0.0589 kJ/mol
   d) 22.4 kJ/mol

   Answer: d Page: 511

72. From the Arrhenius equation one can say that
    a) the activation energy always increases as temperature rises
    b) the activation energy always decreases as temperature rises
    c) the rate constant always decreases as temperature rises
    d) the rate constant always increases as temperature rises
    e) the rate constant always increases as the activation energy increases

    Answer: d Page: 511

73. A reaction with activation energy of 123 kJ/mol has a rate constant of 0.200 s^{-1} at 311 K. At what temperature will its rate constant be double that at 311 K?
    a) 304 K
    b) 316 K
    c) 622 K
    d) 349 K
    e) 246 K

    Answer: b Page: 511

74. What is the activation energy in kJ of a reaction whose rate constant increases by a factor of 10 upon increasing the temperature from 303 K to 333 K?
    a) 30
    b) 33
    c) 46
    d) 64
    e) 89

    Answer: d Page: 511

75. What is the intermediate in the following mechanism?

    $$A + B \rightarrow C + D$$
    $$B + D \rightarrow X$$

    a) A
    b) B
    c) C
    d) D
    e) X

    Answer: d Page: 513

76. Each of the choices below gives a reaction and the corresponding rate law. Of these choices, which one could be an elementary process?
    a) $2A \rightarrow P$ rate = k[A]
    b) $A + B \rightarrow P$ rate = k[A][B]
    c) $A + 2B \rightarrow P$ rate = $k[A]^2$
    d) $A + B + C \rightarrow P$ rate = k[A][C]

    Answer: b Page: 513

77. Which type of elementary process below is the slowest?
    a) unimolecular
    b) bimolecular
    c) termolecular

    Answer: c Page: 513

78. For the elementary reaction $NO_3 + CO \rightarrow NO_2 + CO_2$
    a) the molecularity is 2 and rate = $k[NO_3][CO]$
    b) the molecularity is 4 and rate = $k[NO_3][CO][NO_2][CO_2]$
    c) the molecularity is 2 and rate = $k[NO_2][CO_2]$
    d) the molecularity is 2 and rate = $k[NO_3][CO]/[NO_2][CO_2]$
    e) the moleccularity is 4 and rate = $k[NO_2][CO_2]/[NO_3][CO]$

    Answer: a Page: 513

79. For mechanistic purposes, elementary reactions of which of the molecularities below are considered plausible?
    a) 2
    b) 4
    c) 5
    d) 6
    e) both 2 and 4

    Answer: a Page: 513

80. Given the following mechanism, which species below may be classified as intermediates in the formation of XO_2 from X and O_2?

    $X + YO_2 \rightarrow XO + YO$
    $XO + YO \rightarrow XO_2 + YC$
    $YO + O_2 \rightarrow YO + O$
    $YO + O \rightarrow YO_2$

    a) X only
    b) YO only
    c) both X and YO_2
    d) both XO and YO
    e) both YO_2 and O_2

    Answer: d Page: 513

81. The first step of a mechanism involving the reactant I_2 is shown below. The expression relating [I] to [I_2] is

$$I_2 \underset{k_{-1}}{\overset{k_1}{\rightleftarrows}} 2I \qquad \text{fast, equilibrium}$$

a) $[I] = k_1[I_2]$

b) $[I] = k_1[I_2]^{1/2}$

c) $[I] = (k_1/k_{-1})^{1/2}[I_2]^{1/2}$

d) $[I] = (k_1/k_{-1})^2[I_2]^2$

e) $[I] = (k_1/k_{-1})^2[I_2]^{1/2}$

Answer: c Page: 513

82. A possible mechanism for the reaction $Br_2 + 2NO \rightarrow 2NOBr$ is shown below. The proper form of its rate law should be rate =

$$2NO \underset{k_{-1}}{\overset{k_1}{\rightleftarrows}} N_2O_2 \qquad \text{fast, equilibrium}$$

$$N_2O_2 + Br_2 \rightarrow 2NOBr \qquad \text{slow}$$

a) $k_1[NO]^{1/2}$

b) $k_1[Br_2]^{1/2}$

c) $(k_2k_1/k_{-1})[NO]^2[Br_2]$

d) $(k_1/k_{-1})^2[NO]^2$

e) $(k_2k_1/k_{-1})[NO][Br_2]^2$

Answer: c Page: 513

83. In any multistep reaction mechanism, the rate of the overall reaction is determined by the rate of the _______ step in the mechanism.
a) first
b) last
c) slowest
d) fastest

Answer: c Page: 513

84. Consider the following hypothetical chemical reaction.

$2A + 2B \rightarrow C$

The mechanism for this reaction is

1) $A + B \rightarrow D$ (slow)
2) $D + B \rightarrow E$ (fast)
3) $A + E \rightarrow C$ (fast)

Which one of the following is the correct rate law for this reaction?

a) Rate = k[A][B]
b) Rate = k[A][E]
c) Rate = $k[A]^2[B]^2$
d) Rate = k[D][B]

Answer: a Page: 513

85. Consider the following hypothetical chemical reaction.

$A + 2B \rightarrow E$

The mechanism for this reaction is

1) $2A + B \rightarrow C$ (slow)
2) $B + C \rightarrow D$ (fast)
3) $D \rightarrow E$ (fast)

Which one of the following is the correct rate law for this reaction?

a) Rate = k[A][B]
b) Rate = k[A][E]
c) Rate = $k[A]^2[B]$
d) Rate = k[D][B]

Answer: c Page: 513

ESSAY

86. Name one of the three scientists who were awarded the Nobel Prize in chemistry for pioneering work in the field of reaction dynamics.

Answer: Yuan Lee, Dudley Herschbach, or John Polanyi Page: 514

MULTIPLE CHOICE

87. Which of the following will lower the activation energy for a reaction?
    a) increasing the concentrations of reactants
    b) raising the temperature of the reaction
    c) adding a suitable catalyst
    d) all of the above

    Answer: c Page: 521

88. Consider the following reaction and its associated rate law.

    $A + B \rightarrow C \qquad R = k[A]^2$

    Which of the following will not increase the rate of the reaction?
    a) increasing the concentration of reactant A
    b) increasing the concentration of reactant B
    c) increasing the temperature of the reaction
    d) adding a suitable catalyst

    Answer: b Page: 521

89. A catalyst
    a) increases reaction rate by decreasing the heat of reaction
    b) increases reaction rate by lowering the activation energy of the forward reaction only
    c) increases reaction rate by increasing the activation energy of the reverse reaction
    d) increases reaction rate by providing an alternative pathway with a lower activation energy

    Answer: d Page: 521

90. Given the following mechanism, which of the species below is a catalyst in the formation of XO_2 from X and O_2?

    $X + YO_2 \rightarrow XO + YO$
    $XO + YO_2 \rightarrow XO_2 + YO$
    $YO + O_2 \rightarrow YO_2 + O$
    $YO + O \rightarrow YO_2$

    a) X
    b) O_2
    c) YO_2
    d) XO
    e) XO_2

    Answer: c Page: 521

91. Chlorine atoms photochemically derived from Freons help destroy stratospheric ozone in the two-step mechanism below. We classify the respective species Cl and ClO for the overall balanced reaction as

$Cl + O_3 \rightarrow ClO + O_2$
$ClO + O \rightarrow Cl + O_2$

a) both catalysts
b) both intermediates
c) catalyst and intermediate
d) intermediate and catalyst
e) both activated complexes

Answer: c Page: 521

92. The reaction of NO with one in the following reaction mechanism is an example of

$NO_{(g)} + O_{3(g)} \rightarrow NO_{2(g)} + O_{2(g)}$
$NO_{2(g)} + O_{(g)} \rightarrow NO_{(g)} + O_{2(g)}$

a) homogeneous catalysis
b) heterogeneous catalysis

Answer: a Page: 522

93. The process of a molecule bonding to the surface of another substance is called
a) absorption
b) absorbtion
c) adsorption
d) induction
e) substration

Answer: c Page: 523

94. Which one of the following is not true about heterogeneous catalysts?
a) they work by adsorbing reactants to their surfaces
b) to be effective, they must have large surface areas
c) they are in a different phase than the reactants
d) they attach themselves to portions of the reactant molecules called active sites

Answer: d Page: 523

ESSAY

95. An automotive catalytic converter contains two different catalysts. State the function of each catalyst in a catalytic converter.

Answer:
One oxidizes CO and hydrocarbons to H_2O and CO_2 and the other converts nitrogen oxides to N_2

Page: 525

MULTIPLE CHOICE

96. What type of catalyst is used in automotive catalytic converters?
    a) heterogeneous
    b) homogeneous
    c) enzymes
    d) noble gas
    e) nonmetal oxides

    Answer: a Page: 525

ESSAY

97. Why is it necessary to avoid the use of leaded gasoline in a catalytic converter equipped car?

    Answer:
    the lead in the gasoline poisons the catalyst in the catalytic convertor by binding to and blocking active sites

    Page: 525

MULTIPLE CHOICE

98. According to current theory, what is the primary source of the specificity of enzymes?
    a) their polarity
    b) their delocalized electron cloud
    c) their bonded transition metal
    d) their locations within the cell
    e) their shape

    Answer: e Page: 526

ESSAY

99. What is meant by nitrogen fixation?

    Answer: the conversion of nitrogen into a form that plants can utilize

    Page: 527

MULTIPLE CHOICE

100. The enzyme, nitrogenase, converts ____ into ____.
    a) ammonia, urea
    b) CO and unburned hydrocarbons, H_2O and CO_2
    c) nitrogen, ammonia
    d) nitrogen oxides, N_2
    e) nitroglycerine, nitric acid and glycerine

    Answer: c Page: 527

101. What is currently thought to be the active site of nitrogenase is a cofactor that contains two transition metals. What transition metals are contained in this cofactor?
    a) Cr and Mg
    b) Mn and V
    c) Os and Ir
    d) Fe and Zn
    e) Fe and Mo

    Answer: e Page: 527

102. Why is nitrogen fixation a difficult process?
    a) because there is so little nitrogen in the atmosphere
    b) because nitrogen exists primarily as its oxides which are very unreactive
    c) because nitrogen is very unreactive, largely due to its triple bond
    d) because of the extreme toxicity of nitrogen
    e) because of the high polarity of nitrogen molecules preventing them from dissolving in biological fluids, such as those inside cells

    Answer: c Page: 527

103. How is elemental nitrogen formed in the nitrogen cycle on Earth?
    a) by the action of nitrogenase on animal tissue and waste
    b) by lightning in the atmosphere
    c) by legumes such as clover and alfalfa
    d) by the action of bacteria on animal waste and dead plants and animals
    e) by photosynthesis in bluegreen algae

    Answer: d Page: 527

Chapter 15: Chemical Equilibrium

MULTIPLE CHOICE

1. At equilibrium
   a) All chemical processes have ceased.
   b) The rate of the forward reaction equals that of the reverse.
   c) The rate constant for the forward reaction equals that of the reverse.
   d) Both the rate of the forward reaction equals that of the reverse and the rate constant for the forward reaction equals that of the reverse.
   e) none of the above

   Answer: b Page: 539

2. What is the relationship between the rate constants for the forward and reverse reactions and the equilibrium constant for a process?
   a) $K = k_f k_r$
   b) $K = k_f - k_r$
   c) $K = k_f + k_r$
   d) $K = k_f / k_r$

   Answer: d Page: 540

3. The value of K_c for the following reaction is 962 at 1258°C.

   $$2Br(g) \rightleftharpoons Br_2(g)$$

   If k_f is the rate constant for the forward reaction and k_r is the rate constant for the reverse reaction, then at equilibrium
   a) $k_f > k_r$
   b) $k_f < k_r$
   c) $k_f = k_r$
   d) $k_f \leq k_r$

   Answer: a Page: 540

4. Which one of the following will change the value of an equilibrium constant?
   a) changing temperature
   b) adding other substances that do not react with any of the species involved in the equilibrium
   c) varying the initial concentrations of reactants
   d) varying the initial concentrations of products

   Answer: a Page: 543

5. The equilibrium expression depends on the _______ of the reaction.
   a) stoichiometry
   b) mechanism
   c) stoichiometry and the mechanism
   d) rate
   e) equilibrium position

   Answer: a Page: 543

6. An aqueous equilibrium mixture of $CoCl_4^{2-}$, $CoBr_4^{2-}$, Cl^-, and Br^- is present in a flask at 25°C. Which action below will change the value of the equilibrium constant from that which currently describes the concentration relationships of the four species above:
   a) add more Cl^- to the solution
   b) add more Br^- to the solution
   c) add more $CoBr_4^{2-}$ to the solution
   d) add more $CoCl_4^{2-}$ to the solution
   e) put the flask into an 80°C water bath

   Answer: e Page: 543

7. For the gas-phase reaction $CO + 3H_2 \leftrightharpoons CH_4 + H_2O$, which expression represents K_c correctly?
   a) $[CO]^3[H_2]/[CH_4][H_2O]$
   b) $[CO][H_2]^3/[CH_4][H_2O]$
   c) $[CH_4][H_2O]/[CO][H_2]^3$
   d) $[CH_4][H_2O]/[CO]^3[H_2]$
   e) $[CH_4][H_2O]/[CO](3[H_2])^3$

   Answer: c Page: 543

8. Identify the equation that would give the gaseous equilibrium expression

$$K_c = \frac{[H_2]^2[O_2]}{[H_2O]^2}$$

   a) $2H_2(g) + O_2(g) \leftrightharpoons 2H_2O(g)$
   b) $H_2O(g) \leftrightharpoons H_2(g) = 1/2\ O_2(g)$
   c) $H_2O(g) \leftrightharpoons 2H(g) + O(g)$
   d) $2H_2O(g) \leftrightharpoons 2H_2(g) + O_2(g)$

   Answer: d Page: 543

9. The Haber process allowed the Germans to continue production of explosives even though their supply of nitrates from the outside was cut off. Which war did this prolong?
   a) World War II
   b) Vietnam
   c) World War I
   d) Civil War
   e) Russian Revolution

   Answer: c Page: 542

10. What roll did Karl Bosch play in development of the Haber-Bosch process?
    a) he discovered the reaction conditions necessary for formation of ammonia
    b) he originally isolated ammonia from camel dung and found a method for purifying it
    c) Haber was working in his lab with his instructor at the time he worked out the process
    d) he developed the equipment necessary for industrial production of ammonia
    e) he was the German industrialist who financed the research done by Haber

    Answer: d Page: 542

11. How did the Haber process affect World War I?
    a) it did not
    b) it allowed the Russians to continue growing adequate food by improving their fertilizers
    c) it allowed the United States to increase manufacture of plastics necessary for food preservation and shipment
    d) it allowed the Germans to continue to manufacture explosives even though their supply of nitrates from Chile was cut off
    e) it prevented the depletion of Middle Eastern petroleum reserves by substituting as a fuel

    Answer: d Page: 542

12. In what year was Fritz Haber awarded the Nobel Prize in chemistry?
    a) 1954
    b) 1933
    c) 1918
    d) 1900
    e) 1912

    Answer: c Page: 542

13. Which one of the following is true concerning the Haber process?
    a) it is a process used for shifting equilibrium positions to the right for more economical chemical synthesis of a variety of substances
    b) it is a process used for the synthesis of ammonia
    c) it is another way of stating LeChatelier's principle
    d) it is an industrial synthesis of sodium chloride that was discovered by Karl Haber

    Answer: b Page: 542

14. An equilibrium constant with a large magnitude indicates that a system favors ___ when it reaches equilibrium.
    a) reactants
    b) products
    c) neither reactants nor products

    Answer: b Page: 546

15. The balanced homogeneous vapor-phase reaction $A + B \leftrightharpoons X + Y$ has $K_c = 997$ at 472 K. At equilibrium
    a) products predominate
    b) reactants predominate
    c) roughly equal molar amounts of products and reactants are present
    d) only products exist
    e) only reactants exist

    Answer: a Page: 546

16. The balanced homogeneous vapor-phase reaction $X + Y \leftrightharpoons 2M$ has $K_c = 0.89$ at 672 K. At equilibrium
    a) products predominate
    b) reactants predominate
    c) roughly equal molar amounts of products and reactants are present
    d) only products exist
    e) only reactants exist

    Answer: c Page: 546

17. The equilibrium constant for reaction (1) below is 4.22×10^{-3}. What is the value of the equilibrium constant for reaction (2)?
    $3\,A + 2\,B \leftrightharpoons 2\,D + E$ (1)
    $2\,D + E \leftrightharpoons 3\,A + 2\,B$ (2)

    a) 5.78×10^{-2}
    b) 4.22×10^{-3}
    c) 1.78×10^{-5}
    d) 237

    Answer: d Page: 547

18. The equilibrium constant for reaction (1) is K. What is the equilibrium constant for equation (2)?

    (1) $SO_2(g) + 1/2O_2(g) \leftrightharpoons SO_3(g)$

    (2) $2SO_3(g) \leftrightharpoons 2SO_2(g) + O_2(g)$

    a) K^2
    b) 2K
    c) 1/2K
    d) $1/K^2$

    Answer: d Page: 547

19. The equilibrium constant for reaction (1) is K. What is the equilibrium constant for equation (2)?

    (1) $1/3N_2(g) + H_2(g) \leftrightharpoons 2/3NH_3(g)$

    (2) $2NH_3(g) \leftrightharpoons N_2(g) + 3H_2(g)$

    a) K^3
    b) 3K
    c) K/3
    d) $1/K^3$

    Answer: d Page: 547

20. The value of K_c for the following reaction is 0.25.

    $SO_2(g) + NO_2(g) \leftrightharpoons SO_3(g) + NO(g)$

    What is the value of K_c for the reaction shown below?

    $2SO_2(g) + 2NO_2(g) \leftrightharpoons 2SO_3(g) + 2NO(g)$

    a) 0.50
    b) 0.062
    c) 0.12
    d) 0.25

    Answer: b Page: 547

21. The value of K_c for the following reaction is 2×10^{-10} at 100°C.

$$COCl_2(g) \rightleftharpoons CO(g) + Cl_2(g)$$

What is the value of K_c for the reaction shown below?

$$CO(g) + Cl_2(g) \rightleftharpoons COCl_2(g)$$

a) -2×10^{-10}
b) 5×10^{9}
c) 2×10^{10}
d) -5×10^{9}

Answer: b Page: 547

22. The concentration of a pure substance in its pure liquid or pure solid phase is given by
a) (Avogadro's number)(specific volume)
b) (molar volume)(molecular weight)
c) $\frac{\text{molar mass}}{\text{density}}$
d) (mass)(specific gravity)
e) $\frac{\text{density}}{\text{molar mass}}$

Answer: e Page: 548

23. Which one of the following choices is the correct expression for the equilibrium constant for the reaction below?

$$Al_2(SO_3)_3(s) + 6HCl_{(g)} \rightleftharpoons 2AlCl_{3(s)} + 3H_2O_{(l)} + 3SO_{2(g)}$$

a) $K_c = \frac{[AlCl_3]^2[H_2O]^3[SO_2]^3}{[Al_2(SO_3)_3][P_{HCl}]^6}$

b) $K_c = \frac{[AlCl_3]^2(PSO_2)^3}{Al_2(SO_3)_3](PHCl)^6}$

c) $K_c = \frac{(PSO_2)^3}{(P_{HCl})^6}$

d) $K_c = \frac{[AlCl_3]^2[H_2O]^3}{[Al_2(SO_3)_3]}$

e) $K_c = \frac{[AlCl_3]^2}{[Al_2(SO_3)^3]}$

f) $K_c = \frac{[SO_2]^3}{[HCl]^6}$

Answer: f Page: 548

24. Which of the reactants and/or products do not appear in the properly written heterogeneous K_c expression for the reaction $NiCO_3(s) + 2H^+(aq) \leftrightharpoons Ni^{2+}(aq) + CO(g) + H_2O(\ell)$?
    a) $NiCO_3(s)$
    b) $CO_2(g) + H_2O(\ell)$
    c) $H^+(aq)$ and $Ni^{2+}(aq)$
    d) $CO_2(g)$
    e) $NiCO_3(s)$ and $H_2O(\ell)$

    Answer: e Page: 548

25. The proper K_c expression for the reaction below is:

    $NiCO_3(s) + 2H^+(aq) \leftrightharpoons Ni^{2+}(aq) + CO_2(g) + H_2O(\ell)$

    a) $[Ni^{2+}]/[NiCO_3]$
    b) $[NiCO_3]/[Ni^{2+}]$
    c) $[Ni^{2+}][CO_2]/[H^+]^2$
    d) $[Ni^{2+}][H^+]^2$
    e) $[CO_2]$

    Answer: c Page: 548

26. The proper K_C expression for the reaction below is

    $4CuO(s) + CH_4(g) \leftrightharpoons CO_2(g) + 4Cu(s) + 2H_2O(g)$

    a) $[CuO]/[Cu]$
    b) $[CuO]^4/[Cu]^4$
    c) $[Cu]^4/[CuO]^4$
    d) $[CO_2][H_2O]^2/[CH_4]$
    e) $[CH_4]/[CO_2][H_2O]^2$

    Answer: d Page: 548

27. Identify the correct equilibrium expression (K_c) for the reaction shown below.

$$3SO_2(g) \rightleftharpoons 2SO_3(g) + S(s)$$

a) $\frac{[SO_2]^3}{[SO_3]^2[S]}$

b) $\frac{[SO_3]^2[S]}{[SO_2]^3}$

c) $\frac{[SO_3]^2}{[SO_2]^3}$

d) $\frac{[SO_2]^3}{[SO_3]^2}$

Answer: c Page: 548

28. Identify the correct equilibrium expression (K_c) for the reaction shown below.

$$NH_4HS(s) \rightleftharpoons NH_3(g) + H_2S(g)$$

a) $[NH_3][H_2S]$

b) $\frac{1}{[NH_3][H_2S]}$

c) $\frac{[NH_3][H_2S]}{[NH_4HS]}$

d) $\frac{[NH_4HS]}{[NH_3][H_2S]}$

Answer: a Page: 548

29. Identify the correct equilibrium expression (K_c) for the following reaction.

$$6CO_2(g) + 6H_2O(\ell) \rightleftharpoons C_6H_{12}O_6(s) + 6O_2(g)$$

a) $\frac{[C_6H_{12}O_6][O_2]^6}{[CO_6][H_2O]^6}$

b) $\frac{[CO_2]^6}{[O_2]^6}$

c) $\frac{[O_2]^6}{[CO_2]^6}$

d) $\frac{[O_2]^6}{[CO_2]^6[H_2O]^6}$

Answer: c Page: 548

30. $$BaS(s) + 2O_2(g) \rightleftharpoons BaSO_4(s)$$

Which one of the following is the correct expression for K_c for this above equation?

a) $\frac{1}{[O_2]^2}$

b) $\frac{[BaSO_4]}{[BaS][O_2]^2}$

c) $[O_2]^2$

d) $\frac{[BaS][O_2]^2}{[BaSO_4]}$

Answer: a Page: 548

31. $4CuO(s) + CH_4(g) \leftrightharpoons CO_2(g) + 4Cu(s) + 2H_2O(g)$

Which one of the following is the correct expression for K_c for this equation?

a) $\frac{[CH_4]}{[CO_2][H_2]^2}$

b) $\frac{[CO_2][Cu][H_2O]^2}{[CuO]^4[CH_4]}$

c) $\frac{[H_2O]^2[CO_2]}{[CH_4]}$

d) $\frac{[CO_2][H_2O]}{[CH_4][CuO]}$

Answer: c Page: 548

32. Calculate K_c for the following reaction if the equilibrium concentrations of H_2, CO, and H_2O are 2.0 X 10^{-2} M, 2.0 X 10^{-2} M, and 5.0 X 10^{-2} M respectively.

$C(s) + H_2O(g) \leftrightharpoons CO(g) + H_2(g)$

a) 0.0080
b) 5.0 X 10^{-3}
c) 12.5
d) 200

Answer: a Page: 548

33. Calculate the equilibrium constant for the reaction below if a 3.25 L tank was found to contain 0.343 mol O_2, 0.0212 mol SO_3, and 0.00419 mol SO_2.

$2SO_{3(g)} \leftrightharpoons 2SO_{2(g)} + O_{2(g)}$

a) 6.78 x 10^{-2}
b) 1.34 x 10^{-2}
c) 4.12 x 10^{-3}
d) 4.35 x 10^{-2}

Answer: c Page: 548

34. Consider the following chemical reaction.

$$H_2(g) + I_2(g) \leftrightharpoons 2HI(g)$$

At equilibrium, the concentration of H_2, I_2, and HI were found to be 0.15 M, 0.033 M, and 0.55 M respectively. What is the value of K_c for this reaction?
a) 23
b) 111
c) 0.0090
d) 6.1

Answer: d Page: 550

35. 0.50 mol of I_2 and 0.50 mol of Br_2 are placed in a 1.00 L flask and allowed to reach equilibrium. At equilibrium, the flask contains 0.84 mol of IBr. What is the value of K_c for this reaction?

$$I_2(g) + Br_2(g) \leftrightharpoons 2IBr(g)$$

a) 11
b) 4.0
c) 110
d) 6.1

Answer: c Page: 550

36. Consider the following equation.

$$PCl_5(g) \leftrightharpoons PCl_3(g) + Cl_2(g)$$

Initially, 0.84 mole of $PCl_5(g)$ is placed in a 1.0 L flask. At equilibrium, 0.72 mole of $PCl_5(g)$ is present. What is the value of K_c for this reaction?
a) 0.62
b) 0.020
c) 0.72
d) 0.12

Answer: b Page: 550

37. The following reaction was carried out at 25°C with the initial concentration of NO_2 being 0.70 mol/L and no NO(g) or $O_2(g)$ initially present. At equilibrium the NO_2 concentration was found to be 0.28 mol/L. Calculate K_c for the reaction.

$$2NO_2(g) \rightleftharpoons 2NO(g) + O_2(g)$$

a) 1.9
b) 0.94
c) 0.47
d) 0.14

Answer: c Page: 550

38. Consider the reaction shown here.

$$CO(g) + H_2O(g) \rightleftharpoons CO_2(g) + H_2(g)$$

In an experiment, CO(g) and $H_2O(g)$ are mixed together in such a way that their initial concentrations are 0.35 mol/L and 0.40 mol/L respectively (there is no CO_2 or H_2 initially present). At equilibrium it is found that the concentration of CO(g) is 0.19 mol/L. What is the value of the equilibrium constant for this reaction?
a) 1.0
b) 0.90
c) 0.56
d) 0.34

Answer: c Page: 550

39. For which one of the following equations is K_c equal to K_p?
a) $H_2(g) + Cl_2(g) \rightleftharpoons 2HCl(g)$
b) $2SO_3(g) \rightleftharpoons 2SO_2(g) + O_2(g)$
c) $N_2O_4(g) \rightleftharpoons 2NO_2(g)$
d) $C(s) + CO_2(g) \rightleftharpoons 2CO(g)$

Answer: a Page: 552

40. The value of K_c for this reaction is 0.13 at 200°C. What is the value of K_p for the reaction? (R = 0.0821 L•atm/k•mol)
a) 8.6×10^{-5}
b) 3.3×10^{-3}
c) 2.0×10^{2}
d) 4.8×10^{-4}

Answer: a Page: 552

41. Assume that $K_c = 3.0 \times 10^5$ for the following reaction at 25°C. What is K_p?

$$2H_2S(g) + 3O_2(g) \rightleftharpoons 2H_2O(g) + 2SO_2(g)$$

a) 1.2×10^4
b) 8.2×10^{-5}
c) 3.3×10^{-6}
d) 3.0×10^5

Answer: a Page: 552

42. $$4CuO(s) + CH_4(g) \rightleftharpoons CO_2(g) + 4Cu(s) + 2H_2O(g)$$

The value of K_c for this reaction is 1.10 at 25.0°C. What is the value of K_p for this reaction? (R = 0.0821 L•atm/K•mol)

a) 658
b) 37.2
c) 26.9
d) 4.63

Answer: a Page: 552

43. For which one of the following is the value of K_p smaller than that of K_c at 25°C?

a) $H_{2(g)} + F_{2(g)} \rightleftharpoons 2HF_{(g)}$
b) $2SO_{3(g)} \rightleftharpoons 2SO_{2(g)} + O_{2(g)}$
c) $Al_2(SO_3)_{3(s)} + 6HCl_{(g)} \rightleftharpoons 2AlCl_{3(s)} + 3H_2O_{(l)} + 3SO_{2(g)}$
d) $NH_4Br_{(s)} + KOH_{(s)} \rightleftharpoons NH_{3(g)} + KBr_{(s)} + H_2O_{(l)}$

Answer: c Page: 552

44. For which one of the following does $K_c = K_p$ at 25°C?

a) $H_{2(g)} + F_{2(g)} \rightleftharpoons 2HF_{(g)}$
b) $2SO_{3(g)} \rightleftharpoons 2SO_{2(g)} + O_{2(g)}$
c) $Al_2(SO_3)_{3(s)} + 6HCl_{(g)} \rightleftharpoons 2AlCl_{3(s)} + 3H_2O_{(l)} + 3SO_{2(g)}$
d) $NH_4Br_{(s)} + KOH_{(s)} \rightleftharpoons NH_{3(g)} + KBr_{(s)} + H_2O_{(l)}$

Answer: a Page: 552

45. For the gas-phase reaction $H_2 + X_2 \leftrightharpoons 2HX$, calculate the equilibrium constant at 501 K for the following equilibrium concentrations: [H] = 0.0025 M, [X] = 0.0050 M, and [HX] = 0.0075 M.
 a) 0.22
 b) 60
 c) 1200
 d) 18
 e) 4.5

 Answer: e Page: 552

46. A 2.21 L vessel was found to contain 4.18×10^{-2} mol of CO_2, 2.81×10^{-2} mol of CO, and 8.89×10^{-3} mol of O_2. Is the system at equilibrium for thc following reaction? If not, which direction must the reaction proceed to achieve equilibrium?

 $2CO_2 \leftrightharpoons 2CO + O_2 \qquad K_c = 1.2 \times 10^{-13}$

 a) yes
 b) no, to the right
 c) no, to the left

 Answer: c Page: 553

47. A 2.21 L vessel was found to contain 6.89×10^{-12} mol of CO_2, $9.78 \times 10^{-}$ mol of CO, and 8.45×10^{-15} mol of O_2. Is the system at equilibrium for the following reaction? If not, which direction must the reaction proceed to achieve equilibrium?

 $2\ CO_2 \leftrightharpoons 2CO + O_2 \qquad K_c = 1.2 \times 10^{-13}$

 a) yes
 b) no, to the right
 c) no, to the left

 Answer: c Page: 553

48. For the reaction $Y_4(g) \leftrightharpoons 2Y_2(g)$, $K_c = 0.100$ M at 611 K. If a cold mixture of Y_4 and Y_2 in a closed container (both gases 0.100 M) is warmed to 611 K, which following <u>net</u> conversion occurs as equilibrium is reached?
 a) most Y_4 will change into Y_2
 b) most Y_2 will change into Y_4
 c) some Y_4 will change into Y_2
 d) some Y_2 will change into Y_4
 e) no net interconversion of Y_4 and Y_2 will occur

 Answer: e Page: 553

49. Which one of the following is true for a reaction that is approaching equilibrium from the right?
a) $Q > K$
b) $Q < K$
c) $Q = K$
d) Q \\ K

Answer: a Page: 553

50. The value of K_c for the following reaction is 1.6.

$$C(s) + CO_2(g) \rightleftharpoons 2CO(g)$$

What is the equilibrium concentration of CO if the equilibrium concentration of CO_2 is 0.50 M?
a) 0.80
b) 0.75
c) 0.89
d) 0.31

Answer: c Page: 554

51. $C_6H_6(g) + 3H_2(g) \rightleftharpoons C_6H_{12}(g)$. When 1.00 mol C_6H_6 and 3.00 mol H_2 are put into a 200 L container and allowed to reach equilibrium over a catalyst at an elevated temperature, the resulting mixture contains 0.137 mol C_6H_{12}. What is the equilibrium amount of H_2 in moles?
a) 0.137
b) 0.411
c) 0.0457
d) 2.59
e) 2.86

Answer: d Page: 554

52. Calculate the equilibrium partial pressure of PCl_3 in a 3.00 L vessel that was charged with 0.123 atm of PCl_5.

$$PCl_{5(g)} \rightleftharpoons PCl_{3(g)} + Cl_{2(g)} \qquad K_p = 0.0121$$

a) 0.078 atm
b) 0.0450 atm
c) 0.0900 atm
d) 0.0330 atm

Answer: d Page: 554

53. Calculate the equilibrium partial pressure of BCl_3 in a 2.00 L container that was evacuated, then charged with 4.29 g of PH_3BCl_3 and allowed to come to equilibrium.

$PH_3BCl_{3(s)} \rightleftharpoons PH_{3(g)} + BCl_{3(g)}$ $K_p = 0.052$

a) 0.026 atm
b) 0.23 atm
c) 0.10 atm
d) 0.32 atm

Answer: b Page: 554

54. The value of K_c for the following reaction is 0.070. What is the equilibrium concentration of C_4H_{10} if the equilibrium concentrations of C_2H_6 and C_2H_4 are both 0.035 M?

$C_4H_{10}(g) \rightleftharpoons C_2H_6(g) + C_2H_4(g)$

a) 0.018 M
b) 57 M
c) 0.50 M
d) 2.0 M

Answer: a Page: 554

55. Under a set of equilibrium conditions [HI] = 0.10 M and $[H_2] = [I_2]$. Calculate the concentration of I_2. ($K_c = 0.016$)

$2HI(g) \rightleftharpoons H_2(g) + I_2(g)$

a) 1.3×10^{-2} M
b) 4.0×10^{-2} M
c) 3.1×10^{-1} M
d) 1.3 M

Answer: a Page: 554

56. Consider the reaction shown below.

$N_2O_4(g) \rightleftharpoons 2NO_2(g)$

Determine the value of the equilibrium constant for this reaction if an initial concentration of $N_2O_4(g)$ of 0.0400 mol/L is reduced to 0.0055 mol/L at equilibrium. There is no $NO_2(g)$ present at the start of the reaction.
a) 0.87
b) 13
c) 0.22
d) 0.022

Answer: a Page: 554

57. K_c for the following reaction at 25°C is 4.8 X 10^{-6}. Calculate the equilibrium concentration (in mol/L) of $Cl_2(g)$ if the initial concentration of ICl(g) is 1.33 mol/L. There is no I_2 or Cl_2 initially present.

$$2ICl(g) \rightleftharpoons I_2(g) + Cl_2(g)$$

a) 2.9 X 10^{-3}
b) 5.8 X 10^{-3}
c) 3.2 X 10^{-6}
d) 6.4 X 10^{-6}

Answer: a Page: 554

58. Nitrosyl bromide decomposes according to the following equation:

$$2NOBr(g) \rightleftharpoons 2NO(g) + Br_2(g)$$

There are 0.64 mol of NOBr placed in a 1.00 L flask containing no NO or Br_2. At equilibrium the flask is found to contain 0.46 mol of NOBr. How many moles of NO and Br_2 respectively are in the flask at equilibrium?
a) 0.18, 0.18
b) 0.46, 0.23
c) 0.18, 0.09
d) 0.18, 0.36

Answer: c Page: 554

59. For the vapor-phase reaction 2AZ = A_2 + Z_2, K_c = 16 at 523 K. If 0.030 mol AZ is introduced into a 1.00 L vessel at 523 K, then at equilibrium $[Z_2]$ is
a) 0.003 M
b) 0.013 M
c) 0.015 M
d) 0.24 M
e) 0.0052 M

Answer: b Page: 554

60. For the reaction $3A_2(g) + 2X_2(g) \rightleftharpoons 2A_3X_2(g)$, K_c = 9.9 at 417 K. What is $[A_3X_2]$ at 417 K if $[A_2]$ = 0.010 M and $[X_2]$ = 0.020 M?
a) 4.0 x 10^{-10} M
b) 6.3 x 10^{-5} M
c) 4.0 x 10^{-8} M
d) 2.0 x 10^{-4} M
e) 4.9 x 10^{-6} M

Answer: b Page: 554

61. For the reaction $2HI(g) \rightleftharpoons H_2(g) + I_2(g)$, $K_c = 0.0198$ at 721 K. What is [HI] at 721 K if $[H_2] = 0.0120$ M and $[I_2] = 0.0150$ M?
a) 0.133 M
b) 0.0334 M
c) 0.0953 M
d) 0.00211 M
e) 0.006567 M

Answer: c Page: 554

62. Consider the following reaction at equilibrium.

$$2SO_2(g) + O_2(g) \rightleftharpoons 2SO_3(g)$$

What is the relationship between the reaction quotient (Q) and the equilibrium constant (K_c) for this reaction at the moment excess $O_2(g)$ is added?
a) $Q = K_c$
b) $Q < K_c$
c) $Q > K_c$

Answer: b Page: 557

63. The following equilibrium was established. What would happen if the container was cooled?
$Ba(OH)_2 \cdot 8H_2O_{(s)} + 2\ NH_4NO_{3(s)} \rightleftharpoons$
$Ba(NO_3)_{2(aq)} + 3\ NH_{3(aq)} + 10\ H_2O_{(l)} \quad \Delta H = +$

a) nothing
b) some barium hydroxide octahydrate and ammonium nitrate would be used up and some barium nitrate, ammonia, and water would be produced
c) some barium nitrate, ammonia, and water would be used up and some barium hydroxide octahydrate and ammonium nitrate would be produced

Answer: c Page: 557

64. The following equilibrium was established. What would happen if some barium hydroxide octahydrate was added to the container?
$Ba(OH)_2 \cdot 8H_2O_{(s)} + 2\ NH_4NO_{3(s)} \rightleftharpoons$
$Ba(NO_3)_{2(aq)} + 3\ NH_{3(aq)} + 10\ H_2O_{(l)} \quad \Delta H = +$

a) nothing
b) some barium hydroxide octahydrate and ammonium nitrate would be used up and some barium nitrate, ammonia, and water would be produced
c) some barium nitrate, ammonia, and water would be used up and some barium hydroxide octahydrate and ammonium nitrate would be produced

Answer: a Page: 557

65. The following equilibrium was established. What would happen if water was added to the container?
$Ba(OH)_2 \cdot 8H_2O_{(s)} + 2\ NH_4NO_{3(s)} \leftrightharpoons$
$Ba(NO_3)_{2(aq)} + 3\ NH_{3(aq)} + 10\ H_2O_{(l)}$ $\Delta H = +$

a) nothing
b) some barium hydroxide octahydrate and ammonium nitrate would be used up and some barium nitrate, ammonia, and water would be produced
c) some barium nitrate, ammonia, and water would be used up and some barium hydroxide octahydrate and ammonium nitrate would be produced

Answer: c Page: 557

66. Of the following equilibria, which one will shift to the left in response to a decrease in volume?

a) $H_{2(g)} + Cl_{2(g)} \leftrightharpoons 2\ HCl_{(g)}$

b) $2\ SO_{3(g)} \leftrightharpoons 2\ SO_{2(g)} + O_{2(g)}$

c) $N_{2(g)} + 3\ H_{2(g)} \leftrightharpoons 2\ NH_{3(g)}$

d) $4\ Fe_{(s)} + 3\ O_{2(g)} \leftrightharpoons 2\ Fe_2O_{3(s)}$

Answer: b Page: 557

67. What will be the effect of addition of argon gas to a container in which the following equilibrium is established?
$2\ SO_{3(g)} \leftrightharpoons 2\ SO_{2(g)} + O_{2(g)}$

a) none
b) shift to the left
c) shift to the right

Answer: a Page: 557

68. Le Chatelier's Principle predicts which action(s) below to cause the endothermic reaction $CH_3CH{=}CH_2(g) \rightarrow c\text{-}C_3H_6(g)$ to form more $CH_3CH{=}CH_2$ than initially present at equilibrium?
a) increasing the system temperature
b) decreasing the system temperature
c) increasing the system pressure
d) decreasing the system pressure
e) decreasing <u>both</u> the system temperature <u>and</u> the system pressure

Answer: b Page: 557

69. For the endothermic reaction $CaCO_3(s) = CaO(s) + CO_2(g)$, which of the following actions would favor shifting the equilibrium position to form more CO_2 gas?
    a) increasing the system temperature
    b) decreasing the system temperature
    c) increasing the system pressure
    d) increasing both the system temperature and the system pressure
    e) both decreasing the system temperature and increasing the system pressure

    Answer: a Page: 557

70. In which of the following completely vapor-phase reactions would increasing system pressure at constant temperature not change the concentrations of reactants and products?
    a) $N_2(g) + 3H_2(g) \rightarrow 2NH_3(g)$
    b) $N_2O_4(g) \rightarrow 2NO_2(g)$
    c) $N_2(g) + 2O_2(g) \rightarrow 2NO_2(g)$
    d) $2N_2(g) + O_2(g) \rightarrow 2N_2O(g)$
    e) $N_2(g) + O_2(g) \rightarrow 2NO(g)$

    Answer: e Page: 557

71. Consider the following reaction at equilibrium.

    $$2NH_3(g) \rightleftharpoons N_2(g) + 3H_2(g) \qquad \Delta H° = +92.4 \text{ kJ}$$

    Adding $N_2(g)$ to this reaction will
    a) decrease the concentration of $NH_3(g)$ at equilibrium
    b) decrease the concentration of $H_2(g)$ at equilibrium
    c) increase the value of the equilibrium constant
    d) cause the reaction to shift to the right

    Answer: b Page: 557

72. Consider the following reaction at equilibrium.

    $$2NH_3(g) \rightleftharpoons N_2(g) + 3H_2(g) \qquad \Delta H° = +92.4 \text{ kJ}$$

    This reaction can be driven further to completion by using conditions of
    a) high temperature and high pressure
    b) high temperature and low pressure
    c) low temperature and low pressure
    d) low temperature and high pressure

    Answer: b Page: 557

73. Consider the following reaction at equilibrium.

$$2CO_2(g) \rightleftharpoons 2CO(g) + O_2(g) \qquad \Delta H° = -514 \text{ kJ}$$

Adding $O_2(g)$ to the reaction will
a) increase the concentration of CO(g) at equilibrium
b) decrease the concentration of $CO_2(g)$ at equilibrium
c) increase the value of the equilibrium constant
d) cause the reaction to shift to the left

Answer: d Page: 557

74. Consider the following reaction at equilibrium.

$$2CO_2(g) \rightleftharpoons 2CO(g) + O_2(g) \qquad \Delta H° = -514 \text{ kJ}$$

Increasing the temperature of this reaction at equilibrium will
a) increase the concentration of $O_2(g)$ at equilibrium
b) decrease the concentration of $CO_2(g)$ at equilibrium
c) decrease the value of the equilibrium constant
d) cause the reaction to shift right

Answer: c Page: 557

75. Consider the following reaction at equilibrium.

$$2CO_2(g) \rightleftharpoons 2CO(g) + O_2(g) \qquad \Delta H° = -514 \text{ kJ}$$

The amount of CO(g) produced by this reaction can be maximized by carrying out the reaction at
a) high temperature and high pressure
b) high temperature and low pressure
c) low temperature and low pressure
d) low temperature and high pressure

Answer: c Page: 557

76. What is the consequence of heating the following equilibrium system at constant pressure?

$$2SO_2(g) + O_2(g) \rightleftharpoons 2SO_3(g) \qquad \Delta H° = -99 \text{ kJ/mol}$$

a) the concentration of SO_3 will decrease
b) the partial pressure of SO_2 will decrease
c) the equilibrium constant will increase
d) the total volume of the system will decrease

Answer: a Page: 557

77. A vessel containing X and Y was allowed to come to equilibrium according to the reaction below. When the vessel was heated, the concentration of X increased and the concentration of Y decreased. What is the sign of ΔH associated with this reaction?

$$X \rightleftharpoons Y$$

a) +
b) -

Answer: b Page: 562

78. What effect does a catalyst have on an equilibrium?
a) it increases the rate of the forward reaction
b) it increases the equilibrium constant so that products are favored
c) it slows the reverse reaction
d) it increases the rate at which equilibrium is achieved without changing the composition of the equilibrium mixture
e) it shifts the equilibrium to the right

Answer: d Page: 563

79. How does a catalyst affect a chemical reaction?
a) it lowers the energy of the transition state
b) it accelerates the forward reaction
c) it makes reactions more exothermic
d) it increases the entropy change associated with a reaction
e) it reacts with product, effectively removing it and shifting the equilibrium to the right

Answer: a Page: 563

80. What condition used in the Haber process favors products as a result of equilibrium considerations?
a) high temperature
b) low temperature
c) high pressure
d) low pressure
e) use of a catalyst

Answer: c Page: 563

Chapter 16: Acid-Base Equilibria

ESSAY

1. Acids taste __________ and bases taste __________.

   Answer: sour, bitter Page: 573

MULTIPLE CHOICE

2. The concentration of water in pure water is approximately
   a) 18 *M*
   b) 100 *M*
   c) 55 *M*
   d) 0.100 *M*
   e) 83 *M*

   Answer: c Page: 574

3. In basic solution
   a) $[H_3O^+] = [OH^-]$
   b) $[H_3O^+] > [OH^-]$
   c) $[H_3O^+] < [OH^-]$
   d) $[H_3O^+] = 0$ M

   Answer: c Page: 574

4. What is the concentration of hydronium ions in a solution with a hydroxide ion concentration of 2.31×10^{-4} M ?
   a) 4.33×10^{-11} M
   b) 2.31×10^{10} M
   c) 9.72×10^{-4} M
   d) 1.01×10^{-5} M

   Answer: a Page: 574

5. What is the pH of an aqueous solution at 25°C in which $[H^+]$ is 0.0025 M?
   a) +3.40
   b) +2.60
   c) -2.60
   d) -3.40
   e) +2.25

   Answer: b Page: 574

6. What is the pH of an aqueous solution at 25°C in which $[OH^-]$ is 0.0025 M?
   a) +2.60
   b) -2.60
   c) +11.40
   d) -11.40
   e) -2.25

   Answer: c Page: 575

ESSAY

7. The concentration of hydroxide ions in neutral aqueous solution is

   Answer: 1×10^{-7} *M* Page: 575

MULTIPLE CHOICE

8. What is the pH of a solution that contains 3.98×10^{-9} *M* hydronium ion?
   a) 8.400
   b) 5.600
   c) 9.000
   d) 3.980
   e) 7.000

   Answer: a Page: 576

9. What is the pH of a solution that contains 3.98×10^{-9} *M* hydroxide ion?
   a) 8.400
   b) 5.600
   c) 9.000
   d) 3.980
   e) 7.000

   Answer: b Page: 576

10. What is the concentration of hydronium ions in a solution with pH = 4.282?
   a) 4.282 *M*
   b) 9.718 *M*
   c) 1.92×10^{-10} *M*
   d) 5.22×10^{-5} *M*
   e) 1.66×10^{4} *M*

   Answer: d Page: 576

11. What is the concentration of hydroxide ions in a solution with pH = 4.282?
    a) 4.282 *M*
    b) 9.718 *M*
    c) 1.92×10^{-10} *M*
    d) 5.22×10^{-5} *M*
    e) 1.66×10^{4} *M*

    Answer: c Page: 576

12. Calculate the pOH of a solution that contains 1.94×10^{-10} *M* hydronium ions.
    a) 1.940
    b) 4.288
    c) 7.000
    d) 14.000
    e) 9.712

    Answer: b Page: 576

13. Calculate the concentration of hydronium ions in a solution with a pOH of 4.223.
    a) 5.98×10^{-5} *M*
    b) 1.67×10^{-10} *M*
    c) 1.67×10^{4} *M*
    d) 5.99×10^{-19} *M*
    e) 1.00×10^{-7} *M*

    Answer: b Page: 576

14. In basic solution, pH is ____ and pOH is ____.
    a) = 7, = 7
    b) >7, <7
    c) <7, >7

    Answer: c Page: 576

15. Which solution below has the highest concentration of hydroxide ions?
    a) pH = 3.21
    b) pH = 12.59
    c) pH = 7.93
    d) pH = 9.82

    Answer: b Page: 576

ESSAY

16. Calculate the pH and pOH of a solution containing 0.0727 M H_3O^+.

    Answer: pH = $-\log[H_3O^+]$ = 1.138 pOH = 14 - pH = 14 - 1.138 = 12.862

    Page: 576

17. Calculate the hydroxide ion concentration in a solution that has a pOH of 7.927.

Answer:
$pOH = -\log [OH^-]$
$7.927 = -\log [OH^-]$
$[OH^-] = 1.18 \times 10^{-8}$ M

Page: 576

MULTIPLE CHOICE

18. What is $[H^+]$ for an aqueous solution whose pH at 25°C is 8.11?
a) 7.8×10^{-9} M
b) 1.3×10^{8} M
c) 7.8×10^{9} M
d) 1.3×10^{-8} M
e) 8.1×10^{-8} M

Answer: a Page: 576

19. Determine the $[H^+]$ in a solution with a pH of 4.39.
a) 3.9×10^{-4} M
b) 0.64 M
c) 0.012 M
d) 4.1×10^{-5} M

Answer: d Page: 576

20. What is the concentration of H^+ in a solution with a pH of 7.35?
a) 3.5×10^{-7} M
b) 2.2×10^{-7} M
c) 6.4×10^{-4} M
d) 4.5×10^{-8} M

Answer: d Page: 576

21. What is the H^+ concentration in a solution with a pH of 3.75?
a) 5.6×10^{3} M
b) 7.5×10^{-3} M
c) 5.6×10^{-11} M
d) 1.8×10^{-4} M

Answer: d Page: 576

22. Of the following, which is a weak acid?
    a) HF
    b) HCl
    c) HI
    d) HBr
    e) HNO_3
    f) $HClO_4$

    Answer: a Page: 576

23. According to Arrhenius, an acid is a substance that
    a) is capable of donating one or more H^+
    b) causes an increase in the concentration of H+ in aqueous solutions
    c) can accept a pair of electrons to form a coordinate covalent bond
    d) reacts with the solvent to form the cation formed by autoionization of that solvent
    e) tastes bitter

    Answer: b Page: 580

24. Which one of the following would be considered a base according to the Bronsted-Lowry definition but not by the Arrhenius definition?
    a) $NH_3(g)$
    b) $HBr(aq)$
    c) $Ba(OH)_2(aq)$
    d) $HF(g)$
    e) $KOH(aq)$

    Answer: a Page: 580

25. Which one of the following is a Bronsted-Lowry acid?
    a) $(CH_3)_3NH^+$
    b) CH_3COOH
    c) HF
    d) HNO_2
    e) all of these

    Answer: e Page: 580

26. In the following reaction, which substance is acting as a base?
    $HN_3 + H_2O \rightarrow H_3O^+ + N_3^-$

    a) H_2O
    b) HN_3

    Answer: a Page: 580

ESSAY

27. Write the reactions that occur when sodium fluoride is placed in water.

    Answer:
    $NaF \rightarrow Na^+ + F^-$
    $F^- + H_2O \rightarrow HF + OH^-$
    $2H_2O \rightarrow H_3O^+ + OH^-$
    Page: 580

MULTIPLE CHOICE

28. A Bronsted-Lowry base is defined as a substance which
    a) increases $[H^+]$ when placed in H_2O
    b) decreases $[H^+]$ when placed in H_2O
    c) increases $[OH^-]$ when placed in H_2O
    d) acts as a proton acceptor in any system
    e) acts as a proton donor in any system

    Answer: d Page: 580

29. A Bronsted-Lowry acid is defined as a substance that
    a) increases $[H^+]$ when placed in H_2O
    b) decreases $[H^+]$ when placed in H_2O
    c) increases $[OH^-]$ when placed in H_2O
    d) acts as a proton acceptor in any system
    e) acts as a proton donor in any system

    Answer: e Page: 580

30. A substance that is capable of acting as both acid and as base is called
    a) autosomal
    b) conjugated
    c) amphoteric
    d) autocratic
    e) contrapunctal

    Answer: c Page: 581

ESSAY

31. What is the formula of the conjugate base of hypochlorous acid?

    Answer: ClO^- or OCl^- Page: 581

MULTIPLE CHOICE

32. What is the conjugate acid of NH_3?
   a) NH_3
   b) NH_2^+
   c) NH_3^+
   d) NH_4^+

   Answer: d Page: 581

33. What is the conjugate base of OH^-?
   a) O_2
   b) O^-
   c) H_2O
   d) O^{2-}

   Answer: d Page: 581

ESSAY

34. The following acids are listed in order of increasing strength. List their conjugate bases in order of increasing strength.
   HCN, CH_3COOH, HF, $HClO_4$

   Answer: ClO_4^-, F^-, CH_3COO^-, CN^- Page: 583

MULTIPLE CHOICE

35. What is the strongest base that can exist in water?
   a) OH^-
   b) KOH
   c) NaOH
   d) NH_3

   Answer: a Page: 583

36. The hydride ion, H^-, is a stronger base than the hydroxide ion, OH^-. What reaction will occur if sodium hydride is dissolved in water?
   a) $H^-(aq) + H_2O(l) \rightarrow H_3O^-(aq)$
   b) $H^-(aq) + H_2O(l) \rightarrow OH^-(aq) + H_2(g)$
   c) $H^-(aq) + H^2O(l) \rightarrow OH^-(aq) + 2H^+(aq)$
   d) $H^-(aq) + H_2O(l) \rightarrow$ No Reaction

   Answer: b Page: 583

37. The $[OH^-]$ and pH of 0.035 M KOH at 25°C are respectively
   a) 0.035 M and +1.46
   b) 0.035 M and -1.46
   c) 2.9×10^{-13} M and -12.54
   d) 0.035 M and +12.54
   e) 2.9×10^{-13} M and +12.54

   Answer: d Page: 585

38. The $[OH^-]$ and pH of 0.0012 M $Ba(OH)_2$ at 25°C are respectively
   a) 0.00060 M and -2.62
   b) 0.0012 M and +2.92
   c) 0.0024 M and +11.38
   d) 0.0024 M and +2.62
   e) 0.0012 M and -2.92

   Answer: c Page: 585

39. Calculate the pH of a 0.011 M NaOH solution.
   a) 1.96
   b) 4.51
   c) 12.04
   d) 12.90

   Answer: c Page: 585

40. Calculate the $[OH^-]$ in a NaOH solution with a pH of 12.73.
   a) 1.27
   b) 1.9×10^{-13}
   c) 0.054
   d) 2.3×10^{-12}

   Answer: c Page: 585

41. Which of the following possesses the greatest concentration of hydroxide ion?
   a) a solution with a pH of 3.0
   b) a 1×10^{-4} M solution of HNO_3
   c) a solution with a pOH of 12.0
   d) water

   Answer: d Page: 585

42. What is the pH of a 0.053 M solution of KOH?
   a) 6.9
   b) 12.7
   c) 7.3
   d) 1.3

   Answer: b Page: 585

43. What is the pH of a 0.053 M solution of $Ca(OH)_2$?
a) 1.3
b) 12.7
c) 0.97
d) 13.0

Answer: d Page: 585

44. Calculate the pH of 0.00756 M HNO_3.
a) 11.879
b) 7.091
c) 2.121
d) 12.947

Answer: c Page: 585

ESSAY

45. Calculate the pOH of 1.826 M KOH.

Answer:
pOH = -log[OH^-]
pOH = -log(1.826) = 0.2615
Page: 585

MULTIPLE CHOICE

46. The [H^+] and pH of 0.021 M HNO_3 at 25°C are respectively
a) 4.8×10^{-13} M and 12.32
b) 4.8×10^{-13} M and -12.32
c) 0.021 M and +1.68
d) 0.021 M and -1.68
e) 4.8×10^{-6} M and +5.32

Answer: c Page: 585

47. Calculate the pH of a 0.030 M HCl solution.
a) 3.00
b) 1.52
c) 3.51
d) 0.52

Answer: b Page: 585

48. Calculate the pH of a 0.025 M HI solution.
   a) 1.06
   b) 1.60
   c) 3.69
   d) 4.12

   Answer: b Page: 585

49. The $[H^+]$ and PH of 0.0037 M HBr at 25°C are respectively
   a) 0.0074 M and +2.43
   b) 0.0037 M and +2.43
   c) 0.0074 M and +2.13
   d) 0.0037 M and +2.13
   e) 0.0037 M and -2.13

   Answer: b Page: 585

50. Which of the following acids is <u>not</u> a strong acid?
   a) H_2CO_3
   b) H_2SO_4
   c) HNO_3
   d) $HClO_4$

   Answer: a Page: 585

51. Which one of the following is the weakest acid?
   a) HF ($K_a = 6.8 \times 10^{-4}$)
   b) HClO ($K_a = 3.0 \times 10^{-8}$)
   c) HNO_2 ($K_a = 4.5 \times 10^{-4}$)
   d) HCN ($K_a = 4.9 \times 10^{-10}$)

   Answer: d Page: 587

52. HZ is a weak acid. An aqueous solution nominally 0.020 M in HZ has a pH of 4.93 at 25°C. What is K_a for HZ?
   a) 1.2×10^{-5}
   b) 6.9×10^{-9}
   c) 1.4×10^{-10}
   d) 9.9×10^{-2}
   e) 2.8×10^{-12}

   Answer: b Page: 587

53.

Acid	K_a
HOAc	1.8×10^{-5}
$HCHO_2$	1.8×10^{-4}
HClO	3.0×10^{-8}
HF	6.8×10^{-4}

Which one of the acids shown in the table is the strongest?

a) HOAc
b) $HCHO_2$
c) HClO
d) HF

Answer: d Page: 587

54. What is the % ionization of hypochlorous acid (HClO) in a 0.015 M solution of HClO? ($K_a = 3.0 \times 10^{-8}$)
a) 4.5×10^{-8}
b) 14
c) 2.1×10^{-5}
d) 0.14

Answer: d Page: 587

55. The pH of a 0.55 M solution of HBrO is 4.48. What is the value of K_a for HBrO?
a) 2.0×10^{-9}
b) 1.1×10^{-9}
c) 6.0×10^{-5}
d) 3.3×10^{-5}

Answer: a Page: 587

56. A 0.15 M solution of the weak acid HA has a pH of 5.35. What is the value of K_a for HA?
a) 3.0×10^{-5}
b) 1.8×10^{-5}
c) 7.1×10^{-9}
d) 1.3×10^{-10}

Answer: d Page: 587

57. Calculate the pH of 0.0385 M hypochlorous acid, $K_a = 3.0 \times 10^{-8}$.
a) 1.41
b) 8.94
c) 4.47
d) 7.52

Answer: c Page: 590

58. K_a for HClO is 3.0×10^{-8}. What is the pH at 25°C of an aqueous solution that is 0.020 M in HClO?
a) +2.45
b) -2.45
c) -9.22
d) +9.22
e) +4.61

Answer: e Page: 590

59.

Acid	K_a
HOAc	1.8×10^{-5}
HN_3	1.9×10^{-5}
$HCHO_2$	1.8×10^{-4}
HClO	3.0×10^{-8}

What is the pH of a 0.15 M solution of HOAc?

a) 5.57
b) 7.35
c) 2.78
d) 9.18

Answer: c Page: 590

60. K_a for HF is 6.8×10^{-4}. What is the pH of a 0.35 M solution of HF?
a) 3.17
b) 1.81
c) 3.62
d) 0.46

Answer: b Page: 590

61. K_a for HN_3 is 1.9×10^{-5}. What is the pH of a 0.35 M solution of HN_3?
a) 11.41
b) 2.37
c) 5.18
d) 2.59

Answer: d Page: 590

62. What is the value of K_a for the weak acid HA if a 0.35 M solution of HA has a pH of 5.95?
a) 3.2×10^{-6}
b) 1.7
c) 1.1×10^{-6}
d) 3.6×10^{-12}

Answer: d Page: 590

63. A 0.25 M solution of the weak acid HX has a pH of 4.15. What is the value of K_a for HX?
    a) 2.8×10^{-4}
    b) 1.7×10^{-10}
    c) 7.1×10^{-5}
    d) 2.0×10^{-8}

    Answer: d Page: 590

ESSAY

64. Write the K_{a2} reaction for phosphoric acid.

    Answer: $H_2PO_4^- + H_2O \rightarrow H_3O^+ + HPO_4^{2-}$ Page: 594

MULTIPLE CHOICE

65. Of the following, which is the weakest acid?
    a) H_3PO_4
    b) $H_2PO_4^-$
    c) HPO_4^{2-}

    Answer: c Page: 594

66. Calculate the pH of a solution of 0.163 M sulfurous acid, $K_{a1} = 1.7 \times 10^{-}$, $K_{a2} = 6.4 \times 10^{-8}$.
    a) 4.48
    b) 1.35
    c) 1.77
    d) 7.19

    Answer: b Page: 594

67. Calculate the value of K_3.
    $H_2C_4H_2O_4 + H_2O \rightarrow HC_4H_2O_4^- + H_3O^+$ $K_1 = 9.3 \times 10^{-4}$
    $HC_4H_2O_4^- + H_2 \rightarrow C_4H_2O_4^{2-} + H_3O^+$ $K_2 = 3.4 \times 10^{-5}$
    $H_2C_4H_2O_4 + 2\ H_2O \rightarrow C_4H_2O_4^{2-} + 2\ H_3O^+$ K_3

    a) 9.6×10^{-4}
    b) 27
    c) 3.6×10^{-2}
    d) 3.2×10^{-8}

    Answer: d Page: 594

68. Which species from the following list would be the strongest Bronsted base?
a) Cl^-
b) Br^-
c) NO_3^-
d) F^-

Answer: d Page: 596

69. Which species from the following list would be the strongest Bronsted base?
a) ClO_4^-
b) NO_3^-
c) CN^-
d) Br^-

Answer: c Page: 596

70. Calculate the pOH of 0.0827 M sodium cyanide solution (for cyanide ion, $K_b = 4.9 \times 10^{-10}$.
a) 9.31
b) 10.39
c) 5.20
d) 1.08

Answer: c Page: 596

71. Which one of the following is not a weak base?
a) $(CH_3)_3N$
b) NaOCl
c) NaF
d) $NaClO_4$

Answer: d Page: 596

72. Calculate the pH of a solution made by dissolving 1.87 g of sodium caproate, $NaC_6H_{11}O_2$, $K_b = 7.58 \times 10^{-10}$, in water and diluting to a total volume of 500.0 mL.
a) 5.344
b) 8.656
c) 5.494
d) 8.505

Answer: b Page: 596

73. Determine the pH of a 0.15 M solution of KF ($K_a = 7.0 \text{ X } 10^{-4}$).
a) 12.01
b) 5.83
c) 8.17
d) 2.33

Answer: c Page: 596

74. Calculate the pH of a 0.50 M solution of NH_3. The K_b of NH_3 is 1.8 X 10^{-}

a) 8.95
b) 11.48
c) 2.52
d) 5.05

Answer: b Page: 596

75. Determine the pH of a 0.35 M solution of CH_3NH_2 (methylamine). The K_b of methylamine is 4.4 X 10^{-4}.
a) 10.19
b) 3.81
c) 12.09
d) 1.91

Answer: c Page: 596

76. Calculate the pH of 0.726 M anilinium hydrochloride, $C_6H_5NH_3Cl$, given that the K_b for aniline is 3.83 x 10^{-4}.
a) 1.778
b) 12.222
c) 5.361
d) 8.639

Answer: c Page: 596

77.

Acid	K_a
HOAc	1.8 X 10^{-5}
$HCHO_2$	1.8 X 10^{-4}
HClO	3.0 X 10^{-8}
HF	6.8 X 10^{-4}

Which one of the following is the strongest base?

a) OAc^-
b) CHO_2^-
c) ClO^-
d) F^-

Answer: c Page: 596

78. Which one of the following does not form hydroxide ions when placed in water?
a) ionic hydrides
b) ionic metal oxides
c) nonmetal oxides
d) ionic nitrides

Answer: c Page: 598

ESSAY

79. For any conjugate acid-base pair, the product of the K_a for the acid and the K_b for the base has the numerical value

Answer: 1×10^{-14} Page: 600

MULTIPLE CHOICE

80. Given that the K_a for gallic acid, $HC_7H_5O_5$, is 4.57×10^{-3}, what is the K_b for sodium gallate, $NaC_7H_5O_5$?
a) 4.57×10^{-3}
b) 2.19×10^{-12}
c) 5.43×10^{-5}
d) 7.81×10^{-6}

Answer: b Page: 600

81. K_b for C_5H_5N is 1.4×10^{-9}. K_a for $C_5H_5NH^+$ is
a) 1.0×10^{-7}
b) 1.4×10^{-23}
c) 7.1×10^{-4}
d) 1.4×10^{-5}
e) 7.1×10^{-6}

Answer: e Page: 600

82. K_b for NH_3 is 1.8×10^{-5}. What is the pH of a 0.35 M solution of NH_4Cl?
a) 9.71
b) 4.29
c) 9.14
d) 4.86

Answer: d Page: 600

83. The K_a for formic acid ($HCHO_2$) is 1.8×10^{-4}. What is the pH of a 0.35 M solution of sodium formate ($NaCHO_2$)?
a) 10.71
b) 5.36
c) 3.29
d) 8.64

Answer: d Page: 600

84. The K_a for HCN is 4.9×10^{-10}. What is the value of K_b for CN^-?
a) 2.0×10^{-5}
b) 4.0×10^{-6}
c) 4.9×10^{4}
d) 4.9×10^{-24}

Answer: a Page: 600

85. What is K_b for NaF? K_a for HF is 7.0×10^{-4}.
a) 2.0×10^{-8}
b) 1.4×10^{-11}
c) 7.0×10^{-18}
d) 7.0×10^{-4}

Answer: b Page: 600

ESSAY

86. Why are amines, such as amphetamine, converted to acid salts?

Answer:
In the acid salt form they are more stable, less volatile, and more water soluble

Page: 601

MULTIPLE CHOICE

87. A 0.100 M solution of sodium hydrogen succinate, $NaHC_4H_4O_4$, (given that, for succinic acid, $K_{a1} = 6.4 \times 10^{-6}$ and $K_{a2} = 2.7 \times 10^{-6}$) will be ____.
a) acidic
b) basic
c) neutral

Answer: a Page: 603

88. A 0.10 M aqueous solution of which of the following salts will have the lowest pH?
a) KNO_3
b) $Ca(NO_3)_2$
c) $Ni(NO_3)_2$
d) KCl
e) $BaBr_2$

Answer: c Page: 603

89. A 0.10 M aqueous solution of which of the following salts will have the highest pH?
a) $CoCl_2$
b) CoI_2
c) NH_4I
d) NaF
e) KBr

Answer: d Page: 603

90. Which one of the following substances will react completely with NaF?
a) NaOAc
b) HCl
c) NH_3
d) $NaNO_3$

Answer: b Page: 603

91. Of the following four substances, which would form <u>basic</u> solutions?

NH_4Cl $Cu(NO_3)_2$ K_2CO_3 NaF

a) NH_4Cl, $Cu(NO_3)_2$
b) K_2CO_3, NH_4Cl
c) NaF only
d) NaF, K_2CO_3

Answer: d Page: 603

92. Which one of the following 0.1 M solutions would have a pH of 7.0?
a) NaOCl
b) KCl
c) NH_4Cl
d) $Ca(OAc)_2$
e) none of these

Answer: b Page: 603

93. Which one of the following 0.1 M solutions would have the <u>highest</u> pH?
a) KCN (K_a HCN = 4.0×10^{-10})
b) NH_4NO_3 (K_b NH_3 = 1.8×10^{-5})
c) NaOAc (K_a HOAc = 1.8×10^{-5})
d) NaClO (K_a HClO = 3.2×10^{-8})

Answer: a Page: 603

94. Which one of the following 0.1 M solutions would have a pH of 7.0?
a) Na_2S
b) KF
c) $NaNO_3$
d) NH_4Cl

Answer: c Page: 603

95. The strength of an acid ______ as the polarity of the R-H bond ______.
a) increases, increases
b) decreases, decreases
c) increases, decreases
d) decreases, increases
e) remains constant, increases

Answer: a Page: 606

ESSAY

96. How does the strength of oxoacids with the same central atom relate to the number of oxygen atoms bound to the central atom?

Answer: strength increases as the number of bound oxygen atoms increases

Page: 606

MULTIPLE CHOICE

97. For oxoacids with the same number of oxygen atoms, the strength will depend on the
a) metallic character of the central atom
b) electronegativity of the central atom
c) size of the central atom
d) electron affinity of the central atom
e) number of hydrogen atoms in the molecule

Answer: b Page: 606

98. An acid containing the group, COOH, is called a
a) strong acid
b) carbonaceous acid
c) carboxylic acid
d) double oxoacid
e) carbo-oxo acid

Answer: c Page: 606

99. Which one of the following does not act as an acid in water?
a) Al^{3+}
b) Cr^{3+}
c) Fe^{2+}
d) Ca^{2+}

Answer: d Page: 606

100. An aqueous solution of which one of the following will be basic?
a) NH_4ClO_4
b) KBr
c) $CrCl_3$
d) $Fe(NO_3)_3$
e) none of these

Answer: e Page: 606

ESSAY

101. Which hydrogen halide is a weak acid?

Answer: HF Page: 606

MULTIPLE CHOICE

102. Metal hydrides
    a) are either acidic or show no acid-base characteristics at all
    b) are usually neutral
    c) are generally amphoteric
    d) are either basic or show no acid-base character

    Answer: d Page: 606

103. Which one of the following is the most acidic?
    a) H_2Te
    b) H_2Se
    c) H_2O
    d) H_2S

    Answer: a Page: 606

104. Of the following choices, which is the strongest acid?
    a) $HBrO_2$
    b) HIO_2
    c) $HClO_2$

    Answer: c Page: 606

105. Of the following, which is the strongest acid?
    a) HIO
    b) HIO_4
    c) HIO_2
    d) HIO_3

    Answer: b Page: 606

106. Of the following, which is the strongest acid?
    a) CH_3COOH
    b) $ClCH_2COOH$
    c) $Cl_2CHCOOH$
    d) Cl_3CCOOH

    Answer: d Page: 606

107. Which one of the following is the strongest acid?
    a) ClCOOH
    b) HCOOH
    c) BrCOOH
    d) FCOOH

    Answer: d Page: 606

108. Which of the following acids will be the strongest?
a) H_2SO_4
b) HSO_4^-
c) H_2SO_3
d) H_2SeO_4
e) HSO_3^-

Answer: a Page: 606

109. A 0.10 M solution of the sodium salt of which of the following anions would have the highest pH?
a) IO_2^-
b) ClO_2^-
c) ClO^-
d) IO^-
e) IO_3^-

Answer: d Page: 606

110. Of the following, which one of the following is the strongest acid?
a) $HClO$
b) $HClO_3$
c) $HClO_2$
d) $HClO_4$

Answer: d Page: 606

111. Of the following, which one of the following is the strongest acid?
a) $HClO$
b) HF
c) HBr
d) HI

Answer: d Page: 606

112. Of the following, which one of the following is the strongest acid?
a) H_2SeO_3
b) H_2SO_3
c) H_2SO_4
d) H_2SeO_4

Answer: c Page: 606

113. Which definition of acids and bases is the most general?
a) Bronsted-Lowry
b) Arrhenius
c) Lewis

Answer: c Page: 611

114. Which one of the following cannot act as a Lewis base?
 a) Cl^-
 b) NH_3
 c) Cr^{3+}
 d) CN^-

 Answer: c Page: 611

115. In the reaction $BF_3 + F^- \rightarrow BF_4^-$, BF_3 is acting as what type of acid?
 a) Arrhenius only
 b) Bronsted-Lowry only
 c) Lewis only
 d) Arrhenius, Bronsted-Lowry, and Lewis
 e) Arrhenius and Bronsted-Lowry

 Answer: c Page: 611

116. Sulfur dioxide neutralizes calcium oxide to produce
 a) calcium sulfide
 b) elemental sulfur
 c) calcium sulfite
 d) calcium hydroxide

 Answer: c Page: 611

117. Which equation does <u>NOT</u> represent a Lewis acid-base reaction?
 a) $Cu^{2+}(aq) + 4NH_3(aq) \rightarrow [Cu(NH_3)_4]^{2+}(aq)$
 b) $HCl(g) + NH_3(g) \rightarrow NH_4Cl(s)$
 c) $H^+(aq) + OH^-(aq) \rightarrow H_2O(l)$
 d) $2Na(s) + Cl_2(g) \rightarrow 2NaCl(s)$

 Answer: d Page: 611

118. Identify the Lewis base in the following equation.

$$Cu^{2+}(aq) + 4CN^-(aq) \rightarrow Cu(CN)_4^{2-}(aq)$$

 a) CN^-
 b) Cu^{2+}
 c) $Cu(CN)_4^{2-}$

 Answer: a Page: 611

119. In the reaction shown below, the NH_3 is acting as a(n) ________ base but not as a(n) ________ base.

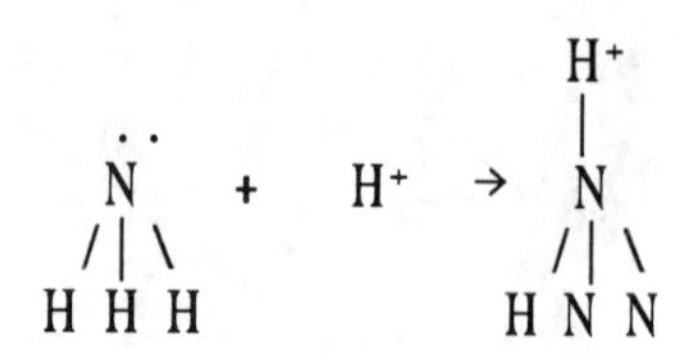

a) Arrhenius, Bronsted-Lowry
b) Bronsted-Lowry, Leis
c) Lewis, Arrhenius
d) Lewis, Bronsted-Lowry

Answer: c Page: 611

120. In the following reaction, the BF_3 is serving as a(n) ________ acid.

$$BF_3 + F^- \rightarrow BF_4$$

a) Arrhenius
b) Bronsted-Lowry
c) Lewis
d) all of the above

Answer: c Page: 611

121. The simplest amino acid is
a) alanine
b) valine
c) histidine
d) lycine
e) glycine

Answer: e Page: 610

ESSAY

122. Amino acids are amphoteric, why?

Answer: they contain both COOH and NH_2 Page: 610

MULTIPLE CHOICE

123. When the proton in the COOH of an amino acid is transferred to the NH_2 group of that same amino acid molecule, a(n) _________ is formed.
    a) cation
    b) amphoter
    c) zwitterion
    d) dianion
    e) dication

    Answer: c Page: 610

Chapter 17: Additional Aspects of Aqueous Equilibria

MULTIPLE CHOICE

1. The common ion effect
   a) reduces the dissociation of a weak acid
   b) increases the dissociation of a weak acid
   c) has no effect on the dissociation of a weak acid

   Answer: a Page: 621

2. Calculate the pH of a solution containing 0.818 M acetic acid (K_a = 1.76 x 10^{-5}) and 0.172 M sodium acetate.
   a) 4.077
   b) 5.432
   c) 8.568
   d) 8.370

   Answer: a Page: 621

3. Which of the following actions will most decrease the degree of dissociation of acetic acid in an aqueous solution nominally 0.10 M of volume 879 mL?
   a) addition of 0.010 mol solid KCl
   b) bubbling in 0.010 mol gaseous HCl (absorbed by solution)
   c) bubbling in 0.020 mol gaseous HBr (absorbed by solution)
   d) addition of 0.010 mol solid KI
   e) addition of 0.010 mol solid sodium acetate

   Answer: c Page: 621

4. Which of the following actions will increase the degree of dissociation of formic acid in an aqueous solution nominally 0.20 M of volume 711 mL?
   a) addition of 183 mL 0.90 M sodium formate
   b) addition of 183 mL H_2O
   c) addition of 183 mL 0.90 M potassium formate
   d) bubbling in 0.010 mol gaseous HCl (absorbed by solution)
   e) bubbling in 0.020 mol gaseous HBr (absorbed by solution)

   Answer: b Page: 621

5. Which one of the following pairs cannot be mixed together to form a buffer?
   a) NH_3, NH_4Cl
   b) $NaC_2H_3O_2$, HCl
   c) RbOH, HBr
   d) KOH, HF
   e) H_3PO_4, KH_2PO_4

   Answer: c Page: 624

6. A solution containing which one of the following pairs of substances could be a buffer?
   a) NaI, HI
   b) KBr, HBr
   c) RbCl, HCl
   d) CsF, HF
   e) none of these

   Answer: d Page: 624

7. What change will be caused by addition of a small amount of a strong acid to a solution containing fluoride and hydrogen fluoride?
   a) the concentration of hydronium ion will significantly increase
   b) the concentration of fluoride will increase as will the concentration of hydronium ion
   c) the concentration of hydrogen fluoride will be decreased and the concentration of fluoride will be increased
   d) the concentration of fluoride will be decreased and the concentration of hydrogen fluoride will be increased
   e) the fluoride ion will precipitate out of solution as its acid salt

   Answer: d Page: 624

8. The Henderson-Hasselbalch equation is
   a) $[H^+] = K_a + \frac{[base]}{[acid]}$
   b) $pH = pK_a - \log\frac{[base]}{[acid]}$
   c) $pH = pK_a + \log\frac{[base]}{[acid]}$
   d) $pH = pK_a + \log\frac{[acid]}{[base]}$
   e) $pH = \log\frac{[acid]}{[base]}$

   Answer: c Page: 624

9. Consider a solution containing 0.100 *M* fluoride ion and 0.126 *M* hydrogen fluoride. Calculate the concentration of fluoride ion after addition of 5.00 mL of 0.0100 *M* HCl to 25.0 mL of this solution.
   a) 0.0850 *M*
   b) 0.00167 *M*
   c) 0.0980 *M*
   d) 0.0817 *M*
   e) 0.00253 *M*

   Answer: d Page: 624

10. Consider a solution containing 0.100 *M* fluoride ion and 0.126 *M* hydrogen fluoride. Calculate the concentration of hydrogen fluoride after addition of 5.00 mL of 0.0100 *M* HCl to 25.0 mL of this solution.
a) 0.107 *M*
b) 0.100 *M*
c) 0.126 *M*
d) 0.00976 *M*
e) 0.00193 *M*

Answer: a Page: 624

11. 50.0 mL of a solution with which one of the following compositions can absorb the most acid without changing pH?
a) 0.821 M HF and 0.217 M NaF
b) 0.821 M HF and 0.909 M NaF
c) 0.100 M HF and 0.217 M NaF
d) 0.121 M HF and 0.667 M NaF

Answer: b Page: 624

ESSAY

12. Write the reaction that occurs when acid (write it as H_3O^+) is added to an ammonia/ammonium buffer.

Answer: $H_3O^+ + NH_3 \rightarrow NH^+_4 + H_2O$ Page: 624

MULTIPLE CHOICE

13. Of the following, which solution has the greatest buffering capacity?
a) 0.821 M HF and 0.217 M NaF
b) 0.821 M HF and 0.909 M NaF
c) 0.100 M HF and 0.217 M NaF
d) 0.121 M HF and 0.667 M NaF

Answer: b Page: 624

14. K_a for acetic acid is 1.7×10^{-5}. The pH of a buffer prepared by combining 50.0 mL 1.00 M potassium acetate and 50.0 mL 1.00 M acetic acid is
a) 1.70
b) 0.85
c) 3.40
d) 4.77
e) 2.38

Answer: d Page: 624

15. K_b for ammonia is 1.8×10^{-5}. The pH of a buffer prepared by combining 50.0 mL 1.00 M ammonia and 50.0 mL 1.00 M ammonium nitrate is
    a) 4.63
    b) 9.26
    c) 4.74
    d) 9.37
    e) 7.00

    Answer: b Page: 624

16. Calculate the pH of a solution prepared by dissolving 0.37 moles of formic acid (HCO_2H) and 0.23 moles of sodium formate ($NaCO_2H$) in 1.00 L of solution. ($K_a = 1.8 \times 10^{-4}$)
    a) 2.09
    b) 10.46
    c) 3.54
    d) 2.30

    Answer: c Page: 624

17. Determine the pH of a solution prepared by dissolving 0.75 moles of NH_3 and 0.25 moles of NH_4Cl in a liter of solution.
    (K_b NH_3 = 1.8×10^{-4})
    a) 4.27
    b) 8.78
    c) 9.73
    d) 5.22

    Answer: c Page: 624

18. Calculate the pH of a solution prepared by dissolving 0.25 moles of benzoic acid ($C_7H_5O_2H$) and 0.15 moles of sodium benzoate ($NaC_7H_5O_2$) in 1.00 L of solution. ($K_a = 6.5 \times 10^{-5}$)
    a) 4.41
    b) 2.39
    c) 3.97
    d) 10.03

    Answer: c Page: 624

19. Calculate the pH of a solution prepared by dissolving 0.15 mol of benzoic acid (HBz) and 0.30 mol of sodium benzoate (NaBz) in 1.00 L of solution. (K_a of HBz = 6.5×10^{-5})
    a) 2.51
    b) 3.89
    c) 4.49
    d) 10.11

    Answer: c Page: 624

20. Consider a solution prepared by dissolving 0.15 mol of benzoic acid (HBz) and 0.30 mol of sodium benzoate (NaBz) in 1.00 L of solution. (K_a of HBz = 6.5 X 10^{-5}) If 0.05 mol of HCl is added to this buffer solution, the pH of the solution will drop slightly. The pH does not drastically decrease because the HCl reacts with the ________ present in the buffer solution.
a) Bz^-
b) H^+
c) H_2O
d) HBz

Answer: a Page: 624

21. Determine the pH of a solution prepared by adding 0.45 moles of KOAc to 1.00 L of 2.00 M HOAc. (K_a = 1.8 X 10^{-5})
a) 2.22
b) 4.10
c) 2.52
d) 5.39

Answer: b Page: 624

22. Consider a solution prepared by adding 0.45 moles of KOAc to 1.00 L of 2.00 M HOAc. (K_a = 1.8 X 10^{-5}) If 0.05 mol of HCl is added to this buffer solution, the pH of the solution will drop slightly. The pH does not drastically decrease because the HCl reacts with the ________ present in the buffer solution.
a) OAc^-
b) H^+
c) H_2O
d) HOAc

Answer: a Page: 624

23. Consider a solution prepared by mixing 0.43 moles of acetic acid with 0.28 moles of sodium acetate in 1.00 liter of solution. The addition of 0.01 moles of HCl to this solution will cause the pH to ________ slightly because the HCl reacts with the ________ that is present.
a) increase, acetate ion
b) increase, sodium ion
c) decrease, acetate
d) decrease, acetic acid

Answer: c Page: 624

24. What is the pH of a solution prepared by dissolving 0.35 mol of CH_3NH_3Cl (methylamine hydrochloride) in 1.00 L of 1.1 M CH_3NH_2 (methylamine). The K_b for methylamine is 4.4 X 10^{-4}.
a) 1.66
b) 2.86
c) 10.15
d) 11.14

Answer: d Page: 624

25. Consider a solution prepared by dissolving 0.35 mol of CH_3NH_3Cl (methylamine hydrochloride) in 1.00 L of 1.1 M CH_3NH_2 (methylamine). The K_b for methylamine is 4.4 X 10^{-4}. If 10 mL of 0.01 M HCl is added to this buffer solution, the pH of the solution will ________ slightly because the HCl reacts with the ________ present in the solution.
a) increase, OH^-
b) increase, CH_3NH_2
c) decrease, CH_3NH_2
d) decrease, $CH_3NH_3^+$

Answer: c Page: 624

26. Which one of the following pairs could be used to make a buffer solution?
a) NH_3, NaOAc
b) $NaNO_3$, NH_4Cl
c) HOAc, NaOH
d) NaOH, NaCl

Answer: c Page: 624

27. Which of the following substances, when added to a solution of nitrous acid (HNO_2), could be used to prepare a buffer solution?
a) HCl
b) NaCl
c) HOAc
d) $NaNO_2$

Answer: d Page: 624

28. Which of the following substances, when added to a solution of hydrofluoric acid, could be used to prepare a buffer solution?
a) HCl
b) $NaNO_3$
c) NaF
d) NaCl

Answer: c Page: 624

29. Human blood is
    a) neutral
    b) very basic
    c) slightly acidic
    d) very acidic
    e) slightly basic

    Answer: e Page: 631

ESSAY

30. What is the condition called when the pH of the blood falls below 7.35?

    Answer: acidosis Page: 647

31. When the pH of the blood rises above _____, the condition is called alkalosis.

    Answer: 7.45 Page: 631

MULTIPLE CHOICE

32. The primary buffer system that controls the pH of the blood is the ______ buffer system.
    a) carbon dioxide, carbonate
    b) carbonate, bicarbonate
    c) carbonic acid, carbon dioxide
    d) carbonate, carbonic acid
    e) carbonic acid, bicarbonate

    Answer: e Page: 631

33. If carbon dioxide is expelled from the blood, what happens to the pH of the blood?
    a) it rises
    b) it falls
    c) it does not change

    Answer: a Page: 631

34. The primary buffer system in the blood
    a) has a high capacity to neutralize acids and a low capacity to neutralize bases
    b) has a high capacity to neutralize bases and a low capacity to neutralize acids
    c) has an equal capacity for neutralizing both acids and bases

    Answer: a Page: 631

35. What are the prinicipal organs that regulate the pH of the carbonic acid-bicarbonate buffer system in the blood?
    a) kidneys, liver
    b) lungs, kidneys
    c) spleen, liver
    d) lungs, skin
    e) brain stem, heart

    Answer: b Page: 631

36. Which one of the following will cause hemoglobin to release oxygen?
    a) increase in pH
    b) decrease in pH
    c) decrease in temperature
    d) decrease in CO_2 concentration
    e) increase in O_2 concentration

    Answer: b Page: 631

ESSAY

37. Explain the reason that a larger number of indicators can be used for strong acid-strong base titrations than for titrations of weak acids or weak bases.

    Answer:
    because the pH change at the equivalence point in a strong acid-strong base titration is so large and in the titration of a weak acid or base is considerably smaller

    Page: 632

38. On the axes below, draw the titration curve for the titration of HF with KOH. Clearly label the axes and the equivalence point. Also indicate whether the pH of the equivalence point is 7, >7, or < 7.

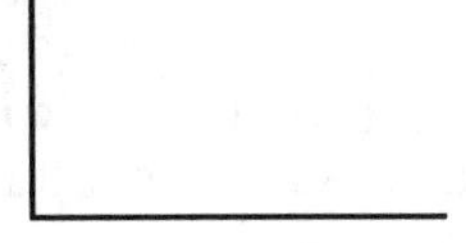

Answer:

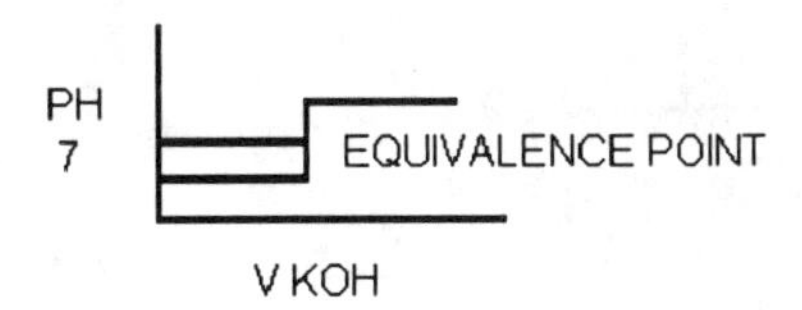

Page: 632

Chapter 17: Additional Aspects of Aqueous Equilibria

MULTIPLE CHOICE

39. Consider the titration of 25.0 mL of 0.723 M $HClO_4$ with 0.273 M KOH. Calculate the H_3O^+ concentration before any KOH is added.
a) 0.439 M
b) 1.00×10^{-7} M
c) 0.723 M
d) 2.81×10^{-13} M

Answer: c Page: 632

40. Consider the titration of 25.00 mL of 0.723 M $HClO_4$ with 0.273 M KOH. Calculate the H_3O^+ concentration after addition of 10.0 mL of KOH.
a) 0.439 M
b) 1.00×10^{-7} M
c) 0.723 M
d) 2.81×10^{-13} M

Answer: a Page: 632

41. Consider the titration of 25.0 mL of 0.723 M $HClO_4$ with 0.273 M KOH. Calculate the H_3O^+ concentration after addition of 66.2 mL of KOH.
a) 0.439 M
b) 1.00×10^{-7} M
c) 0.723 M
d) 2.81×10^{-13} M

Answer: b Page: 632

42. Consider the titration of 25.0 mL of 0.723 M $HClO_4$ with 0.273 M KOH. Calculate the H_3O^+ concentration after addition of 80.0 mL of KOH.
a) 0.439 M
b) 1.00×10^{-7} M
c) 0.723 M
d) 2.79×10^{-13} M

Answer: d Page: 632

43. Consider the titration of 50.0 mL of 0.217 M HN_3 ($K_a = 2.6 \times 10^{-5}$) with 0.183 M NaOH. Calculate the pH of the solution before any NaOH is added.
a) 2.62
b) 8.79
c) 12.21
d) 4.59
e) 7.00

Answer: a Page: 632

44. Consider the titration of 50.0 mL of 0.217 M HN_3 (K_a = 2.6 x 10^{-5}) with 0.183 M NaOH. Calculate the pH of the solution after addition of 29.7 mL of NaOH solution.
a) 2.61
b) 8.79
c) 12.21
d) 4.59
e) 7.00

Answer: d Page: 632

45. Consider the titration of 50.0 mL of 0.217 M HN_3 (K_a = 2.6 x 10^{-5}) with 0.183 M NaOH. Calculate the pH of the solution after addition of 70.0 mL of NaOH solution.
a) 2.61
b) 8.79
c) 12.21
d) 4.59
e) 7.00

Answer: c Page: 632

46. Consider the titration of 50.0 mL of 0.217 M HN_3 (K_a = 2.6 x 10^{-5}) with 0.183 M NaOH. Calculate the pH of the solution after addition of 59.3 mL of NaOH solution.
a) 2.61
b) 8.75
c) 12.21
d) 4.59
e) 7.00

Answer: b Page: 632

47. An initial pH of 1.00, an equivalence point at pH 7.0, and a relatively long, nearly vertical middle section correspond to a titration curve for
a) strong acid titrated by strong base
b) strong base titrated by strong acid
c) weak acid titrated by strong base
d) weak base titrated by strong acid
e) weak base titrated by weak acid

Answer: a Page: 632

48. An initial pH of 4.00, an equivalence point at pH 9.35, and a moderately short, nearly vertical middle section correspond to a titration curve for
a) strong acid titrated by strong base
b) strong base titrated by strong acid
c) weak acid titrated by strong base
d) weak base titrated by strong acid
e) weak base titrated by weak acid

Answer: c Page: 632

49. An initial pH of 13.00, an equivalence point at pH 7.0, and a relatively long, nearly vertical middle section correspond to a titration curve for
    a) strong acid titrated by strong base
    b) strong base titrated by strong acid
    c) weak acid titrated by strong acid
    d) weak base titrated by strong acid
    e) weak base titrated by weak acid

    Answer: b Page: 632

50. Determine the pH of a solution prepared by mixing 45 mL of 0.183 M KOH with 65 mL of 0.145 M HCl.
    a) 1.31
    b) 2.92
    c) 0.74
    d) 1.97

    Answer: d Page: 632

51. Determine the pH of a solution prepared by mixing 50 mL of 0.125 M KOH with 50 mL of 0.125 M HCl.
    a) 6.3
    b) 7.0
    c) 8.1
    d) 5.8

    Answer: b Page: 632

52. What is the molarity of an HOAc solution if 25.5 mL of this solution required 37.5 mL of 0.175 M NaOH to reach the equivalence point?
    a) 0.119
    b) 1.83×10^{-4}
    c) 0.257
    d) 0.365

    Answer: c Page: 632

53. Estimate the pH at the equivalence point of an HOAc solution if 25.5 mL of this solution required 37.5 mL of 0.175 M NaOH to reach the equivalence point.
    a) 4
    b) 7
    c) 9
    d) 12

    Answer: c Page: 632

54. In a titration experiment it was found that 15.38 mL of 0.139 M NaOH was required to neutralize a 25.00 mL sample of HCl. What was the molarity of the HCl sample?
a) 11.7 M
b) 0.00214 M
c) 0.0855 M
d) 0.267 M

Answer: c Page: 632

55. In a titration experiment it was found that a 50.00 mL sample of H_2SO_4 was neutralized by 62.50 mL of 0.375 M NaOH. What was the molarity of the H_2SO_4 sample?
a) 0.234 M
b) 0.469 M
c) 0.150 M
d) 0.300 M

Answer: a Page: 632

56. Consider the diagram of a potentiometric titration curve shown below.

What type of substance was originally in the flask?
a) a strong acid
b) a weak acid
c) a strong base
d) a weak base

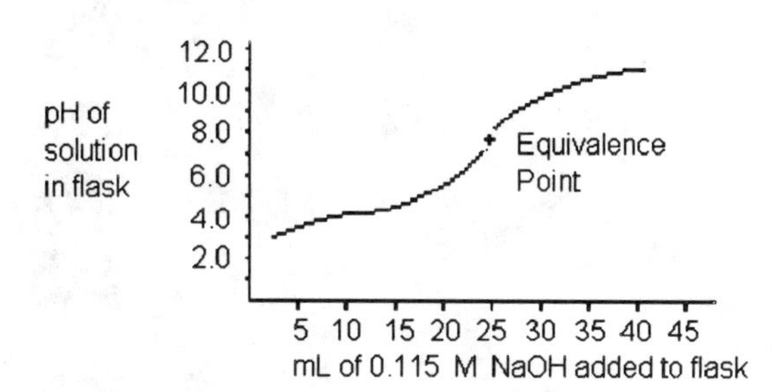

Answer: b Page: 632

57. Consider the diagram of a potentiometric titration curve shown below.

Assume that the flask originally contained 50.00 mL of the solution to be titrated. What was the concentration (in mol/L) of that solution?
a) 0.230
b) 4.35
c) 17.4
d) 0.0575

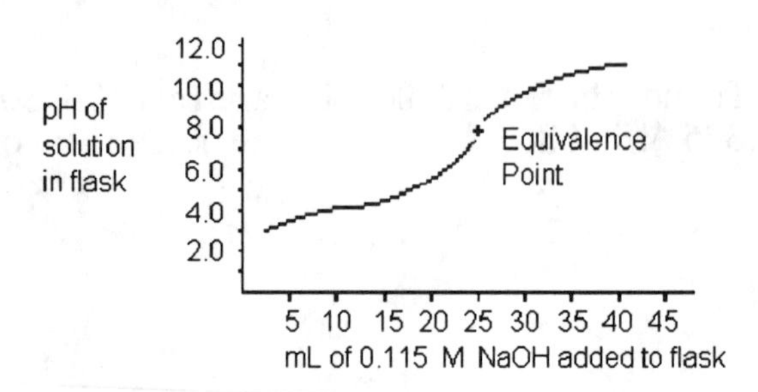

Answer: d Page: 632

58. Consider the diagram of a potentiometric titration curve shown below.

Which one of the following indicators would be the best one to use for this titration?

Indicator	pK_a
methyl red	5.3
bromthymol blue	6.8
thymol blue	8.8
phenolpthalein	9.1

a) methyl red
b) bromthymol blue
c) thymol blue
d) phenopthalein

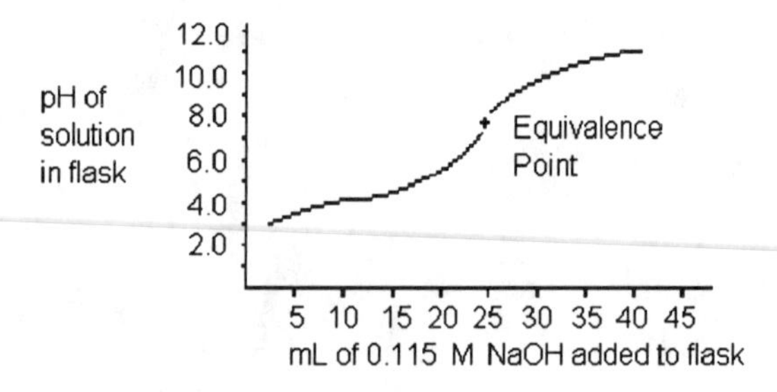

Answer: c Page: 632

59. Consider the diagram of a potentiometic titration curve shown below.

What type of substance was originally in the flask?
a) a strong acid
b) a weak acid
c) a strong base
d) a weak base

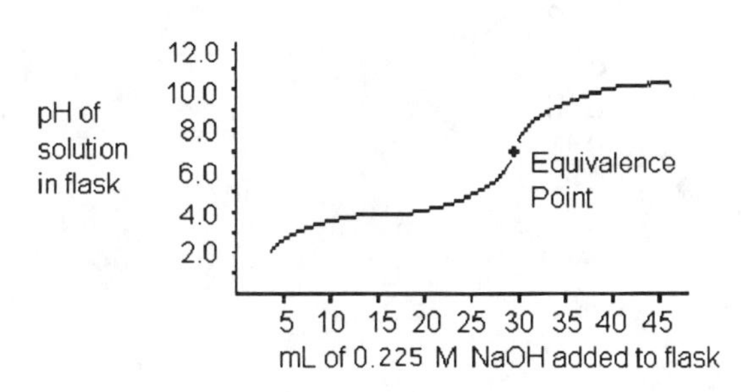

Answer: a Page: 632

60. Consider the diagram of a potentiometic titration curve shown below.

Assume that the flask originally contained 25.00 mL of the solution to be titrated. What was the concentration (in mol/L) of that solution?
a) 3.3
b) 0.22
c) 0.19
d) 0.27

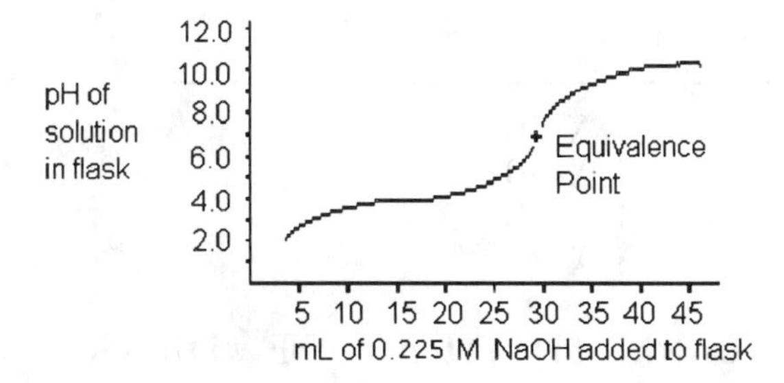

Answer: d Page: 632

61. Consider the diagram of a potentiometric titration curve shown below.

Which one of the following indicators would be the best one to use for this titration?

Indicator	pK_a
methyl red	5.3
bromthymol blue	6.8
thymol blue	8.8
phenolpthalein	9.1

a) methyl red
b) bromthymol blue
c) thymol blue
d) phenolpthalein

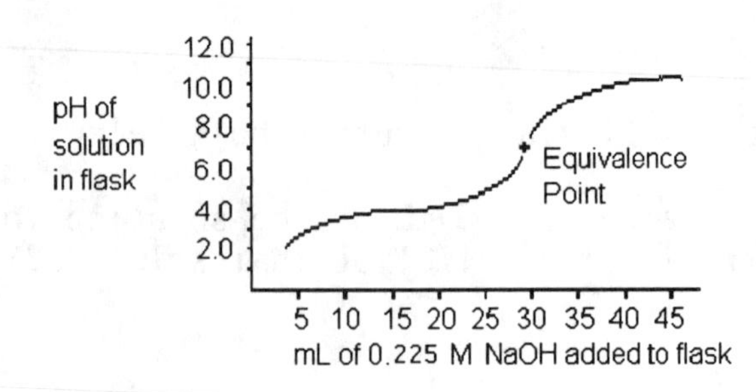

Answer: b Page: 632

62.

Indicator	K_a
methyl orange	$1 X 10^{-4}$
m-cresol purple	$1 X 10^{-8}$
indigo carmine	$1 X 10^{-12}$
bromthymol blue	$1 X 10^{-7}$

Which would be the best indicator for the titration of HF with NaOH?
a) methyl orange
b) m-cresol purple
c) indigo carmine
d) bromthymol blue

Answer: b Page: 632

63.

Indicator	K_a
methyl orange	$1 X 10^{-4}$
m-cresol purple	$1 X 10^{-8}$
indigo carmine	$1 X 10^{-12}$
bromthymol blue	$1 X 10^{-7}$

The indicator indigo carmine can be considered to be a weak acid with the general formula HIn. Determine the ratio $[In^-]/[HIn]$ for indigo carmine in a solution with a pH of 10.0.
a) 10
b) 100
c) 0.01
d) $1 X 10^{-10}$

Answer: c Page: 632

64. Consider an experiment where 35.0 mL of 0.175 HOAc is titrated with 0.25 M NaOH. What is the pH at the equivalence point of this titration? The K_a for HOAc is $1.8 X 10^{-5}$.
a) 5.12
b) 2.87
c) 11.13
d) 8.88

Answer: d Page: 632

65. If each of the following salts has a K_{sp} value of 1.00 x 10-9, which is the most soluble in pure water?
a) XY
b) XY_2
c) X_3Y
d) X_2Y_3
e) X_3Y_4

Answer: d Page: 641

66. If each of the following salts has a K_{sp} value of $1.00 x 10^{-9}$, which is the least soluble in pure water?
a) XY
b) XY_2
c) X_3Y
d) X_2Y_3
e) XY_4

Answer: a Page: 641

67. The solubility of which one of the following will not be affected by the pH of the solution?
a) Na_3PO_4
b) NaF
c) KNO_3
d) $AlCl_3$
e) MnS

Answer: c Page: 641

ESSAY

68. Write the expression relating solubility to K_{sp} for silver sulfide.

Answer:

$S = \sqrt[3]{K_{sp}/4}$

Page: 641

MULTIPLE CHOICE

69. Calculate the concentration of iodide ions in a saturated solution of lead iodide ($K_{sp} = 1.39 \times 10^{-8}$).
a) 4.21×10^{-4} M
b) 3.03×10^{-3} M
c) 1.51×10^{-3} M
d) 3.48×10^{-9} M

Answer: b Page: 641

70. Calculate the molar solubility of silver carbonate ($K_{sp} = 6.15 \times 10^{-12}$).
a) 1.15×10^{-4} M
b) 2.48×10^{-6} M
c) 6.20×10^{-7} M
d) 1.24×10^{-6} M

Answer: a Page: 641

71. Calculate the molar concentration of bromide ions in a saturated solution of mercury(II) bromide, $K_{sp} = 8.0 \times 10^{-20}$.
a) 1.4×10^{-10} M
b) 2.0×10^{-20} M
c) 5.4×10^{-7} M
d) 2.7×10^{-7} M

Answer: c Page: 641

72. If each of the salts below has solubility of 0.0020 mol/L, which has the largest value of K_{sp}?
a) CX_2
b) MY
c) A_2Z
d) B_2Z_3
e) N_3Y_2

Answer: b Page: 641

73. The solubility of ZX_3 (as $Z^{3+} + 3X^-$) in water at 298 K is 4.0×10^{-4} M. K_{sp} for ZX_3 is
a) 2.6×10^{-14}
b) 6.9×10^{-13}
c) 9.5×10^{-16}
d) 0.062
e) 1.6×10^{-7}

Answer: b Page: 641

74. Consider the following table of K_{sp} values.

Compound	K_{sp}
CdS	8.0×10^{-27}
CuS	6.3×10^{-36}
PbS	8.0×10^{-28}
$MnCO_3$	1.8×10^{-11}

Which one of the compounds shown in the table is the least soluble?
a) CdS
b) CuS
c) PbS
d) $MnCO_3$

Answer: b Page: 641

75. What is the molar solubility of PbS?
a) 4.0×10^{-28}
b) 2.8×10^{-14}
c) 6.4×10^{-55}
d) 8.0×10^{-19}

Answer: b Page: 641

76. What is the maximum concentration of Cd^{2+} that can exist in a solution in which the S^{2-} concentration is 2.5×10^{-6}?
a) 3.2×10^{-21}
b) 8.9×10^{-14}
c) 2.0×10^{-32}
d) 2.2×10^{-19}

Answer: a Page: 641

77. The solubility of $PbCl_2$ is 1.6×10^{-2} mol/L. What is the K_{sp} of $PbCl_2$?
    a) 5.0×10^{-4}
    b) 4.1×10^{-6}
    c) 3.1×10^{-7}
    d) 1.6×10^{-5}

    Answer: d Page: 641

78. The K_{sp} for Ag_2S is 1.0×10^{-51}. What is the molar solubility of sp Ag_2 S?
    a) 1.0×10^{-17}
    b) 7.9×10^{-18}
    c) 6.3×10^{-18}
    d) 8.3×10^{-53}

    Answer: c Page: 641

79. The solubility of $Mn(OH)_2$ is 2.2×10^{-5} mol/L. What is the K_{sp} of $Mn(OH)_2$?
    a) 1.1×10^{-14}
    b) 4.3×10^{-14}
    c) 2.1×10^{-14}
    d) 4.8×10^{-10}

    Answer: b Page: 641

80. The solubility of $Mg(OH)_2$ is 1.4×10^{-4} mol/L. Determine the K_{sp} for $Mg(OH)_2$.
    a) 2.7×10^{-12}
    b) 1.1×10^{-1}
    c) 2.0×10^{-8}
    d) 3.9×10^{-8}

    Answer: b Page: 641

81. What is the maximum concentration of chloride ions that can be in a solution containing 0.100 M Pb^{2+} without precipitating any lead ions? The K_{sp} for lead chloride is 1.0×10^{-4}.
    a) 0.058 M
    b) 0.029 M
    c) 0.0.0010 M
    d) 0.032 M

    Answer: d Page: 641

ESSAY

82. What is the value that the K_{sp} for the salt X_2Y must have in order for a saturated solution of X_2Y to contain 0.847 M X^+ and 0.464 M Y^{2-}?

Answer:
That would be the value that would make this solution just saturated with X_2Y. It would be

$K_{sp} = [X^+]^2[Y] = (0.847)^2(0.464) = 0.333$
Page: 641

MULTIPLE CHOICE

83. Calculate the solubility of aluminum hydroxide, $K_{sp} = 1.9 \times 10^{-33}$, in 0.0182 M KOH solution.
a) 3.2×10^{-28} M
b) 2.9×10^{-9} M
c) 1.2×10^{-11} M
d) 3.1×10^{-12} M

Answer: a Page: 644

84. $[Pb^{2+}]$ as x M can be calculated by which equation for excess solid PbI_2 placed into 1.5 M HI?
a) $K_{sp} = 4x^3$
b) $K_{sp} = (x)(x + 1.5)$
c) $K_{sp} = (x)(2x + 1)^2$
d) $K_{sp} = (2x)(x - 1.5)^2$
e) $K_{sp} = (2x)(x - 1.5)^3$

Answer: c Page: 644

85. Calculate the concentration (in mol/L) of Ag^+ in a saturated solution of Ag_2CO_3 when the concentration of CO_3^{2-} ion is 0.025 M. The K_{sp} of Ag_2CO_3 is 8.1×10^{-12}.
a) 1.8×10^{-5}
b) 1.4×10^{-6}
c) 2.8×10^{-6}
d) 3.2×10^{-10}

Answer: a Page: 644

86. What is the solubility (in moles/L) of $PbCl_2$ in a 0.15 M solution of HCl? (K_{sp} $PbCl_2$ = 1.6×10^{-5})
a) 2.0×10^{-3}
b) 1.1×10^{-4}
c) 1.8×10^{-4}
d) 7.1×10^{-4}

Answer: d Page: 644

87. The K_{sp} for $Zn(OH)_2$ is 5.0×10^{-17}. Determine the solubility of $Zn(OH)_2$ in a buffer solution with a pH of 11.50.
a) 5.0×10^{6}
b) 1.2×10^{-12}
c) 1.6×10^{-14}
d) 5.0×10^{-12}

Answer: d Page: 644

88. In which type of solution will silver oxalate be the most soluble?
a) acidic
b) neutral
c) basic

Answer: a Page: 644

89. In which one of the following solutions is cadmium chloride the most soluble?
a) 0.181 M HCl
b) 0.0176 M NH_3
c) 0.744 M $LiNO_3$
d) pure water

Answer: b Page: 664

90. Which one of the following is amphoteric?
a) $Al(OH)_3$
b) $Ca(OH)_2$
c) $Fe(OH)_2$
d) $Fe(OH)_3$

Answer: a Page: 644

91. For which salt should the aqueous solubility be most sensitive to pH?
a) $Ca(NO_3)_2$
b) CaF_2
c) $CaCl_2$
d) $CaBr_2$
e) CaI_2

Answer: b Page: 644

92. In which aqueous system is PbI_2 least soluble?
a) H_2O
b) 0.5 M HI
c) 0.2 M HI
d) 1.0 M_3HNO
e) 0.8 M KI

Answer: e Page: 644

93. The equation that can be used to solve for x = $[Ni^{2+}]$ in a solution nominally 0.20 M $Ni(NO_3)_2$ and 1.00 M ethylenediamine (en), where $Ni(en)_3{}^{2}$ forms with $K_f = 2.0 \times 10^{18}$, is
a) $K_f = (0.20 - x)(x)/(1.0 + x)^3$
b) $K_f = (0.20 - x)/(x)(0.40 + 3x)^3$
c) $K_f = (0.40 - 3x)^3/(x)(1.0 + 3x)$
d) $K_f = (1.20 + x)/(x)(0.40 - 3x)^3$
e) $K_f = (x)^2/(0.20 - 3x)$

Answer: b Page: 644

94. $AgCl(s) + 2NH_3(aq) \rightarrow Ag(NH_3)_2{}^+(aq) + Cl^-(aq)$. Given that $K_c = K_{sp}K_f$ (where K_{sp} is for AgCl and K_f is for $Ag(NH_3)_2{}^+$), the molar solubility (z) of AgCl in 2.0 M NH_3 can be calculated according to which of the following equations?
a) $K_{sp}K_f = z/(2.0 - z)^2$
b) $K_{sp}K_f = z^2/(2.0 - z)$
c) $K_{sp}K_f = z^2/(2.0 - 2z)^2$
d) $K_{sp}K_f = z/(2.0 + 2z)^2$
e) $K_{sp}K_f = (2.0 + 2z)^2/z$

Answer: c Page: 644

95. Which below best describe(s) behavior of an amphoteric hydroxide in water?
a) with conc. aq. NaOH, its suspension dissolves
b) with conc. aq. HCl, its suspension dissolves
c) with conc. aq. NaOH, its clear solution forms a precipitate
d) with conc. aq. HCl, its clear solution forms a precipitate
e) with <u>both</u> conc. aq. NAOH <u>and</u> conc. aq. HCl, its suspension dissolves

Answer: e Page: 644

96. Which one of the following substances, when added to a saturated solution of $Pb(OH)_2$, will <u>decrease</u> the solubility of $Pb(OH)_2$ in the solution?
a) $NaNO_3$
b) H_2O_2
c) HNO_3
d) $Pb(NO_3)_2$

Answer: d Page: 644

97. Which one of the following compounds will <u>increase</u> in solubility if the pH of a saturated solution of the compound is lowered?
 a) $AgCl$
 b) AgI
 c) $PbCl_2$
 d) $Pb(OAc)_2$

 Answer: d Page: 644

98. Which one of the following substances, when added to a saturated solution of $CaCO_3$, will <u>decrease</u> the solubility of $CaCO_3$ in the solution?
 a) $NaCl$
 b) HCl
 c) $CaCl_2$
 d) HNO_3

 Answer: c Page: 644

ESSAY

99. Give the name and formula of the compound that is the main component of tooth enamel.

 Answer: hydroxyapatite, $Ca_5(PO_4)_3OH$ Page: 648

MULTIPLE CHOICE

100. Why does fluoride treatment render teeth more resistant to decay?
 a) fluoride kills the bacteria in the mouth that make the acids that decay teeth
 b) fluoride stimulates production of tooth enamel to replace that lost to decay
 c) fluoride reduces saliva production, keeping teeth drier and thus reducing decay
 d) fluoride converts hydroxyapatite to fluoroapatite that is less reactive with acids
 e) fluoride dissolves plaque, reducing its decaying contact with teeth

 Answer: d Page: 648

101. What is the typical concentration of fluoride in fluoridated water?
 a) 0.100 *M*
 b) 1 ppm
 c) 0.100 ppm
 d) 5 ppb
 e) 5%

 Answer: b Page: 648

102. A solution contains 0.837 M Li^+ and 7.32 x 10^{-2} M $CO^{2-}{}_3$. What type of solution is this with respect to lithium carbonate,
K_{sp} = 1.7 x 10^{-3}?
a) saturated
b) not saturated
c) supersaturated

Answer: c Page: 651

103. The K_{sp} of silver bromide is 4.1 x 10^{-13}. Will a precipitate form if 25.0 mL of 0.0345 M silver nitrate solution is mixed with 25.0 mL of 3.63 x 10^{-4} M sodium bromide solution?
a) yes
b) no

Answer: a Page: 651

104. Consider a solution containing 0.181 M lead ions and 0.174 M mercury(II) ions. The K_{sp} for lead sulfide is 3.4 x 10^{-28} and that for mercury(II) sulfide is 4.0 x 10^{-53}. Calculate the maximum concentration of sulfide ions that can be in solution without precipitating any lead ions.
a) 9.4 x 10^{-28} M
b) 1.9 x 10^{-27} M
c) 1.5 x 10^{-26} M
d) 3.0 x 10^{-25} M

Answer: b Page: 651

105. Consider a solution containing 0.181 M lead ions and 0.174 M mercury(II) ions. The K_{sp} for lead sulfide is 3.4 x 10^{-28} and that for mercury(II) sulfide is 4.0 x 10^{-53}. Calculate the concentration of sulfide ions required to reduce the concentration of mecury(II) ions to 1.0 x 10^{-6} M.
a) 4.0 x 10^{-47} M
b) 3.4 x 10^{-22} M
c) 1.2 x 10^{-25} M
d) 5.6 x 10^{-13} M

Answer: a Page: 651

106. Consider a solution containing 0.181 M lead ions and 0.365 M iron(II) ions. The K_{sp} for lead sulfide is 3.4 x 10^{-28} and that for iron(II) sulfide is 3.7 x 10^{-19}. Calculate the $[H_3O^+]$ required to reduce the concentration of lead ions to 1.0 x 10^{-6} M using H_2S.
a) 4.3 x 10^{-5} M
b) 7.7 x 10^{-9} M
c) 2.1 M
d) 9.2 x 10^{-6} M

Answer: c Page: 651

107. If 0.1 M aqueous solutions of the following pairs of substances are mixed together, which pair could result in the formation of a precipitate?
a) Na_2S, $FeCl_3$
b) NaOH, KNO_3
c) KCl, $Al(NO_3)_3$
d) $Ni(NO_3)_2$, $Mg(NO_3)_2$

Answer: a Page: 651

108. If treatment of a solution, known to contain at least one type of cation, with dilute HCl did not result in the formation of a precipitate, which ion below might the solution contain?
a) Ag
b) Hg_2^{2+}
c) Cd
d) Pb

Answer: c Page: 654

109. The ions Cu^{2+}, Cd^{2+}, Pb^{2+}, Ni^{2+}, Zn^{2+}, and Co^{2+} all form insoluble sulfides; yet sulfide formation can be used to separate the first three from the last three. The technique used entails
a) bubbling H_2S into a moderately strongly acidic solution
b) bubbling H_2S into a slightly basic solution
c) adding $(NH_4)_2S$ followed by $(NH_4)_2HPO_4$
d) adding conc. NaOH followed by $(NH_4)_2S$
e) adding conc. NH_3 followed by $(NH_4)_2S$

Answer: a Page: 654

110. Of AgCl, $PbCl_2$, and Hg_2Cl_2, only _______ dissolve(s) in 6 M NH_3.
a) AgCl
b) $PbCl_2$
c) Hg_2Cl_2
d) AgCl and $PbCl_2$
e) $PbCl_2$ and Hg_2Cl_2

Answer: a Page: 654

Chapter 18: Chemistry of the Environment

MULTIPLE CHOICE

1. The liquid portion of the Earth is called the
   a) stratosphere
   b) lithosphere
   c) atmosphere
   d) hydrosphere
   e) mesposphere

   Answer: d Page: 663

2. Below the tropopause, temperature _____ with increasing altitude. Above the tropopause, temperature _____ with increasing altitude.
   a) increases, increases
   b) decreases, decreases
   c) increases, decreases
   d) decreases, increases
   e) decreases, remains constant

   Answer: d Page: 663

3. The layer of the atmosphere that contains our weather is called the
   a) mesosphere
   b) heterosphere
   c) stratosphere
   d) thermosphere
   e) troposphere

   Answer: e Page: 663

4. What percentage of the atmosphere's mass is contained in the troposphere?
   a) 75%
   b) 99.9%
   c) 45%
   d) 58%
   e) 25%

   Answer: a Page: 663

5. Which noble gas is present in highest concentration in dry air at sea level?
   a) Ne
   b) He
   c) Xe
   d) Kr
   e) Ar

   Answer: e Page: 663

6. Dry air near sea level contains hydrogen at a mole fraction of 5×10^{-7}. Calculate the concentration of hydrogen in dry, sea level air in the units of ppm.
   a) 5 ppm
   b) 0.5 ppm
   c) 500 ppm
   d) 50 ppm

   Answer: b Page: 663

7. Which of the following truly describes the atmosphere?
   a) Temperature increases in a regular way with increasing altitude.
   b) Pressure increases in a regular way with increasing altitude.
   c) Concentrations of all major air pollutants increase in a regular way with increasing altitude.
   d) Temperature decreases in a regular way with increasing altitude.
   e) Pressure decreases in a regular way with increasing altitude.

   Answer: e Page: 663

8. The region between the troposphere and stratosphere is known as the
   a) mesosphere
   b) tropopause
   c) thermosphere
   d) stratopause

   Answer: b Page: 663

9. The region of the atmosphere closest to the surface of the earth is called the
   a) mesosphere
   b) stratosphere
   c) thermosphere
   d) troposphere

   Answer: d Page: 663

10.

Components of Air	Mole Fraction
Nitrogen	0.781
Oxygen	0.209
Argon	0.010

What is the partial pressure or oxygen (in mmHg) in the atmosphere when the atmospheric pressure is 760 mmHg?
a) 159
b) 430
c) 601
d) 720

Answer: a Page: 663

11. Which one of the following substances has the highest ionization energy?
    a) O_2
    b) O
    c) N_2
    d) NO

    Answer: c Page: 666

12. The energy of a photon is ___ related to its wavelength and ___ related to its frequency.
    a) inversely, inversely
    b) directly, directly
    c) inversely, directly
    d) directly, inversely
    e) not, directly
    f) not, not

    Answer: c Page: 666

13. Why does the upper atmosphere contain only very little dissociated nitrogen?
    a) most of the nitrogen is in the troposphere and not in the upper atmosphere
    b) the dissociated nitrogen very rapidly diffuses out of the atmosphere and into space
    c) nitrogen atoms are extremely reactive and so react with other substances immediately upon their formation
    d) the bond energy of nitrogen is very high and it does not absorb radiation very efficiently

    Answer: d Page: 666

14. Of the following substances, which one requires the shortest wavelength for photoionization?
    a) O
    b) O_2
    c) NO
    d) N_2

    Answer: d Page: 666

15. Photoionization processes (e.g., $N_2 + h\upsilon \rightarrow N_2^+ + e^-$) remove UV of <150 nm. Which photoreaction is the principal absorber of UV in the 150-200 nm range in the upper atmosphere?
    a) $N_2 + h\upsilon \rightarrow 2N$
    b) $O_2 + h\upsilon \rightarrow 2O$
    c) $O_3 + h\upsilon \rightarrow O_2 + O$
    d) $N_2 + O_2 + h\upsilon \rightarrow 2NO$
    e) $NO + O_2 + h\upsilon \rightarrow NO_3$

    Answer: b Page: 666

16. The amount of atomic O relative to O_2
    a) is highest in the troposphere
    b) is highest in the stratosphere
    c) increases with altitude in the thermosphere
    d) decreases with altitude in the thermosphere
    e) is essentially independent of altitude in the thermosphere

    Answer: c Page: 666

17. The C-Cl bond dissociation energy in CF_3Cl is 339 kJ/mol. What is the maximum wavelength of photons that can rupture this bond? ($h = 6.63 \times 10^{-34}$ J•s, $c = 3.00 \times 10^{8}$ m/s)
    a) 275 nm
    b) 45.0 nm
    c) 742 nm
    d) 353 nm

    Answer: c Page: 666

18. The C-F bond dissociation energy in CF_3Cl is 482 kJ/mol. What is the maximum wavelength of photons that can rupture this bond? ($h = 6.63 \times 10^{-34}$ J•s, $c = 3.00 \times 10^{8}$ m/s)
    a) 413 nm
    b) 249 nm
    c) 182 nm
    d) 654 nm

    Answer: b Page: 666

ESSAY

19. In the equation below, what is the meaning of the asterisk?

    $$O + O_2 \rightarrow O_3^*$$

    Answer: The asterisk indicates that the ozone formed contains excess energy

    Page: 668

MULTIPLE CHOICE

20. In the equation below, what is M most likely to be?

    $$O + O_2 + M \rightarrow O_3 + M^*$$

    a) Cl_2
    b) N_2
    c) Ne
    d) CO_2
    e) H_2O

    Answer: b Page: 668

21. Why does ozone not form in high concentrations in the atmosphere above 50 km?
    a) insufficient oxygen is available
    b) insufficient molecules exist for removal of excess energy from ozone upon its formation
    c) light of the required wavelength is not available at those altitudes
    d) atomic oxygen concentration is too low at high altitudes

    Answer: b Page: 668

22. Why are chlorofluorocarbons so damaging to the ozone layer when they are such stable molecules?
    a) they contain a double bond that ozone readily attacks, resulting in the destruction of the ozone
    b) they are very light molecules that rapidly diffuse into the upper atmosphere and block the radiation that causes formation of ozone
    c) they are greenhouse gases that raise the temperature above the dissociation temperature of ozone
    d) the radiation in the stratosphere dissociates them producing chlorine atoms that catalytically destroy ozone

    Answer: d Page: 668

23. Cl atoms formed via photolysis in the stratosphere of C-Cl bonds of chlorofluorocarbons are particularly effective in destroying ozone at these altitudes because
    a) Cl atoms absorb UV, which generate O atoms to react with O_2 to produce ozone
    b) Cl atoms catalytically convert O_3 to O_2
    c) Cl atoms stoichiometrically convert O_3 to O_2
    d) Cl atoms react with H atoms, which catalyze conversion of O_2 to O_3
    e) Cl atoms react with N atoms, which catalyze conversion of O_2 to O_3

    Answer: b Page: 668

24. Select the substance that is thought to be partially responsible for depleting the concentration of ozone in the stratosphere.
    a) $CFCl_3$
    b) CO_2
    c) O_2
    d) N_2

    Answer: a Page: 668

ESSAY

25. Polar stratospheric clouds aid in the destruction of stratospheric ozone in two ways. What are these ways?

    Answer:
    they remove NO_2, thus stopping removal of ClO and they catalyze the recombination of HCl and $ClONO_2$ to form Cl_2

    Page: 671

MULTIPLE CHOICE

26. How is the substance Cl_2O_2 damaging to ozone in the stratosphere?
    a) it reacts rapidly with ozone at very low temperatures
    b) even at very low temperatures, it dissociates to form a large number of oxygen atoms
    c) it photodissociates to produce Cl
    d) it forms a solid that has a surface that will adsorb a large number of ozone molecules and thus precipitate them out of the stratosphere
    e) when it decomposes, it emits radiation of the exact wavelength to photodissociate ozone molecules

    Answer: c Page: 671

ESSAY

27. Why is ozone depletion in the Arctic generally much less severe than that in the Antarctic?

    Answer:
    the Arctic generally does not get cold enough for polar stratospheric clouds to form

    Page: 671

MULTIPLE CHOICE

28. Which one of the following is a source of carbon dioxide in the troposphere?
    a) natural gas seepage
    b) electrical discharges
    c) fossil-fuel combustion
    d) volcanic gases
    e) forest fires

    Answer: c Page: 672

29. What is the typical pH of natural, unpolluted rainwater?
    a) 7
    b) 6
    c) 9
    d) 12
    e) 5

    Answer: e Page: 672

30. Natural, unpolluted rainwater is typically acidic. What is the source of this natural acidity?
    a) CO_2
    b) SO_2
    c) NO_2
    d) HCl
    e) chlorofluorocarbons

    Answer: a Page: 672

31. What compound in limestone and marble is attacked by acid rain?
    a) hydroxyapatite
    b) calcium carbonate
    c) gypsum
    d) graphite
    e) potassium hydroxide

    Answer: b Page: 672

32. The major source of sulfur dioxide in the atmosphere is
    a) volcanic activity
    b) forest fires
    c) roasting of ores
    d) burning of coal

    Answer: d Page: 672

33. Which one of the following does not result in the formation of acid rain?
    a) carbon dioxide
    b) nitrogen dioxide
    c) sulfur dioxide
    d) nitrogen monoxide
    e) methane

    Answer: e Page: 672

34. How can lime be used to reduce sulfur dioxide emissions from the burning of coal?
    a) it reacts with the sulfur dioxide to form calcium sulfite solid that can be precipitated
    b) it reduces the sulfur dioxide to elemental sulfur that is harmless to the environment
    c) it oxidizes the sulfur dioxide to tetrathionate that is highly water soluble so it can be scrubbed from the emission gases
    d) it catalyzes the conversion of sulfur dioxide to sulfur trioxide which is much less volatile and can be removed by condensation

    Answer: a Page: 672

35. Why is carbon monoxide toxic?
    a) it causes renal failure
    b) it binds to hemoglobin, thus blocking the transport of oxygen
    c) it blocks acetylcholine receptor sites causing paralysis and rapid death
    d) it induces leukemia

    Answer: b Page: 672

ESSAY

36. What is a key component of photochemical smog and what is its source?

    Answer:
    ozone - it is formed by reaction of oxygen atoms, produced by photochemical decomposition of nitrogen dioxide, with oxygen molecules

    Page: 672

MULTIPLE CHOICE

37. How does carbon dioxide cause atmospheric warming?
    a) by absorbing incoming radiation from the sun and converting it to heat
    b) by absorbing radiation emitted from the surface of the earth preventing its loss to space
    c) by undergoing exothermic reactions extensively in the atmosphere
    d) by increasing the index of refraction of the atmosphere so that infrared radiation from the sun is refracted to the surface of the earth where it is converted to heat

    Answer: b Page: 672

38. CO_2 from hydrocarbon combustion creates a major environmental problem described as
    a) the greenhouse effect
    b) photochemical smog
    c) acid rain
    d) stratospheric ozone depletion
    e) all of the above

    Answer: a Page: 672

39. Which one of the following substances found in the atmosphere will absorb radiation in the infrared portion of the spectrum?
    a) N_2
    b) O_2
    c) CO_2
    d) Ar

    Answer: c Page: 672

40. Which one of the following substances found in the atmosphere will absorb radiation in the infrared portion of the spectrum?
    a) N_2
    b) O_2
    c) Kr
    d) H_2O

    Answer: d Page: 672

41. Which element found in fossil fuels is primarily responsible for acid rain?
    a) sulfur
    b) carbon
    c) hydrogen
    d) phosphorus

    Answer: a Page: 672

42. What is meant by the salinity of seawater?
    a) percent by mass of salt in seawater
    b) ppm salt in seawater
    c) g dry salt per kg seawater
    d) osmotic pressure of seawater
    e) molarity of NaCl in seawater

    Answer: c Page: 679

43. The ion that exists in typical seawater at the highest concentration is
    a) chloride
    b) sodium
    c) magnesium
    d) calcium
    e) sulfate

    Answer: a Page: 679

ESSAY

44. The three most concentrated ions in seawater are

    Answer: chloride, sodium ions, and sulfate ions Page: 679

45. Describe the process of reverse osmosis.

    Answer:
    Water is fed, at high pressure, through tubes of semipermeable material. The water passes through the tubing material and the ions do not.
    Page: 679

MULTIPLE CHOICE

46. Sea water contains about ____ dissolved salts by mass.
   a) 0.03%
   b) 0.1%
   c) 3.5%
   d) 17%
   e) 39%

   Answer: c Page: 679

47. The concentration of Br^- is sea water in 8.3×10^{-4} M. Assuming that a liter of seawater has a mass of 1.0 kg, what is the concentration of Br^- in ppm?
   a) 0.066
   b) 66
   c) 0.83
   d) 8.3

   Answer: b Page: 679

48. A single individual typically uses the greatest quantity of water for
   a) flushing toilets
   b) cooking
   c) cleaning
   d) watering lawns

   Answer: c Page: 681

49. What effect can the presence of large amount of biodegradable organic materials in water have?
   a) it causes death of bottom dwelling organisms because it agglutinates and settles to the bottom, poisoning bottom dwelling organisms
   b) it causes oxygen depletion in the water
   c) it rises to the surface and absorbs wavelengths needed by aquatic plants
   d) it decomposes endothermically causing the temperature of the water to decrease below the limits within which most aquatic organisms can live

   Answer: b Page: 681

ESSAY

50. What is the purpose of adding aluminum sulfate and lime to water in municipal water treatment?

   Answer:
   it forms a gelatinous precipitate that traps suspended solids, including most bacteria, so that they are removed by subsequent filtration
   Page: 681

MULTIPLE CHOICE

51. What is the final stage in municipal water treatment?
    a) filtration through sand and gravel
    b) aeration
    c) settling
    d) treatment with ozone or chlorine

    Answer: d Page: 681

52. In the presence of oxygen, the nitrogen present in biodegradable material ends up mainly as
    a) NH_3
    b) NH_4^+
    c) NO
    d) NO_2
    e) NO_3^-

    Answer: e Page: 681

53. Chemical treatment of municipal water supplies commonly entails use of CaO, $Al_2(SO_4)_3$, and Cl_2. The purpose of adding CaO is to
    a) remove all HCO_3^- as solid $CaCO_3$
    b) remove all SO_4^{2-} as solid $CaSO_4$
    c) remove all Cl^- as solid $CaCl_2$
    d) selectively kill anaerobic (but not aerobic) bacteria
    e) make the water slightly basic so that addition of $Al_2(SO_4)_3$ will afford a gelatinous precipitate of $AL(OH)_3$

    Answer: e Page: 681

54. Chemical treatment of municipal water supplies commonly entails use of CaO, $Al_2(SO_4)_3$, and Cl_2. The purpose of adding Cl_2 is to

    a) remove most Mg^{2+} as solid $MgCl_2$
    b) remove most Al^{3+} as solid $AlCl_2$
    c) oxidize Fe^{2+} to insoluble Fe_2O_3
    d) kill bacteria

    e) both remove most Mg_2^{2+} as solid MgCl and remove most Al^{3+} as solid $AlCl^3$

    Answer: d Page: 681

55. The lime-soda process is used for large-scale water-softening operations. CaO is added to
    a) oxidize Fe^{2+} to insoluble Fe_2O_3
    b) cause precipitation of magnesium as $Mg(OH)_2$
    c) remove most Al^{3+} as solid $Al(OH)_3$
    d) cause precipitation of iron and magnesium as Fe_2MgO_4
    e) reduce the pH to 3-4

    Answer: b Page: 681

56. The principal action of secondary sewage treatment is to
    a) remove inorganic ions via precipitation
    b) remove inorganic ions via reduction to elemental form
    c) lower dissolved oxygen levels in waste water
    d) decompose organic material via aerobic bacterial action
    e) both lower dissolved oxygen levels in waste water and decompose organic material via aerobic bacterial action

    Answer: d Page: 681

57. Which one of the following ions is responsible for making water "hard"?
    a) Ca^{2+}
    b) CO_3^{2-}
    c) Na^+
    d) Cl^-

    Answer: a Page: 681

ESSAY

58. How can the presence of biodegradable waste in a lake result in the death of fish in the lake?

    Answer:
    bacteria utilize oxygen to degrade the waste and deplete the oxygen in the lake water
    Page: 681

MULTIPLE CHOICE

59. Which one of the following could be produced by anaerobic bacteria decomposing biodegradable waste?
    a) nitrate
    b) sulfate
    c) carbon dioxide
    d) hydrogen sulfide
    e) water

    Answer: d Page: 681

ESSAY

60. List two of the three major sources of nitrogen and phosphorus in water.

    Answer:
    domestic sewage, runoff from agricultural land, runoff from livestock areas
    Page: 681

61. Ozone is more efficient at killing bacteria in water yet chlorine is used more commonly for that purpose in municipal water treatment. Why?

    Answer: Ozone must be generated on site, chlorine can be brought in, pg 697

    Page: 681

MULTIPLE CHOICE

62. The sterilizing action of chlorine in water is due to what substance?
    a) Cl^-
    b) Cl_2
    c) HCl
    d) HClO
    e) H^+

    Answer: d Page: 681

Chapter 19: Chemical Thermodynamics

MULTIPLE CHOICE

1. In any spontaneous process, the path between reactants and products is
   a) the path between reactants and products is reversible
   b) the path between reactants and products is irreversible
   c) reactants and products are in equilibrium
   d) both forward and reverse reactions are spontaneous

   Answer: b Page: 691

2. With thermodynamics, one cannot determine
   a) the speed of a reaction
   b) the direction of a reaction
   c) the extent of a reaction
   d) in which direction a reaction is spontaneous
   e) the temperature at which a reaction will be spontaneous

   Answer: a Page: 691

3. Which one of the following is a correct statement of the first law of thermodynamics?
   a) $\Delta E = q + w$
   b) $\Delta H = \Sigma\Delta H_{products} - \Sigma H_{reactants}$
   c) $\Delta S = q/T$
   d) at absolute zero, for a pure crystalline solid, $S = 0$

   Answer: a Page: 691

4. When a reaction is found by thermodynamics to be spontaneous,
   a) it will be very rapid as written
   b) it is possible for it to proceed as written without outside intervention
   c) it is also spontaneous in the reverse direction
   d) the equilibrium position lies very far to the left

   Answer: b Page: 691

5. The thermodynamic quantity that expresses the degree of disorder in a system is
   a) enthalpy
   b) internal energy
   c) bond energy
   d) entropy
   e) heat flow

   Answer: d Page: 694

6. For an isothermal process, ΔS =
   a) q
   b) $\frac{q_{rev}}{T}$
   c) q_{rev}
   d) $(q_{rev})(T)$
   e) $q + w$

   Answer: b Page: 694

7. A cylinder is charged with a gas. Initially the gas occupies a volume of 0.10 L at a pressure of 2.9 atm and 25.0°C. The gas was then isothermally expanded to a volume of 1.0 L. Calculate the entropy change associated with this process.
   a) -2.3J/K
   b) 19J/K
   c) 0.012J/K
   d) 0.0023J/K
   e) 0.23J/K

   Answer: e Page: 694

8. What is the driving force behind the expansion of a gas?
   a) decrease in energy due to decrease in repulsive forces between gas molecules
   b) decrease in energy due the cooling effect
   c) attraction for the container walls
   d) decrease in order

   Answer: d Page: 694

9. The change in which one of the following depends on the pathway of the change?
   a) S
   b) H
   c) q
   d) E

   Answer: c Page: 694

10. Which one of the following is always positive when a spontaneous process occurs?
    a) ΔS_{system}
    b) $\Delta S_{surroundings}$
    c) $\Delta S_{universe}$
    d) $\Delta H_{universe}$

    Answer: c Page: 694

11. Which one of the following can be determined exactly?
   a) E
   b) H
   c) S
   d) all of these
   e) none of these

   Answer: c Page: 694

12. Which reaction below should have $\Delta S° > 0$?
   a) $2H_2(g) + O_2(g) \rightarrow 2H_2O(g)$
   b) $2NO_2(g) \rightarrow N_2O_4(g)$
   c) $H^+(aq) + F^-(aq) \rightarrow HF(aq)$
   d) $BaF_2(s) \rightarrow Ba^{2+}(aq) + 2F^-(aq)$
   e) $2Hg(l) + O_2(g) \rightarrow 2HgO(s)$

   Answer: d Page: 694

13. Which process from the following list would have a negative value of ΔS?
   a) beach erosion
   b) breaking a window
   c) dissolving alcohol in water
   d) making your bed

   Answer: d Page: 694

14. Which of the following processes causes an entropy decrease?
   a) boiling water to form steam
   b) dissolution of solid KCl in water
   c) mixing of two gases into one container
   d) freezing water to form ice

   Answer: d Page: 694

15. Which one of the following reactions would have a positive value for $\Delta S°$?
   a) $Ba(OH)_2(s) + CO_2(g) \rightarrow BaCO_3(s) + H_2O(l)$
   b) $N_2(g) + 3H_2(g) \rightarrow 2NH_3(g)$
   c) $2SO_3(g) \rightarrow 2SO_2(g) + O_2(g)$
   d) $AgNO_3(aq) + HCl(aq) \rightarrow AgCl(s) + HNO_3(aq)$

   Answer: c Page: 694

16. Which equation represents a reaction that is decreasing in entropy as the reaction proceeds?
   a) $CaCO_3(s) \rightarrow CaO(s) + CO_2(g)$
   b) $2C(s) + O_2(g) \rightarrow 2CO(g)$
   c) $2Na(s) + 2H_2O(l) \rightarrow 2NaOH(aq) + H_2(g)$
   d) $2H_2(g) + O_2(g) \rightarrow 2H_2O(l)$

   Answer: d Page: 694

17. Which equation represents a reaction for which $\Delta S°$ is negative at 25°C?
    a) $CaCO_3(s) \rightarrow CaO(s) + CO_2(g)$
    b) $2H_2(g) + O_2(g) \rightarrow 2H_2O(l)$
    c) $2C(s) + O_2(g) \rightarrow 2CO(g)$

    Answer: b Page: 694

18. Of the processes below, which one is accompanied by an increase in entropy?
    a) $Ca(OH)_{2(s)} + 2\ HCl_{(g)} \rightarrow CaCl_{2(s)} + 2\ H_2O_{(g)}$
    b) $CO_{2(s)} \rightarrow CO_{2(g)}$
    c) $H_{2(g)} + Cl_{2(g)} \rightarrow 2\ HCl_{(g)}$
    d) $N_{2(g)} + 3\ H_{2(g)} \rightarrow 2\ NH_{3(g)}$

    Answer: b Page: 694

19. For a reversible process, the change in entropy of the universe is
    a) >0
    b) 0
    c) <0

    Answer: b Page: 698

20. The entropy of the universe is
    a) constant
    b) continually decreasing
    c) continually increasing
    d) zero

    Answer: c Page: 698

21. A system that cannot exchange either matter or energy with its surroundings is called
    a) adiabatic
    b) isolated
    c) isothermal
    d) isobaric
    e) isotonic

    Answer: b Page: 698

22. Which one of the following processes results in a decrease of the entropy of the system?
    a) dissolving sodium chloride in water
    b) sublimation of naphthalene
    c) dissolving oxygen in water
    d) boiling of alcohol
    e) explosion of nitroglycerine

    Answer: c Page: 700

23. For which one of the following reactions should the sign of ΔS be negative?
    a) $2SO_2(g) + O_2(g) \rightarrow 2SO_3(g)$
    b) $NH_3Cl(s) \rightarrow HCl(g) + NH_3(g)$
    c) $2NaCl(s) + H_2SO_3(aq) \rightarrow 2HCl(g) + Na_2SO_4(s)$
    d) $C(s) + O_2(g) \rightarrow CO_2(g)$

    Answer: a Page: 700

24. How does the number of degrees of freedom of a molecule relate to its entropy?
    a) the greater the number of degrees of freedom, the greater the entropy
    b) the fewer the number of degrees of freedom, the lower the entropy
    c) the greater the number of degrees of freedom, the lower the entropy
    d) the fewer the number of degrees of freedom, the greater the entropy
    e) there is no relationship between the number of degrees of freedom and the entropy

    Answer: a Page: 700

25. The third law of thermodynamics states that
    a) during any spontaneous process, the entropy of the universe increases
    b) energy is conserved in any process
    c) $\Delta E = q + w$
    d) the entropy of a pure crystalline substance at absolute zero is zero
    e) $\Delta G = \Delta H + T\Delta S$

    Answer: d Page: 700

ESSAY

26. How many degrees of freedom does a system have if its entropy is zero?

    Answer: zero Page: 700

MULTIPLE CHOICE

27. What happens to the entropy of a system as its temperature increases?
    a) it increases
    b) it decreases
    c) it does not change

    Answer: a Page: 700

28. Consider a pure, crystalline solid being heated from absolute zero to some very high temperature. Which one of the following processes produces the greatest increase in the entropy of the substance?
a) melting the solid
b) heating the liquid
c) heating the gas
d) heating the solid
e) boiling the liquid

Answer: e Page: 700

29. Which one of the following has the greatest entropy?
a) $HCl_{(l)}$
b) $HCl_{(s)}$
c) $HCl_{(g)}$
d) these are all the same

Answer: c Page: 700

30. Which molecule below should have the highest gas-phase absolute entropy at 25°C?
a) H_2
b) C_2H_6
c) C_2H_2
d) CH_4
e) C_2H_2

Answer: b Page: 700

31. Which one of the following substances has the <u>highest</u> absolute entropy at 25°C?
a) $NH_3(g)$
b) $Ne(g)$
c) $H_2O(\ell)$
d) $C(s)$

Answer: a Page: 700

32. Which one of the following substances would have the <u>largest</u> absolute entropy at 25°C and 1 atm pressure?
a) $He(g)$
b) $H_2O(s)$
c) $Ne(g)$
d) $SO_2(g)$

Answer: d Page: 700

33. Which one of the following correctly indicates the relationship between the entropy of a system and the number of different arrangements, W, in the system?
    a) $S = kW$
    b) $S = \frac{k}{W}$
    c) $S = \frac{W}{k}$
    d) $S = k\ \ln(W)$
    e) $S = Wk$

    Answer: d Page: 704

ESSAY

34. Calculate ΔS, for the reaction below at 25°C.
    $4Al_{(s)} + 3O_{2(g)} \rightarrow 2Al_2O_{3(s)}$

Substance	ΔS° (J/mol•K)
$Al_{(s)}$	164
$Al_2O_{3(s)}$	51.0
$O_{2(g)}$	205

Answer:
$\Delta S°, = (2\ mol\ Al_2O_{3(s)})(51.0\ J/mol \cdot K) - (4\ mol\ Al_{(s)})(164\ J/mol \cdot K) - (3\ mol\ O_{2(g)})(205\ J/mol \cdot K) = -1.17\ kJ/K$
Page: 703

35. Calculate ΔS, for the reaction below at 25°C.
    $PCl_{3(g)} + Cl_{2(g)} \rightarrow PCl_{5(g)}$

Substance	ΔS° (J/mol•K)
$PCl_{3(g)}$	312
$Cl_{2(g)}$	223
$PCl_{5(g)}$	353

Answer:
$\Delta S° = (1\ mol\ PCl_{5(g)})(353\ J/mol \cdot K) - (1\ mol\ PCl_{3(g)})(312\ J/mol \cdot K) - (1\ mol\ Cl_{2(g)})(223\ J/mol \cdot K) = -182\ J/K$
Page: 703

MULTIPLE CHOICE

36. Some standard entropies (at 25°C in J/mol K) are given:
diamond 2.43, O_2(g) 205.0, CO(g) 197.9. $\Delta S°$ for the reaction
2C(diamond) + O_2(g) → 2CO(g) at 25°C in J/K is
a) -185.9
b) +185.9
c) -9.5
d) +9.5
e) -195.7

Answer: b Page: 703

37. Some standard entropies (at 25°C in J/mol K) are given:
Fe(s) 27.15, Cl_2(g) 222.96, $FeCl_3$(s) 142.3. $\Delta S°$ for the reaction 2Fe(s) + $3Cl_2$(g) → $2FeCl_3$(s) at 25°C in J/K is
a) -438.6
b) +107.8
c) -107.8
d) -380.0
e) +380.0

Answer: a Page: 703

38. Some standard entropies (at 25°C in J/mol K) are given:
Ca^{2+}(aq) -55.2, F^-(aq) -9.6, CaF_2(s) +68.87. $\Delta S°$ for the reaction CaF_2(s) → Ca^{2+}(aq) + $2F^-$(aq) at 25°C in J/K is
a) -133.7 J/k
b) +133.7 J/k
c) -5.5 J/k
d) -143.3 J/k
e) +143.3 J/k

Answer: d Page: 703

39. During any spontaneous process at constant temperature and pressure, the free energy of the system always
a) increases
b) remains unchanged
c) decreases

Answer: c Page: 706

40. What can be said about a chemical system that has reached a minimum free energy?
a) it is at absolute zero
b) its entropy is zero
c) it is at equilibrium
d) the reaction is complete
e) the reaction is very fast

Answer: c Page: 706

41. When a reaction is at equilibrium, its ΔG
    a) > 0
    b) $= 0$
    c) < 0

    Answer: b Page: 706

42. For which one of the following substances is $\Delta G_f°$ zero?
    a) $H_2O_{(l)}$
    b) $Br_{2(s)}$
    c) $O_{(g)}$
    d) $N_{2(g)}$

    Answer: d Page: 707

43. Consider the following table of thermodynamic data. All values are tabulated for 25°C.

Substance	ΔG_f° (kJ/mol)	$\Delta S°$ (J/mol·K)
$C_2H_2(g)$	209	201
$C_2H_4(g)$	68	219
$C_2H_6(g)$	-33	230
$H_2O(g)$	-229	189
$C_2H_5OH(l)$	-175	161

The value of $\Delta S°$ for the following reaction is -233J/K at 25°C. What is the entropy of $H_2(g)$ at 25°C?

$$C_2H_2(g) + 2H_2(g) \rightarrow C_2H_6(g)$$

a) 131
b) 204
c) 102
d) 262

Answer: a Page: 707

44. Which species below has/have $\Delta G°_f = 0$?
    a) $Co(s)$
    b) $PF_3(g)$
    c) $H_2(g)$
    d) $HCo(PF_3)_4(g)$
    e) both $Co(s)$ and $H_2(g)$

    Answer: e Page: 707

45. Which one of the following is not zero for an element in its standard state at 25°C?
a) ΔG°_f
b) ΔS°
c) ΔH°_f

Answer: b Page: 707

46. Consider the following table of thermodynamic data. All values are tabulated for 25°C.

Substance	ΔG°_f (kJ/mol)	ΔS° (J/mol·K)
$C_2H_2(g)$	209	201
$C_2H_4(g)$	68	219
$C_2H_6(g)$	-33	230
$H_2(g)$	0	131
$H_2O(g)$	-229	189
$C_2H_5OH(l)$	-175	161

Determine the value of ΔG° (in kJ) for the following reaction taking place at 25°C.

$$C_2H_4(g) + H_2O(g) \rightarrow C_2H_5OH(l)$$

a) 122
b) -472
c) -122
d) -14

Answer: d Page: 707

47. Consider the following table of thermodynamic data. All values are tabulated for 25°C.

Substance	ΔG°_f (kJ/mol)	ΔS° (J/mol·K)
$C_2H_2(g)$	209	201
$C_2H_4(g)$	68	219
$C_2H_6(g)$	-33	230
$H_2(g)$	0	131
$H_2O(g)$	-229	189
$C_2H_5OH(l)$	-175	161

What is the value of ΔH° (in kJ) for the reaction described below? Assume the reaction is performed at 25°C.

$$C_2H_2(g) + 2H_2(g) \rightarrow C_2H_6(g)$$

a) -173
b) 236
c) -311
d) -248

Answer: c Page: 707

48. Which of the following processes has a negative standard free energy change at 25°C?
a) $CH_4(g) + 2O_2(g) \rightarrow CO_2(g) + 2H_2O(g)$
b) $2Na(s) + 2H_2O(l) \rightarrow 2NaOH(aq) + H_2(g)$
c) $2H_2O(l) \rightarrow 2H_2(g) + O_2(g)$
d) <u>both</u> $CH_4(g) + 2O_2(g) \rightarrow CO_2(g) + 2H_2O(g)$
<u>and</u> $2Na(s) + 2H_2O(l) \rightarrow 2NaOH(aq) + H_2(g)$

Answer: d Page: 707

49. Consider the following table of thermodynamic data.

Substance	ΔG_f° (kJ/mol)	ΔS° (J/mol·K)
NO(g)	86.7	211
NO_2(g)	51.8	240
NOCl(g)	66.3	264
N_2O(g)	103.6	220

Determine the value of ΔG° (in kJ) for the following reaction taking place at 25°C.

$$2NO(g) + O_2(g) \rightarrow 2NO_2(g)$$

a) -69.8
b) -34.9
c) 104.7
d) -104.7

Answer: a Page: 707

50. Consider the following table of thermodynamic data.

Substance	ΔG_f° (kJ/mol)	ΔS° (J/mol·K)
NO(g)	86.7	211
NO_2(g)	51.8	240
NOCl(g)	66.3	264
N_2O(g)	103.6	220

The value of ΔS° for the following reaction is -117 J/K at 25°C. What is the entropy of Cl_2(g) at 25°C?

$$2NO(g) + Cl_2(g) \rightarrow 2NOCl(g)$$

a) 106
b) 11
c) 223
d) -223

Answer: c Page: 707

51. Consider the following table of thermodynamic data.

Substance	ΔG°_f (kJ/mol)	ΔS° (J/mol·K)
$NO(g)$	86.7	211
$NO_2(g)$	51.8	240
$NOCl(g)$	66.3	264
$N_2O(g)$	103.6	220

What is the value of ΔH° (in kJ) at 25°C for the reaction shown below?

$$N_2O(g) + NO_2(g) \rightarrow 3NO(g)$$

a) 156.2
b) 5.5
c) 53.2
d) 109.0

Answer: a Page: 707

52. Consider the following reaction at 25°C.

$C(s) + H_2O(g) \rightarrow CO(g) + H_2(g)$
$\Delta G^\circ = 91.2$ kJ $\qquad \Delta H^\circ = 131.4$ kJ

What is the value of ΔS° (in J/K) for this reaction at 25°C?
a) -135
b) 1.6
c) -1.6
d) 135

Answer: d Page: 707

53. Consider the following reaction at 25°C.

$C(s) + H_2O(g) \rightarrow CO(g) + H_2(g)$
$\Delta G^\circ = 91.2$ kJ $\qquad \Delta S^\circ = 135$ J

What is the value of ΔH° for this reaction at 25°C?
a) 40.3 kJ
b) 226 kJ
c) 91.3 kJ
d) 131.4 kJ

Answer: d Page: 707

54. Determine the value of $\Delta G°$ (in kJ) for the following reaction using data from the table below.

$$2H_2O(g) + O_2(g) \rightarrow 2H_2O_2(g)$$

Substance	ΔG_f° (kJ/mol)
$H_2O(g)$	-228
$H_2O_2(g)$	-105

a) -246
b) 666
c) 246
d) -666

Answer: c Page: 707

55. Calculate $\Delta G°$ for the reaction below at 25°C

$$2\ SO_{2(g)} + O_{2(g)} \rightarrow 2\ SO_{3(g)}$$

Substance	$\Delta H_f°$ (kJ/mol)	$\Delta S°$ (J/mol·K)
$SO_{2(g)}$	-297	249
$O_{2(g)}$		205
$SO_{3(g)}$	-395	256

a) -196 kJ
b) -191 kJ
c) -5 kJ
d) -139 kJ

Answer: d Page: 707

56. The maximum amount of useful work that can be done by a system on its surroundings in a spontaneous process at constant temperature and pressure is given by
a) ΔH
b) ΔS
c) ΔG
d) $\frac{\Delta H}{T}$
e) $\frac{\Delta S}{T}$

Answer: c Page: 708

57. Assuming ΔH and ΔS do not vary with temperature, at what temperature will the reaction shown below become spontaneous?

$$C(s) + H_2O(g) \rightarrow CO(g) + H_2(g)$$

ΔH = 131.3 kJ   ΔS = 133.6 J/K

a) 273°C
b) 325°C
c) 552°C
d) 710°C

Answer: d Page: 710

58. ΔH° for the reaction is 137 kJ and ΔS° for the reaction is 120 J/K.

$$C_2H_6(g) \rightarrow C_2H_4(g) + H_2(g)$$

This reaction will be:
a) spontaneous at all temperatures
b) spontaneous only at high temperature
c) spontaneous only at low temperature
d) nonspontaneous at all temperatures

Answer: b Page: 710

59. Assuming ΔH and ΔS do not vary with temperature, a reaction that is not spontaneous at low temperature can become spontaneous at high temperature if ΔH is _______ and ΔS is _______.
a) +, +
b) -, -
c) +, -
d) -, +

Answer: a Page: 710

60. The entropy of vaporization ($\Delta S°_{vap}$) for benzene is 96.4 J/K·mol. The enthalpy of vaporization ($\Delta H°_{vap}$) is 33.9 kJ/mol. What is the normal boiling point (in °C) for benzene?
a) 2.8° C
b) 0.35° C
c) 100° C
d) 79° C

Answer: d Page: 710

61. For a reaction to be spontaneous at only high temperatures, the signs of H° and ΔS° are, respectively
a) +, +
b) +. -
c) -, +
d) -, -

Answer: a Page: 710

62. Dissolving ammonium chloride in water lowers the temperature of the system. For this dissolving process
a) ΔH is negative and ΔS is negative
b) ΔH is positive and ΔS is positive
c) ΔH is negative and ΔS is positive
d) ΔH is positive and ΔS is negative

Answer: b Page: 710

63. Consider the following reaction occurring in an automobile engine:

$2C_8H_{18}(l) + 25O_2(g) \rightarrow 16CO_2(g) + 18H_2O(g)$

(gasoline)

The signs of ΔH, ΔS, and ΔG would be:
a) -, +, +
b) +, -, +
c) +, +, -
d) -, +, -

Answer: d Page: 710

64. Consider the following reaction.

$$A + B \rightarrow C$$

This reaction will <u>always</u> be spontaneous when ΔH is _______ and ΔS is _________.
a) +, +
b) -, -
c) -, +
d) +, -

Answer: c Page: 710

65. Solid ammonium nitrate is highly soluble in water. When it dissolves the solution gets very cold. Based on this information alone, what are the signs for ΔH, ΔS, and ΔG for this process?
a) +, +, +
b) +, +, -
c) +, -, -
d) -, -, -

Answer: b Page: 710

66. Solid ammonium nitrate is highly soluble in water. When it dissolves the solution gets very cold. Based on this information alone, what is the driving force for this reaction?
a) enthalpy decrease
b) entropy increase
c) neither of these
d) both of these

Answer: b Page: 710

67. Calculate the equilibrium constant of the reaction below at 25°C.

$2\ SO_{2(g)} + O_{2(g)} \rightarrow 2\ SO_{3(g)}$

Substance	$\Delta H^o{}_f$ (kJ/mol)	ΔS° (J/mol·K)
$SO_{2(g)}$	-297	249
$O_{2(g)}$		205
$SO_{3(g)}$	-395	256

a) 2.32×10^{24}
b) 1.06
c) 1.95
d) 3.82×10^{23}

Answer: a Page: 711

68. A reaction with which one of the following values of ΔG° is farthest from equilibrium?
a) 195 kJ
b) -15 kJ
c) -391 kJ
d) 225 kJ

Answer: c Page: 711

69. For the reaction $A(l) + 2D(g) \rightarrow 3X(g) + Z(s)$ having $\Delta G^\circ = +512$ kJ, the equilibrium mixture
a) will consist almost exclusively of A and D
b) will consist almost exclusively of A and Z
c) will consist almost exclusively of X and Z
d) will consist of significant amounts of A, D, X, and Z
e) has a composition predictable only if one knows T and ΔH°

Answer: a Page: 711

70. The equilibrium position corresponds to which letter on the graph of G = f(course of reaction) below?
a) A
b) B
c) C
d) D
e) E

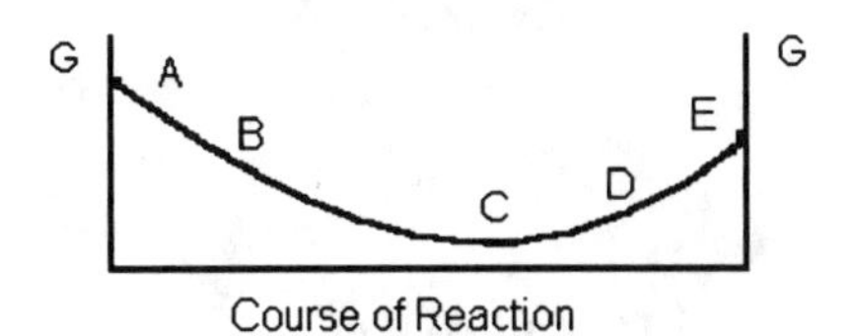

Answer: c Page: 711

71. Which one of the following statements is true about the equilibrium constant for a reaction if ΔG° for the reaction is greater than zero?
a) K = 0
b) K = 1
c) K > 1
d) K < 1

Answer: d Page: 711

72. Which one of the following statements is true about the equilibrium constant for a reaction if ΔG° for the reaction is negative?
a) K = 0
b) K = 1
c) K > 1
d) K < 1

Answer: c Page: 711

73. The value of the equilibrium constant for a particular reaction is 0.48 at 25°C. What is the value of ΔG° (in kJ) for the reaction at 25°C? (R = 8.314 J/K•mol)
a) 1.8
b) -4.2
c) 1.5×10^2
d) 4.2

Answer: a Page: 711

74. Calculate the value of $\Delta G°$ (in kJ) for this reaction at 25°C. ($R = 8.314$ J/K•mol)

$$N_2(g) + 3H_2(g) \rightleftharpoons 2NH_3(g) \qquad K = 5.0 \times 10^8$$

a) 22
b) -4.2
c) -25
d) -50

Answer: d Page: 711

75. Which one of the following reactions releases free energy?
a) $6CO_2 + 6H_2O \rightarrow C_6H_{12}O_6 + 6O_2$
b) ATP → ADP
c) ADP → ATP

Answer: b Page: 713

Chapter 20: Electrochemistry

MULTIPLE CHOICE

1. The gain of electrons is called
   a) reduction
   b) oxidation
   c) disproportionation
   d) fractionation

   Answer: a Page: 723

2. What substance is reduced in the following reaction?

   $Cr_2O_7^{2-} + 6S_2O_3^{2-} + 14H^+ \rightarrow 2Cr^{3+} + 3S_4O_6^{2-} + 7H_2O$

   a) $Cr_2O_7^{2-}$
   b) $S_2O_3^{2-}$
   c) H^+
   d) Cr^{3+}
   e) $S_4O_6^{2-}$
   f) H_2O
   g) none of these; this is not a redox reaction

   Answer: a Page: 723

3. What is the reducing agent in the reaction below?

   $Cr_2O_7^{2-} + 6S_2O_3^{2-} + 14H^+ \rightarrow 2Cr^{3+} + 3S_4O_6^{2-} + 7H_2O$

   a) $Cr_2O_7^{2-}$
   b) $S_2O_3^{2-}$
   c) H^+
   d) Cr^{3+}
   e) $S_4O_6^{2-}$
   f) H_2O
   g) none of these; this is not a redox reaction

   Answer: b Page: 723

4. Which element is reduced in the reaction below?

   $Fe(CO)_5(l) + 2HI(g) \rightarrow Fe(CO)_4I_2(s) + CO(g) + H_2(g)$?

   a) Fe
   b) C
   c) O
   d) H
   e) I

   Answer: d Page: 723

5. Which element is oxidized in the reaction

$Fe(CO)_5(l) + 2HI(g) \rightarrow Fe(CO)_4I_2(s) + CO(g) + H_2(g)$?
a) Fe
b) C
c) O
d) H
e) I

Answer: a Page: 723

6. Which of the following reactions is a redox reaction?
a) $K_2CrO_4 + BaCl_2 \rightarrow BaCrO_4 + 2KCl$
b) $Pb_2^{2+} + 2Br^- \rightarrow PbBr$
c) $Cu + S \rightarrow CuS$
d) both of the following:
$K_2CrO_4 + BaCl_2 \rightarrow BaCrO_4 + 2KCl$
$Pb^{2+} + 2Br^- \rightarrow PbBr_2$

Answer: c Page: 723

7. Which one of the following reactions is a redox reaction?
a) $NaOH + HCl \rightarrow NaCl + H_2O$
b) $Pb^{2+} + 2Cl^- \rightarrow PbCl_2$
c) $AgNO_3 + HCl \rightarrow HNO_3 + AgCl$
d) $2Al + 3Cl_2 \rightarrow 2AlCl_3$

Answer: d Page: 723

8. Which substance is serving as the reducing agent in the following reaction?

$Fe_2S_3 + 12HNO_3 \rightarrow 2Fe(NO_3)_3 + 3S + 6NO_2 + 6H_2O$

a) HNO_3
b) S
c) NO_2
d) Fe_2S_3

Answer: d Page: 723

9. Which substance is serving as the reducing agent in the following reaction?

$14H^+ + Cr_2O_7^{2-} + 3Ni \rightarrow 3Ni^{2+} + 2Cr^{3+} + 7H_2O$

a) Ni
b) H^+
c) $Cr_2O_7^{2-}$
d) H_2O

Answer: a Page: 723

10. Which substance is the oxidizing agent in the reaction below?

$Pb + PbO_2 + 2H_2SO_4 \rightarrow 2PbSO_4 + 2H_2O$

a) Pb
b) H_2SO_4
c) PbO_2
d) $PbSO_4$

Answer: c Page: 723

11. What is the oxidation number of each sulfur atom in osmium(V) sulfate dihydrate?
a) -2
b) +3
c) +6
d) -1
e) 0

Answer: c Page: 723

ESSAY

12. Write the balanced half reaction for the reduction occurring in the reaction below.
$Cr_2O^{2-}_7 + 6\ S_2O^{2-}_3 + 14\ H^+ \rightarrow 2\ Cr^{3+} + 3\ S_4O^{2-}_6 + 7\ H_2O$

Answer: $Cr_2O^{2-}_7 + 6\ e^- + 14\ H^+ \rightarrow 2\ Cr^{3+} + 7\ H_2O$ Page: 725

13. Write the balanced half reaction for the oxidation occurring in the reaction below.
$Cr_2O^{2-}_7 + 6\ S_2O^{2-}_3 + 14\ H^+ \rightarrow 2\ Cr^{3+} + 3\ S_4O^{2-}_6 + 7\ H_2O$

Answer: $2\ S_2O^{2-}_3 \rightarrow S_4O^{2-}_6 + 2\ e^-$ Page: 725

14. Balance the following redox reaction in acidic solution.
$H_3PO_4 + HNO_2 \rightarrow N_2O_4 + HPO_3$

Answer:
$H_3PO_4 + 2\ H^+ + 2\ e^- \rightarrow H_3PO_3 + H_2O$
$2\ HNO_2 \rightarrow N_2O_4 + 2\ H^+ + 2\ e^-$

$H_3PO_4 + 2\ HNO_2 \rightarrow N_2O_4 + H_3PO_3 + H_2O$
Page: 725

15. Balance the following redox reaction in acidic solution.
$HClO_2$ + MnO_2 → Cl_2 + MnO^-_4

Answer:
2 $HClO_2$ + 6 H^+ + 6 e^- → Cl_2 + $4H_2O$
2(MnO_2 + $2H_2O$ → MnO^-_4 + 4 H^+ 3 e^-)

---

2 $HClO_2$ + 2 MnO_2 → Cl_2 + 2 MnO^-_4 + $2H^+$
Page: 725

MULTIPLE CHOICE

16. The balanced half-reaction in which bromite ion is converted to bromide ion is a
a) one-electron oxidation
b) two-electron reduction
c) two-electron oxidation
d) three-electron oxidation
e) four-electron reduction

Answer: e Page: 725

17. How many electrons are involved in the following half-reaction when it is balanced?

$$S_4O_6^{2-} \rightarrow S_2O_3^{2-}$$

a) 6
b) 2
c) 4
d) 1

Answer: b Page: 725

18. What is the coefficient of $Fe(OH)_2$ when the following redox equation is balanced?

BrO^- + $Fe(OH)_2$ → Br^- + $Fe(OH)_3$ (basic solution)

a) 1
b) 3
c) 2
d) 5

Answer: c Page: 725

19. What is the coefficient of the permanganate ion when the following equation is correctly balanced?

$MnO_4^- + Br^- \rightarrow Mn^{2+} + Br_2$ (acidic solution)

a) 1
b) 2
c) 3
d) 5

Answer: b Page: 725

20. What is the coefficient of H_2O when the following equation is corrcctly balanced?

$ClO^- + S_2O_3^{2-} \rightarrow Cl^- + SO_4^{2-}$ (basic solution)

a) 1
b) 2
c) 3
d) 4

Answer: a Page: 725

21. What is the coefficient of the permanganate ion when the following equation is correctly balanced?

$MnO_4^- + I^- \rightarrow Mn^{2+} + I_2$ (acidic solution)

a) 1
b) 2
c) 3
d) 5

Answer: b Page: 725

22. What is the coefficient of Fe^{3+} when the following equation is correctly balanced?

$CN^- + Fe^{3+} \rightarrow CNO^- + Fe^{2+}$ (basic solution)

a) 1
b) 2
c) 3
d) 4

Answer: b Page: 725

ESSAY

23. In what type of electrochemical cell does a spontaneous redox reaction occur?

Answer: galvanic or voltaic Page: 730

MULTIPLE CHOICE

24. The electrode at which oxidation occurs is called the
a) oxidizing agent
b) cathode
c) reducing agent
d) anode

Answer: d Page: 730

ESSAY

25. What is the purpose of the salt bridge in an electrochemical cell?

Answer: To provide ions that maintain electrical neutrality in the half cells.

Page: 730

MULTIPLE CHOICE

26. What is the sign of the cathode in a galvanic cell?
a) +
b) -
c) neither of these

Answer: a Page: 730

ESSAY

27. What are the two possible <u>reduction</u> half reactions that can ccur in this cell?

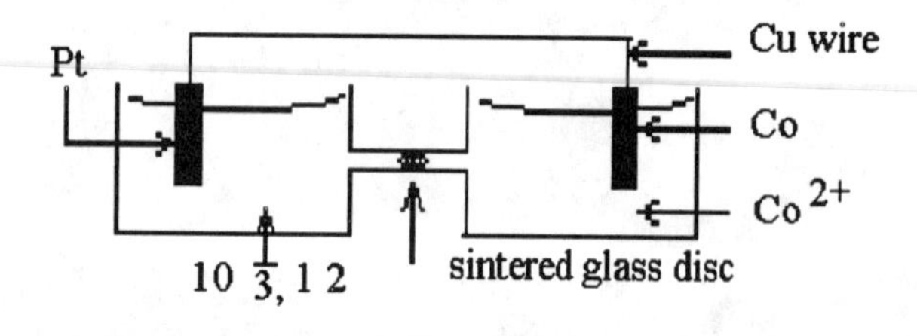

Answer: $2IO_3^- + 10e^- + 12H^+ \rightarrow I_2 + 6H_2O$ and $Co^{2+} + 2e^- \rightarrow Co$

Page: 730

MULTIPLE CHOICE

28. The half-reaction occurring at the cathode in the voltaic reaction $3MnO_4^-(aq) + 24H^+(aq) + 5Fe(s) \rightarrow 3Mn^{2+}(aq) + 5Fe^{3+}(aq) + 12H_2O(l)$ is
a) $MnO_4^-(aq) + 8H^+(aq) + 5e^- \rightarrow Mn^{2+}(aq) + 4H_2O(l)$
b) $2MnO_4^-(aq) + 12H^+(aq) + 6e^- \rightarrow 2Mn^{2+}(aq) + 3H_2O(l)$
c) $Fe(s) \rightarrow Fe^{3+}(aq) + 3e^-$
d) $Fe(s) \rightarrow Fe^{2+}(aq) + 2e^-$
e) $Fe^{2+}(aq) \rightarrow Fe^{3+}(aq) + e^-$

Answer: a Page: 730

29. Which transformation could take place at the anode of an electrochemical cell?
a) Cr^{3+} to $Cr_2O_7^{2-}$
b) F_2 to F^-
c) O_2 to H_2O
d) $HAsO_2$ to As

Answer: a Page: 730

30. In a galvanic cell, which direction do electrons flow?
a) cathode to anode
b) anode to cathode

Answer: b Page: 730

ESSAY

31. The symbol $E°$ indicates that this emf was measured at a temperature of ____°C and with all substances at concentrations of ____ or partial pressures of ____.

Answer: 25, 1 *M*, 1 atm Page: 733

32. The standard hydrogen electrode has been assigned a standard reduction potential value of

Answer: 0 V Page: 733

MULTIPLE CHOICE

33. The reduction half reaction occurring in the standard hydrogen electrode is
a) $H_2(g, 1atm) \rightarrow 2H^+(aq, 1M) + 2e^-$
b) $2H^+(aq) + 2OH^- \rightarrow H_2O(l)$
c) $O_2(g) + 4H^+(aq) + 4e^- \rightarrow 2H_2O(l)$
d) $2H^+(aq, 1M) + 2e^- \rightarrow H_2(g, 1atm)$
e) $2H^+(aq, 1M) + Cl_2(aq) \rightarrow 2HCl(aq)$

Answer: d Page: 733

ESSAY

34. For the reaction, $Fe^{3+} + e^- \rightarrow Fe^{2+}$, $E° = 0.77V$. What is the value of the standard reduction potential for the reaction, $49Fe^{3+} + 49e^- \rightarrow 49Fe^{2+}$?

Answer: 0.77V Page: 733

35. One volt equals
a) 1 amp•s
b) 1 J/s
c) 96485 C
d) 1 J/C

Answer: d Page: 733

36. Determine the overall reaction and determine the cell potential of the following cell given that the standard reduction potential for the Co^{2+}/Co half reaction is -0.534 v and that for the IO_3^-/I_2 half reaction is 1.195 v.

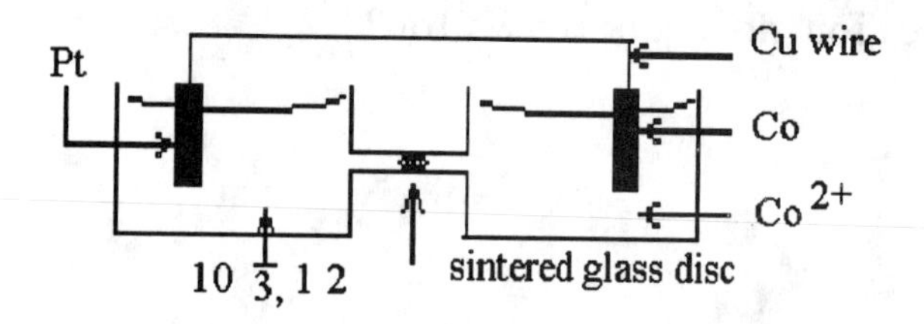

Answer:

$Co^{2+} + 2e^- \rightarrow Co$ E° = -0.534 v
$2IO_3^- + 10e^- + 12H^+ \rightarrow I_2 + 6H_2O$ E° = 1.195 v
$2IO_3^- + 10e^- + 12H^+ \rightarrow I_2 + 6H_2O$ E° = 1.195 v
$5(Co \rightarrow Co^{2+} + 2e^-)$ E° = 0.534 v

$2IO_3^- + 5Co + 12H^+ \rightarrow 5Co^{2+} + 6H_2O$ $E°_{cell}$ = 1.729 v

Page: 733

MULTIPLE CHOICE

37. From the information given, determine which halogen is the strongest oxidizing agent.

Substance	E° (v)
Br_2	1.09
F_2	2.85
I_2	0.54
Cl_2	1.36

a) Cl_2
b) Br_2
c) F_2
d) I_2

Answer: c Page: 733

38. The two electrodes $Cr(s)/Cr^{3+}(aq)$ and $Sn(s)/Sn^{2+}(aq)$ are combined to afford a spontaneous electrochemical reaction. The standard reduction potentials in V for $Cr^{3+}(aq)$ and $Sn^{2+}(aq)$ are -0.74 and -0.14, respectively. E° in V is
a) +0.88 V
b) -0.88 V
c) +0.60 V
d) -0.60 V
e) +2.50 V

Answer: c Page: 733

39. The respective standard reduction potentials in V for Ni^{2+} and Ag^{+} are -0.28 and +0.80. The oxidizing agent in this cell is
a) Ni
b) Ni^{2+}
c) Ag^{+}
d) Ag

Answer: c Page: 733

40. The respective standard reduction potentials in V for Ni^{2+} and Ag^{+} are -0.28 and +0.80. The electrode on the ______ is the cathode and it has a ________ sign.
a) right, +
b) right, -
c) left, -
d) left, +

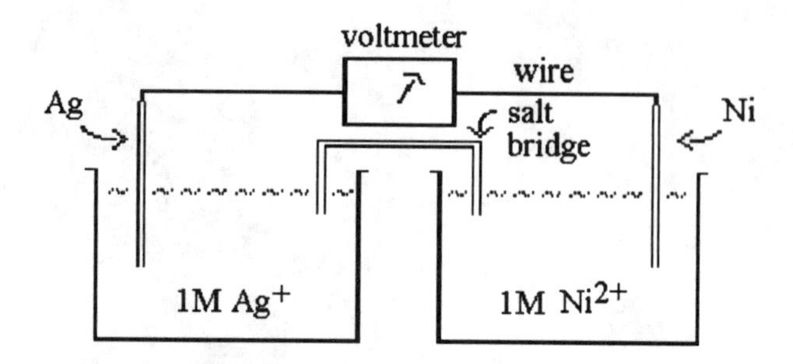

Answer: d Page: 733

41. The standard reduction potentials in V for Ag^{+} and Ni^{2+} are +0.80 and -0.28, respectively. Electrons in the cell flow through the ______ toward the ________.
a) wire, silver electrode
b) wire, nickel electrode
c) salt bridge, nickel electrode
d) salt bridge, silver electrode

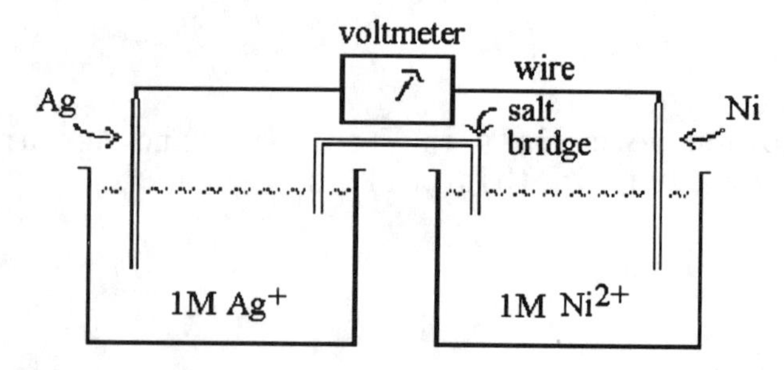

Answer: a Page: 733

42. The standard reduction potentials in V for Pb^{2+} and Ag^{+} are -0.13 and +0.80, respectively. Calculate E° (in volts) for a cell in which the overall reaction is $Pb + 2Ag^{+} \rightarrow Pb^{2+} + 2Ag$
a) 0.93
b) 0.67
c) 1.73
d) 1.47

Answer: a Page: 733

43. Use the following standard reduction potentials in V: Ag^{+} -> Ag, +0.80; Fe^{2+} -> Fe, -0.41; Fe^{3+} -> Fe, -0.04; Mn^{2+} -> Mn, -1.18; Zn^{2+} -> Zn, -0.76. The electrical potential of the cell represented above is 0.46 ± 0.01 volts. Identify X.
a) Ag
b) Fe
c) Mn
d) Zn

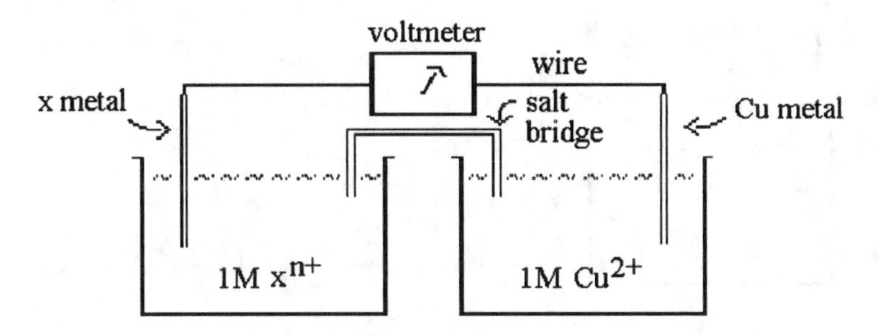

Answer: a Page: 733

44. Respective standard reduction potentials in V for Fe^{2+} and Ag^{+} are -0.44 and +0.80. Determine the value of E° cell for a voltaic cell in which the overall reaction is $Fe + 2Ag^{+} \rightarrow Fe^{2+} + 2Ag$
a) 0.36 V
b) 1.16 V
c) 1.24 V
d) 2.04

Answer: c Page: 733

45. Respective standard reduction potentials in V for Pb^{2+} and Ni^{2+} are -0.13 and -0.28. Which substance will be oxidized in the above voltaic cell?
a) Pb^{2+}
b) Pb
c) Ni^{2+}
d) Ni

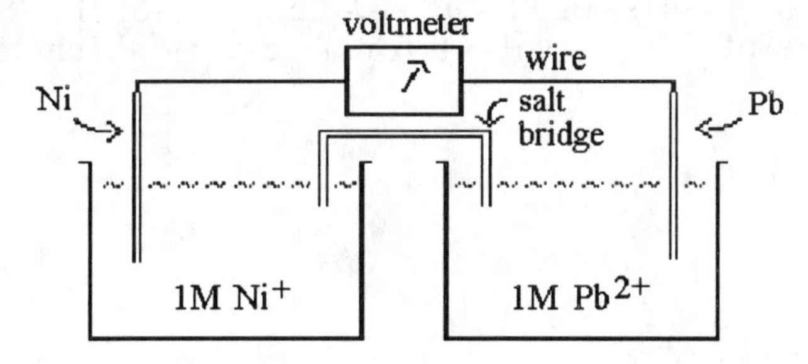

Answer: d Page: 733

46. Respective standard reduction potentials in V for Pb^{2+} and Ni^{2+} are -0.13 and -0.28. The ______ electrode is the electrode where the reduction will occur and it is called the ______.
a) Pb, cathode
b) Pb, anode
c) Ni, cathode
d) Ni, anode

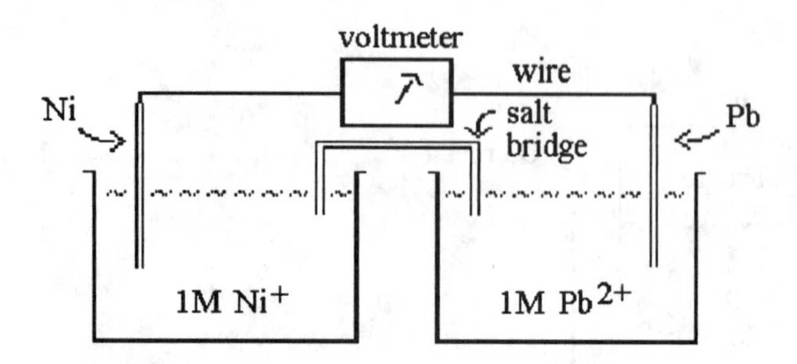

Answer: a Page: 733

47. Respective standard reduction potentials in V for Pb^{2+} and Ni^{2+} are -0.13 and -0.28. What is E° for this cell?
a) -0.15 V
b) 0.15 V
c) -0.38 V
d) 0.38 V

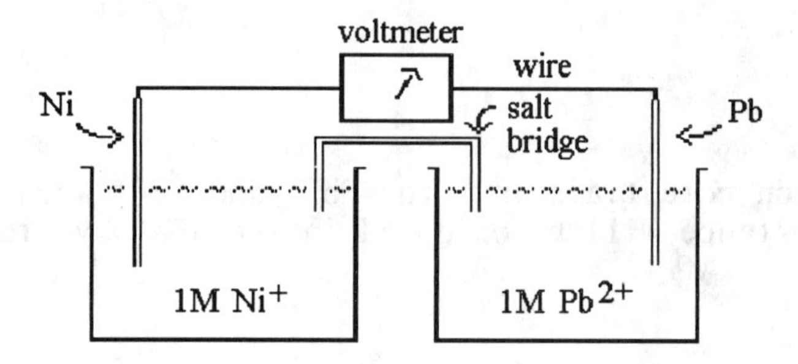

Answer: b Page: 733

48. Use the standard reduction potentials in V: Cu^{2+} -> Cu^{+}, +0.16; I_2 -> I^-, +0.54. Calculate the value of E° (in volts) for a cell in which the overall reaction is

$$2Cu^{+} + I_2 \rightarrow 2Cu^{2+} + 2I^{-}$$

a) 0.38 V
b) -0.38 V
c) 0.68 V
d) 0.83 V

Answer: a Page: 733

49. The respective standard reduction potentials in V for Zn^{2+} and Fe^{2+} are -0.76 and -0.44. Determine the value of $E°_{cell}$ for a voltaic cell in which the overall reaction is

    $Zn + Fe^{2+} \rightarrow Fe + Zn^{2+}$

    a) 0.32 V
    b) -0.32 V
    c) 1.20 V
    d) -1.20 V

    Answer: a Page: 733

50. The respective standard reduction potentials in V for Ag^{+} and Zn^{2+} are +0.80 and -0.76. Which substance will be oxidized in this voltaic cell?
    a) Ag
    b) Ag^{+}
    c) Zn^{2+}
    d) Zn

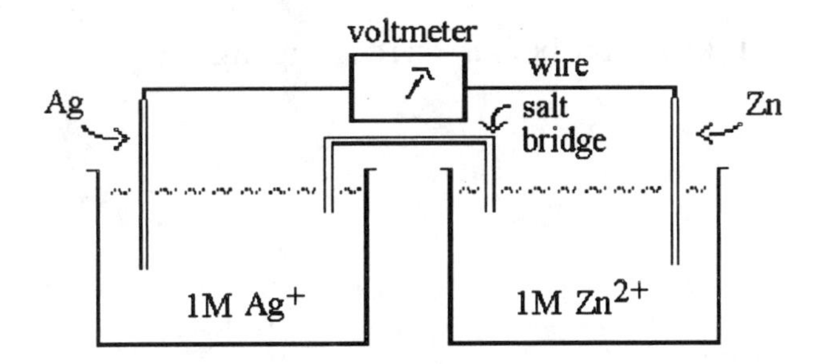

    Answer: d Page: 733

51. The respective standard reduction potentials in V for Ag^{+} and Zn^{2+} are +0.80 and -0.76. What is E° for this cell?
    a) 0.04 V
    b) 1.56 V
    c) -0.04 V
    d) -1.56 V

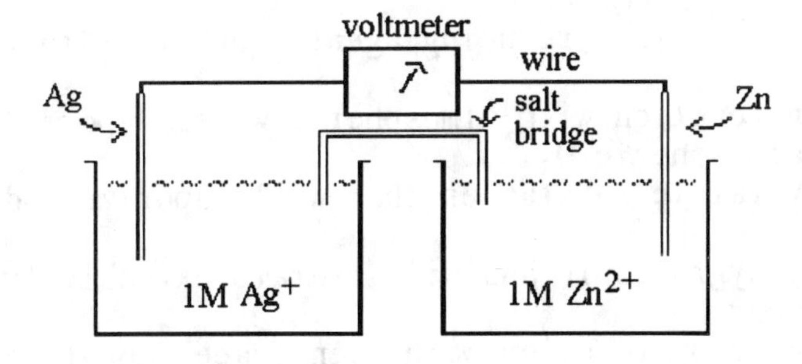

    Answer: b Page: 733

52. The more _____ the $E°$ value for a half-reaction, the greater the tendency for the reactant in the half-reaction to act as an oxidizing agent.
    a) positive
    b) negative
    c) exothermic
    d) endothermic

    Answer: a Page: 738

53. Which one of the following types of elements is most likely to be good oxidizing agents?
    a) alkali metals
    b) lanthanides
    c) alkaline earth elements
    d) transition elements
    e) halogens

    Answer: e Page: 738

54. Which one of the following is likely to be an oxidizing agent?
    a) permanganate ion
    b) fluoride ion
    c) sodium metal
    d) zinc nitrate
    e) lithium ion

    Answer: a Page: 738

55. Which one of the following is not a good reducing agent?
    a) H_2
    b) Na
    c) O_2
    d) Li
    e) Ca

    Answer: c Page: 738

56. Why is it generally necessary to store reducing agents such that they are not in contact with air?
    a) they rapidly degrade upon reaction with atmospheric water vapor
    b) to prevent oxidation by atmospheric O_2
    c) they are usually highly volatile substances that will vaporize and be lost
    d) they are generally highly hygroscopic and will hydrate extensively with atmospheric water vapor
    e) they are rapidly deactivated by reaction with even trace amounts of carbon dioxide

    Answer: b Page: 738

57. Use the following standard reduction potentials in V:
Cl_2 -> Cl^-, +1.36; Zn^{2+} -> Zn, -0.76; Mg^{2+} -> Mg, -2.38; H^+ -> H_2, 0.00; H_2O -> O_2, +1.23. Which one of the following substances can be oxidized by O_2 in acidic solution?
a) Cl^-
b) Zn^{2+}
c) Mg^{2+}
d) H_2

Answer: d Page: 738

58. Use the following standard reduction potentials in V:
I_2 -> I_2^-, +0.54; Br_2 -> Br^-, +1.07; H^+ -> H_2, 0.00; Cu^{2+} -> Cu, +0.34; Ni^{2+} -> Ni, -0.28. Which one of the following species could be used to oxidize I^- to I_2?
a) Br_2
b) H^+
c) Cu^{2+}
d) Ni^{2+}

Answer: a Page: 738

59. In acidic solution, the permanganate ion (MnO_4^-) is a
a) strong reducing agent
b) strong acid
c) strong oxidizing agent
d) good complexing agent

Answer: c Page: 738

60. Bromine can oxidize each of the metals below except

Substance	E° (v)
Br_2	1.09
Ag	0.80
Pt	1.20
Cu	0.34
Pd	0.83

a) Ag
b) Pt
c) Cu
d) Pd

Answer: b Page: 738

61. Given that the following reaction occurs spontaneously, which one of the following half-reactions has the largest *E* ° value in the positive direction associated with it?

$Mg + NiBr_2 \rightarrow Ni + MgBr_2$

a) $Br_2 \rightarrow 2Br^-$
b) $Mg^{2+} + 2e^- \rightarrow Mg$
c) $Ni^{2+} + 2e^- \rightarrow Ni$

Answer: c Page: 740

62. The relationship between the change in free energy and the emf of an electrochemical cell is given by
a) $\Delta G = \frac{-nF}{E}$
b) $\Delta G = \frac{-E}{nF}$
c) $\Delta G = -nFE$
d) $\Delta G = -nRTF$
e) $\Delta G = \frac{-nF}{ERT}$

Answer: c Page: 440

63. Calculate the ΔG, for the reaction of elemental bromine with chloride ion.

Substance	E° (v)
Br_2	1.09
Cl_2	1.36

a) $2.10 \times 10_5$ J
b) -2.62×10^5 J
c) 0.27 J
d) 5.21×10^4 J

Answer: d Page: 740

64. A spontaneous electrochemical reaction has
a) $\Delta G° = 0$, $E° = 0$, and $K >> 1$
b) $\Delta G° < 0$, $E° > 0$, and $K > 1$
c) $\Delta G° > 0$, $E° < 0$, and $K < 1$
d) $\Delta G° > 0$, $E° < 0$, and $K > 1$
e) $\Delta G° < 0$, $E° = 0$, and $K >> 1$

Answer: b Page: 740

65. E° for the following reaction is 0.13 V. What is the value of $\Delta G°$ (in kJ) for the reaction? (F = 96,500 J/V·mol)

$$Pb(s) + 2H^+(aq) \rightarrow Pb^{2+}(aq) + H_2(g)$$

a) -25
b) 25
c) -12
d) 12

Answer: a Page: 740

66. The standard reduction potentials in V for Ag^+ and Fe^{3+} to Fe^{2+} are +0.80 and +0.77, respectively. Calculate $\Delta G°$ for the following reaction. (F = 96,500 J/V·mol)
$Ag^+(aq) + Fe^{2+}(aq) \rightleftharpoons Ag(s) + Fe^{3+}(aq)$
a) 2.89 kJ
b) 151.7 kJ
c) -151.7 kJ
d) -2.89 kJ

Answer: d Page: 740

67. One of the differences between a voltaic cell and an electrolytic cell is that in an electrolytic cell
a) an electric current is produced by a chemical reaction.
b) electrons flow toward the anode.
c) a nonspontaneous reaction is forced to occur.
d) O_2 gas is produced at the cathode.

Answer: c Page: 740

ESSAY

68. What is the value of the emf of an electrochemical cell at equilibrium?

Answer: zero Page: 743

69. Explain the difference between the reaction quotient, *Q*, and the equilibrium constant, *K*.

Answer:
The reaction quotient involves concentrations at the time of measurement, the equilibrium constant involves concentrations at equilibrium only.
Page: 743

MULTIPLE CHOICE

70. The relationship between the standard emf for a redox reaction and its equilibrium constant is given by
a) $K = -nFE°$
b) $\ln K = \frac{\Delta G}{RT}$
c) $\log K = \frac{nE°}{0.0592}$
d) $E = E° - \frac{RT}{nF}\ln K$
e) $\ln K = \frac{\Delta G}{E°}$

Answer: c Page: 743

71. Consider the half reaction below. What will happen to the E° of this half cell if the iodate concentration is increased?

$2IO_3^-{}_{(aq)} + 10e^- + 12H^+{}_{(aq)} \rightarrow I_{2(s)} + 6H_2O_{(l)}$ E° = 1.195 v

a) it will increase
b) it will decrease
c) it will not change

Answer: a Page: 743

72. Consider the half reaction below. What will happen to the E° of this half cell if the pH is increased?
$2IO_3^-{}_{(aq)} + 10e^- + 12H^+{}_{(aq)} \rightarrow I_{2(s)} + 6H_2O_{(l)}$ E° = 1.195 v

a) it will increase
b) it will decrease
c) it will not change

Answer: b Page: 743

ESSAY

73. Calculate the equilibrium constant for the following reaction given that E° for $Cr_2O_7^{2-}/Cr^{3+}$ is 1.36 v and for $S_2O_3^{2-}/S_4O_6^{2-}$ is 0.17 v.
$Cr_2O_7^{2-} + 6S_2O^{2-}{}_3 + 14H^+ \rightarrow 2Cr^{3+} + 3S_4O_6^{2-} + 7H_2O$

Answer:
$E°_{cell}$ = 1.36 v - 0.17 v = 1.19 v
log K = (6)(1.19)/0.0592 = 121
$K = 4 \times 10^{120}$

Page: 743

MULTIPLE CHOICE

74. The standard reduction potentials in V for Zn^{2+} and Cu^{2+} are -0.76 and +0.34, respectively. What is the potential of the cell represented below?

    Zn | Zn^{2+}(1.00 M) || Cu^{2+}(0.100 M) | Cu

    a) -1.14 V
    b) -0.42 V
    c) 1.07 V
    d) 1.10 V

    Answer: c Page: 743

75. The value of E° for the following reaction is 0.63 V. What is the value of E° for this reaction when the concentration of Zn^{2+} is 0.00020 M and the concentration of Pb^{2+} is 1.0 M?

    Pb^{2+}(aq) + Zn(s) → Zn^{2+}(ag) + Pb(s)

    a) 0.52 V
    b) 0.85 V
    c) 0.41 V
    d) 0.74 V

    Answer: d Page: 743

76. The standard reduction potential for Zn^{2+} is -0.76 V. Calculate the voltage of the following cell at 25°C.

    Zn | Zn^{2+} (1.0 M) || H^{+}(.0010 M), H_2 (g, 1.0 atm) | Pt

    a) 0.58 V
    b) 0.41 V
    c) 0.94 V
    d) -0.94 V

    Answer: a Page: 743

77. The value of E° for the following reaction is 1.10 V. What is the value of E° for this reaction when the concentration of Cu^{2+} is 1.0 X 10^{-5} M and the concentration of Zn^{2+} is 1.0 M?

    Zn(s) + Cu^{2+}(aq) → Cu(s) + Zn^{2+}(aq)

    a) 1.40
    b) 1.25
    c) 0.95
    d) 0.80

    Answer: c Page: 743

78. The standard reduction potentials in V for Zn^{2+} and Cu^{2+} are -0.76 and +0.34, respectively. What is the concentration of Zn^{2+} when the following cell has the potential of 1.30 V at 25°C?

    Zn | Zn^{2+} (X M) || Cu^{2+}(4.0×10^{-5} M) | Cu

    a) 1.0
    b) 1.7×10^{-12}
    c) 4.4×10^{-87}
    d) 4.1×10^{-9}

    Answer: b Page: 743

79. The standard reduction potentials of Cu^{2+} and Ag^{+} in V are +0.34 and +0.80, respectively. Determine the value of E° (in volts) for the following cell at 25°C.

    Cu | Cu^{2+} (1.00 M) || Ag^{+}(0.0010 M) | Ag

    a) 0.11 V
    b) 0.28 V
    c) 0.37 V
    d) 0.55 V

    Answer: c Page: 743

80. The standard reduction potentials in V for Ag^{+} and Fe^{3+} to Fe^{2+} are +0.80 and +0.77, respectively. Calculate K, the equilibrium constant, for the following reaction at 25°C.

    (R = 8.314 J/K·mol, F = 96,500 J/V·mol)

    $Ag^{+}(aq) + Fe^{2+}(aq) \rightarrow Ag(s) + Fe^{3+}(aq)$

    a) 10.0
    b) 2.0
    c) 3.2
    d) 1.0

    Answer: c Page: 743

ESSAY

81. Explain why a lead storage battery is rechargeable.

    Answer:
    The products of the redox reactions precipitate onto and cling to the surfaces of the electrodes during discharge. Thus they are readily available to reform the original electrode material when electrical current is forced through the battery in the reverse direction during recharging.

    Page: 747

MULTIPLE CHOICE

82. What happens to the sulfuric acid in a lead storage battery when it is being discharged?
    a) sulfate ions are consumed and their concentration decreases
    b) protons are released so the pH drops
    c) it gets increasingly more viscous due to an increase in concentration
    d) its concentration rises

    Answer: a Page: 747

83. What is the cathode material in a dry cell?
    a) lead
    b) magnesium
    c) graphite
    d) zinc

    Answer: c Page: 747

84. What is the anode in an alkaline dry cell?
    a) MnO_2
    b) KOH
    c) Zn powder
    d) Mn_2O_3

    Answer: c Page: 747

ESSAY

85. What substances are produced at the cathode of a nicad battery during discharge?

    Answer: $Ni(OH)_2$ and OH^- Page: 747

MULTIPLE CHOICE

86. The lead-containing product(s) formed during recharging of a lead storage battery is/are
    a) Pb(s) only
    b) PbO_2(s) only
    c) $PbSO_4$(s) only
    d) both PbO_2(s) and $PbSO_4$(s)
    e) both Pb(s) and PbO_2(s)

    Answer: e Page: 747

87. In use of a lead storage battery, the electrodes are consumed. In such a battery
    a) the anode is Pb
    b) the anode is $PbSO_4$
    c) the anode is PbO_2
    d) the cathode is $PbSO_4$
    e) the cathode is Pb

    Answer: a Page: 747

88. In a common dry cell, the element being reduced during use is
    a) zinc
    b) manganese
    c) iron
    d) nitrogen
    e) oxygen

    Answer: b Page: 747

89. What is overvoltage and what is its cause?
    a) the extra voltage required over the theoretical amount calculated to cause a voltaic cell to function, caused by slow reaction rates at the electrodes
    b) the voltage produced by a battery after its theoretical expiration, caused by corrosion of the electrodes
    c) the extra voltage supplied by lead storage batteries for starting a car engine, possible because of the high electrolyte concentration supplied in manufacture of the battery
    d) the additional voltage required by a real circuit over that of a theoretical circuit to overcome friction (resistance) in the components, caused by resistance of the semiconductor components
    e) the voltage required to cause movement of the ions in the salt bridge of an electrochemical cell, caused by viscosity of the medium

    Answer: a Page: 750

ESSAY

90. In an electrolytic cell, the sign of the cathode is ___ and that of the anode is ___.

    Answer: -, + Page: 750

91. Elemental sodium cannot be produced by electrolysis of aqueous sodium chloride. Why?

    Answer:
    Because water is more easily reduced than sodium ions are, water will be reduced instead of sodium ions and elemental hydrogen will be produced instead of elemental sodium.
    Page: 750

MULTIPLE CHOICE

92. The standard reduction potentials of several common metal ions are listed: Mg^{2+}, -2.38 V; Li^{+}, -3.04 V; Ni^{2+}, -0.28 V; Mn^{2+}, -1.18 V; Ca^{2+}, -2.76 V. Considering that E° for $2H_2O(l) + 2e^- \rightarrow H_2(g) + 2OH^-(aq)$ is -0.83 V, which of the following metals may be produced via electrolysis of an aqueous solution of its nitrate?
a) magnesium
b) lithium
c) nickel
d) manganese
e) calcium

Answer: c Page: 750

93. How long will it take to plate out 2.19 g of chromium metal from a solution of Cr^{3+} using a current of 35.2 amps?
a) 5.77 minutes
b) 346 minutes
c) 115 minutes
d) 1.92 minutes

Answer: a Page: 754

94. What current is required to plate out 1.22 g of nickel from a solution of Ni^{2+} in 1.0 hour?
a) 65.4 amps
b) 4.01×10^3 amps
c) 1.17 amps
d) 12.9 amps

Answer: c Page: 754

95. The work, calculated from the equation below, required to run an electrolytic cell is always
$w = -nFE$

a) less than the actual amount required
b) more than the actual amount required
c) the same as the amount actually required

Answer: a Page: 754

96. The mass of chromium (in mg) deposited by passing a 27.2 mA current through an aqueous solution of $Cr(NO_3)_3$ for 989 s is __________. Use the facts that 1 A·s = 1 C and the total charge on 1 mole of electrons is 9.65×10^4C.
a) 14.5
b) 43.5
c) 4.83
d) 27.9
e) 96.5

Answer: c Page: 754

97. In an electrolytic cell, a 0.064 g sample of copper was deposited from copper(II) sulfate solution. How many grams of sodium would be produced if the same electron flow were passed through molten sodium chloride?
a) 0.012 g
b) 0.023 g
c) 0.046 g
d) 0.088 g

Answer: c Page: 754

98. How many grams of Ca metal could be produced by the electrolysis of molten $CaBr_2$ using a current of 30.0 amp for 10.0 hours?
(F = 96,500 coul/mol)
a) 22.4 g
b) 448 g
c) 0.0622 g
d) 224 g

Answer: d Page: 754

99. How many grams of copper metal can be obtained by passing a current of 12 amps through a solution of $CuSO_4$ for 15 minutes?
(F = 96,500 coul/mol)
a) 0.016 g
b) 3.6 g
c) 7.1 g
d) 14 g

Answer: b Page: 754

100. How many seconds will be required to produce 1.0 g of silver metal by the electrolysis of a $AgNO_3$ solution using a current of 30 amps?
(F = 96,500 coul/mol)
a) 2.7×10^4
b) 3.2×10^3
c) 30
d) 3.7×10^{-5}

Answer: c Page: 754

101. If a piece of aluminum metal was attached to a piece of iron, which metal would corrode first?
   a) the aluminum
   b) the iron
   c) neither, they would protect each other
   d) they would corrode at the same rate as if they were present separately
   e) neither, these metals do not corrode in the environment

   Answer: a Page: 758

102. Consider a piece of iron, such as a car door, that is coated with paint. This paint gets chipped off the iron in a spot by another car door contacting it. The iron will begin to corrode. Where will the pitting of the iron occur?
   a) in the very center of the exposed area
   b) in a ring in the exposed area
   c) just under the paint surrounding the edge of the exposed area
   d) evenly across the exposed area
   e) in the vicinity of any bends in the exposed area

   Answer: c Page: 758

ESSAY

103. Why does raising the pH of water in contact with iron reduce its corrosion rate?

   Answer:
   the reduction of O_2 requires H^+ and raising pH reduces the amount of H^+ available for this process

   Page: 758

104. Why can aluminum be used as a structural material even though it is a very active metal that corrodes very quickly?

   Answer:
   Because it rapidly forms a coating of Al_2O_3 that strongly adheres to the surface of the aluminum and insulates it from further corrosion.

   Page: 758

105. Oxygen is a stronger oxidizing agent in ____ environment than it is in ____ environment.

   Answer: an acidic, a basic Page: 758

Chapter 20: Electrochemistry

MULTIPLE CHOICE

106. Galvanized iron is iron coated with
    a) magnesium
    b) zinc
    c) chromium
    d) phosphate

    Answer: b Page: 758

ESSAY

107. What is meant by cathodic protection?

    Answer:
    A metal is electrically connected to a more active metal. When this set of electrically connected metals is placed in a corrosive environment, the active metal acts as the anode forcing the metal to be protected to act as the cathode. Since it is the cathode, it will not oxidize.

    Page: 758

MULTIPLE CHOICE

108. Cathodic protection of a metal pipe against corrosion usually entails
    a) attaching an active metal to make the pipe the anode in an electrochemical cell
    b) coating the pipe with another metal whose standard reduction potential is less negative than that of the pipe
    c) attaching an active metal to make the pipe the cathode in an electrochemical cell
    d) attaching a dry cell to reduce any metal ions which might be formed
    e) coating the pipe with a fluoropolymer to act as a source of fluoride ion (since the latter is so hard to oxidize)

    Answer: c Page: 758

109. Corrosion of iron is retarded by
    a) the presence of salts
    b) high pH conditions
    c) low pH conditions
    d) both the presence of salts and high pH conditions
    e) both the presence of salts and low pH conditions

    Answer: b Page: 758

Chapter 21: Nuclear Chemistry

MULTIPLE CHOICE

1. All atoms of a given element have the same
   a) mass number
   b) number of nucleons
   c) atomic mass
   d) charge
   e) atomic number

   Answer: e Page: 771

2. Atoms containing radioactive nuclei are called
   a) radionuclides
   b) radioisotopes
   c) nucleons
   d) nuclides
   e) radioisophores

   Answer: b Page: 771

3. What is the atomic number of an alpha particle?
   a) 0
   b) 1
   c) 2
   d) 3
   e) 4

   Answer: c Page: 771

4. What happens to the mass number and the atomic number of an element when it undergoes beta decay?
   a) neither the mass number nor the atomic number change
   b) the mass number decreases by 4 and the atomic number decreases by 2
   c) the mass number does not change and the atomic number increases by 1
   d) the mass number does not change and the atomic number decreases by 2
   e) the mass number increases by 2 and the atomic number increases by 1

   Answer: c Page: 771

5. Which one of the following is a correct representation of a beta particle?

a) ${}^{4}_{2}e$

b) ${}^{1}_{0}\beta$

c) ${}^{0}_{1}e$

d) ${}^{0}_{-1}e$

e) ${}^{2}_{4}\beta$

Answer: d Page: 771

6. Which one of the following processes results in an increase in the atomic number?
a) gamma emission
b) positron emission
c) beta emission
d) alpha emission
e) corrosion

Answer: c Page: 771

ESSAY

7. What happens in the nucleus of an atom that undergoes positron emission?

Answer: a proton is converted to a neutron and a positron Page: 771

MULTIPLE CHOICE

8. What is the mass number of an alpha particle?
a) 0
b) 1
c) 2
d) 3
e) 4

Answer: e Page: 771

ESSAY

9. What happens to the atomic mass number and the atomic number of a radioisotope when it undergoes alpha emission?

   Answer: The mass number drops by 4 and the atomic number decreases by 2.

   Page: 771

10. Electrons do not exist in the nucleus, yet beta emission is ejection of electrons from the nucleus. How does this happen?

    Answer:
    A neutron breaks apart to produce a proton and an electron in the nucleus. The proton remains in the nucleus and the electron is ejected.

    Page: 771

MULTIPLE CHOICE

11. Of the following processes, which one does not change the atomic number?
    a) alpha emission
    b) beta emission
    c) electron capture
    d) gamma emission
    e) positron emission

    Answer: d Page: 771

ESSAY

12. What isotope of what element is produced if krypton-81 undergoes beta decay?

    Answer: rubidium-81 Page: 771

13. When an isotope undergoes electron capture, what happens to the captured electron?

    Answer: It combines with a proton in the nucleus to form a neutron.

    Page: 771

MULTIPLE CHOICE

14. By what process does thorium-230 decay to radium-226?
 a) gamma emission
 b) alpha emission
 c) beta emission
 d) electron capture
 e) positron emission

 Answer: b Page: 771

ESSAY

15. The alpha decay of what isotope of what element produces lead-206?

 Answer: polonium-210 Page: 771

MULTIPLE CHOICE

16. In balancing the nuclear reaction ${}^{238}_{92}U \rightarrow {}^{234}_{90}E + {}^{4}_{2}He$, the identity of element E is determined from its
 a) atomic weight
 b) mass number
 c) atomic number
 d) number of neutrons
 e) number of electrons

 Answer: c Page: 771

17. Which type of radioactive decay results in no change in mass number and atomic number for the starting nucleus?
 a) alpha
 b) beta
 c) positron emission
 d) electron capture
 e) gamma

 Answer: e Page: 771

18. Alpha-decay produces a new nucleus whose ________________ than those respectively of the original nucleus.
 a) atomic number is 2 less and mass number is 2 less
 b) atomic number is 1 less and mass number is 2 less
 c) atomic number is 2 less and mass number is 4 less
 d) atomic number is 2 more and mass number is 4 more
 e) atomic number is 2 more and mass number is 2 less

 Answer: c Page: 771

19. What is the missing product from this reaction?

$$^{32}_{15}P \rightarrow \, ^{32}_{16}S + \_\_\_\_\_\_$$

a) $^{4}_{2}He$

b) $^{0}_{-1}e$

c) $^{0}_{0}.$

d) $^{0}_{1}e$

Answer: b Page: 771

20. This reaction is an example of ______ decay.

$$^{210}_{84}Po \rightarrow \, ^{206}_{82}Pb + \_\_\_\_\_\_$$

a) alpha
b) beta
c) gamma
d) positron

Answer: a Page: 771

21. The missing product from this reaction is

$$^{121}_{53}I \rightarrow \, ^{121}_{52}Te + \_\_\_\_\_\_$$

a) $^{4}_{2}He$

b) $^{0}_{-1}e$

c) $^{1}_{0}n$

d) $^{0}_{1}e$

Answer: d Page: 771

22. This reaction is an example of __________.

$$^{41}_{20}Ca + \_\_\_\_\_\_ \rightarrow ^{41}_{19}K$$

a) alpha decay
b) beta decay
c) positron decay
d) electron capture

Answer: d Page: 771

23. The missing product in this reaction would be found in which group of the periodic table?

$$^{24}_{11}Na \rightarrow ^{0}_{-1}e + \_\_\_\_\_\_$$

a) 1A
b) 2A
c) 3A
d) 8A

Answer: b Page: 771

24. The missing product in this reaction combines with oxygen to form a compound with the formula

$$^{42}_{19}K \rightarrow ^{0}_{-1}e + \_\_\_\_\_\_$$

a) M_2O
b) MO
c) MO_2
d) M_2O_3

Answer: b Page: 771

25. Which one of these radioactive decay products has the shortest average lifetime in the atmosphere?

a) $^{4}_{2}He$

b) $^{0}_{-1}e$

c) $^{0}_{1}e$

d) $^{1}_{0}n$

Answer: c Page: 771

26. Radium undergoes alpha decay. The product of this reaction also undergoes alpha decay. What is the product of this second decay reaction?
a) Po
b) Rn
c) U
d) Th

Answer: a Page: 771

27. ^{41}Ca decays by electron capture. The product of this reaction undergoes positron decay. What is the product of this second decay reaction?
a) Ti
b) Ca
c) Ar
d) Cl

Answer: c Page: 771

28. Nuclei above the belt of stability can lower their proton-to-neutron ratio by
a) beta emission
b) gamma emission
c) positron emission
d) electron capture

Answer: a Page: 774

29. How many radioactive decay series exist in nature?
a) 0
b) 1
c) 2
d) 3
e) 10

Answer: d Page: 774

30. What is the largest number of protons that can exist in a nucleus and still be stable?
a) 206
b) 82
c) 92
d) 83

Answer: d Page: 774

ESSAY

31. Stable nuclei with low atomic numbers, up to 20, have a neutron to proton ratio of ___.

Answer: 1 Page: 774

MULTIPLE CHOICE

32. The three radioactive series that occur in nature end with what element?
a) Bi
b) U
c) Po
d) Pb

Answer: d Page: 774

33. Of the following, which is not a magic number of protons?
a) 20
b) 8
c) 50
d) 126
e) 2
f) 82

Answer: d Page: 774

34. The largest number of stable nuclei have an ___ number of protons and an ___ number of neutrons.
a) even, even
b) odd, odd
c) even, odd
d) odd, even

Answer: a Page: 774

35. Which of these nuclides is most likely to be radioactive?
a) $^{39}_{19}K$
b) $^{27}_{13}Al$
c) $^{127}_{53}I$
d) $^{243}_{95}Am$

Answer: d Page: 774

36. A nucleus is most likely to be unstable when it has an ______ number of protons and an ______ number of neutrons.
a) odd, odd
b) odd, even
c) even, odd
d) even, even

Answer: a Page: 774

37. What is required for a nuclear transmutation to occur?
    a) very high temperature
    b) a corrosive environment
    c) a particle to collide with a nucleus
    d) spontaneous nuclear decay
    e) gamma emission

    Answer: c Page: 779

38. The first nuclear transmutation was performed by ______.
    a) Michael Faraday
    b) Madame Curie
    c) Galileo
    d) Mendeleev
    e) Ernest Rutherford

    Answer: e Page: 779

ESSAY

39. The first nuclear transmutation resulted in the conversion of nitrogen-14 to _____.

    Answer: oxygen-17 Page: 779

MULTIPLE CHOICE

40. The cobalt-60 used in cancer radiation therapy is produced by bombardment of what element with neutrons?
    a) uranium
    b) cobalt
    c) aluminum
    d) iron
    e) chromium

    Answer: d Page: 779

41. In the nuclear transmutation, $16_{8}O(p,\alpha)^{13}{}_{7}N$, what is the bombarding particle?
    a) an alpha particle
    b) a beta particle
    c) a gamma photon
    d) a proton

    Answer: d Page: 779

42. What particle is emitted in the nuclear transmutation, $^{27}_{13}Al(n,?)^{24}_{11}Na$?
    a) an alpha particle
    b) a beta particle
    c) a neutron
    d) a proton

Answer: a Page: 779

43. Which one of the following requires a particle accelerator to occur?

a) $^{59}_{26}Fe \rightarrow ^{59}_{27}Co + ^{0}_{-1}e$

b) $^{59}_{27}Co + ^{1}_{0}n \rightarrow ^{60}_{27}Co$

c) $^{238}_{92}U + ^{1}_{0}n \rightarrow ^{239}_{93}Np + ^{0}_{-1}e$

d) $^{239}_{94}Pu + ^{4}_{2}He \rightarrow ^{242}_{96}Cm + ^{1}_{0}n$

e) none of these

Answer: d Page: 779

44. Bombardment of uranium-238 with a deuteron (hydrogen-2) generates neptunium-238 and ___ neutrons.
    a) 1
    b) 2
    c) 3
    d) 4
    e) 5

Answer: b Page: 779

45. Bombardment of uranium-235 with a neutron generates tellurium-135, 2 neutrons, and
    a) strontium-103
    b) krypton-101
    c) krypton-103
    d) strontium-99
    e) zirconium-99

Answer: e Page: 779

46. The reaction shown below is responsible for creating ^{14}C in the atmosphere. What is the bombarding particle?

$$^{14}_{7}N + \_\_\_\_\_ \rightarrow ^{14}_{6}C + ^{1}_{1}H$$

a) $^{4}_{2}He$ or alpha

b) $^{0}_{-1}e$ or beta

c) neutron
d) positron

Answer: c Page: 779

47. The nuclide ^{77}Se can be formed in a cyclotron by bombarding _____ with alpha particles (assuming no fragmentation).
a) $^{73}_{32}Ge$

b) $^{77}_{35}Br$

c) $^{81}_{36}Kr$

d) $^{77}_{33}As$

Answer: a Page: 779

48. What order process is radioactive decay?
a) zeroth
b) first
c) second
d) third

Answer: b Page: 781

49. Which one of the following can be done to shorten the half life of the radioactive decay of strontium-90?
a) freeze it
b) heat it
c) react it with phosphate to form an insoluble compound
d) oxidize it to the +2 oxidation state
e) none of these

Answer: e Page: 781

ESSAY

50. The half-life for the beta decay of potassium-40 is 1.3×10^9 years. What is the rate constant for this decay?

Answer:
$t_{1/2} = 0.693/k$
1.3×10^9 years $= 0.693/k$
$k = 5.3 \times 10^{-10}$ year^{-1}

Page: 781

MULTIPLE CHOICE

51. The beta decay of cesium-137 is 30 years. How many years must pass to reduce a 25 mg sample of cesium 137 to 0.78 mg?
a) 60 years
b) 150 years
c) 180 years
d) 750 years
e) 5 years

Answer: b Page: 781

52. The half-life for beta decay of strontium-90 is 28.8 years. A milk sample is found to contain 10.3 ppm strontium-90. How many years would pass before the strontium-90 concentration would drop to 1.0 ppm?
a) 92.3
b) 0.112
c) 186
d) 96.9
e) 131

Answer: d Page: 781

53. The carbon-14 dating method can be used to determine the age of a
a) flint arrowhead
b) papyrus scroll
c) stone axe head
d) clay pot

Answer: b Page: 781

54. The basis for the carbon-14 dating method is that
a) the amount of carbon-14 in all objects is the same.
b) carbon-14 is very unstable and is readily lost from the atmosphere.
c) the ratio of carbon-14 to carbon-12 in the atmosphere is a constant.
d) living tissue will not absorb carbon-14 but will absorb carbon-12.

Answer: c Page: 781

55. ^{131}I has a half-life of 8.04 days. Assuming you start with a 1.35 mg sample of ^{131}I, how much will remain after 13.0 days?
 a) 0.835 mg
 b) 0.268 mg
 c) 0.422 mg
 d) 0.440 mg

 Answer: d Page: 781

56. ^{210}Pb has a half-life of 22.3 years and decays to produce ^{206}Hg. If you start with 7.50 g of ^{210}Pb, how many grams of ^{206}Hg will you have after 17.5 years?
 a) 4.35
 b) 3.15
 c) 3.09
 d) 0.0600

 Answer: a Page: 781

ESSAY

57. How does a Geiger counter function to allow detection of radioactive emissions?

 Answer:
 radioactive emissions ionize the atmosphere in the Geiger counter allowing a current to flow

 Page: 786

MULTIPLE CHOICE

58. What is a phosphor?
 a) an oxide of phosphorus
 b) a substance that thermally reduces to phosphorus
 c) a bioluminescent substance
 d) a substance that emits light when excited by radiation
 e) an alkali metal phosphide

 Answer: d Page: 786

59. Which one of the following devices converts radioactive emissions to light for detection?
 a) Geiger counter
 b) photographic film
 c) scintillation counter
 d) none of these

 Answer: c Page: 786

60. Which one of the following is used as a radiotracer to study blood?
    a) iron-59
    b) technetium-99
    c) sodium-23
    d) iodine-131
    e) phosphorus-32

    Answer: a Page: 786

61. Due to the nature of the positron, what is actually detected in positron emission tomagraphy is
    a) alpha radiation
    b) beta radiation
    c) gamma radiation
    d) x-ray emission
    e) neutron emission

    Answer: c Page: 786

ESSAY

62. What is the source of the tremendous energies produced by nuclear reactions?

    Answer: conversion of matter to energy, mass loss Page: 787

MULTIPLE CHOICE

63. Which one of the following is true?
    a) most spontaneous nuclear reactions are exothermic
    b) some spontaneous nuclear reactions are endothermic
    c) all spontaneous nuclear reactions are exothermic
    d) there is no relationship between exothermicity and spontaneity in nuclear reactions

    Answer: c Page: 787

64. Binding energy per nucleon is greatest for nuclei with
    a) large mass number
    b) intermediate mass number
    c) small mass number

    Answer: b Page: 787

65. The greater the binding energy, the ___ stable the nucleus.
    a) more
    b) less

    Answer: a Page: 787

66. The respective masses in amu of the proton, the neutron, and the nickel-60 atom are 1.00728, 1.00867, and 59.9308. What is the mass defect of the nickel-60 atom in amu?
a) 0.5505
b) 0.5449
c) 0.6060
d) 0.6111
e) 0.7280

Answer: a Page: 787

67. The mass of a proton is 1.673×10^{-24} g. The mass of a neutron is 1.675×10^{-24} g. The mass of the nucleus of an ^{56}Fe atom is 9.289×10^{-23} g. What is the nuclear binding energy (in J) for Fe^{56}?
($C = 3.00 \times 10^{8}$ m/s)
a) 2.57×10^{-16}
b) 7.72×10^{-8}
c) 8.36×10^{-9}
d) 7.72×10^{-11}

Answer: d Page: 787

68. When two atoms of ^{2}H are fused to form one atom of ^{4}He, the total energy evolved is 3.83×10^{-12} J. What is the total change in mass for this reaction?
($C = 3.00 \times 10^{8}$ m/s)

a) 1.28×10^{-17} g
b) 4.26×10^{-26} g
c) 3.45×10^{8} g
d) 1.15 g

Answer: b Page: 787

69. What is the typical percent of uranium-235 in the UO_2 pellets used in nuclear reactors?
a) 0.7
b) 1
c) 3
d) 5
e) 14

Answer: c Page: 791

70. Energy is released from a nuclear fission reaction because the total mass of products is ________ than that of the reactants. Energy is released in a nuclear fusion reaction because the total mass of products is ________ than that of the reactants.
a) less, less
b) more, more
c) less, more
d) more, less

Answer: a Page: 791

71. On average, ___ neutrons are produced by every fission of uranium-235.
a) 4
b) 3.5
c) 1
d) 2.4

Answer: d Page: 791

72. When the critical mass of uranium-235 is present, ___ neutron(s) from each fission cause(s) subsequent fission reactions.
a) 4
b) 3.5
c) 1
d) 2.4

Answer: c Page: 791

ESSAY

73. What is the form and concentration of the fuel in a typical nuclear reactor?

Answer: UO_2 pellets with the uranium-235 isotope enriched to about 3%

Page: 791

74. What is the purpose of the moderator in a nuclear reactor?

Answer:
to slow the neutrons so that they can be captured by the fissile uranium-235 and cause subsequent fission reactions

Page: 791

MULTIPLE CHOICE

75. What drives the turbine in a nuclear power plant?
    a) the moderator
    b) steam
    c) the control rods
    d) the primary coolant

    Answer: b Page: 791

76. Fission reactions can be run continuously to generate electric power commercially because
    a) the reactors generate more readily fissionable fuel than they consume
    b) graphite control rods provide additional protons when the process becomes subcritical
    c) many more neutrons are produced in the fission reactions than are consumed
    d) supercritical neutrons split into protons and electrons
    e) the different isotopes of uranium interconvert under reactor conditions to form the necessary uranium-235

    Answer: c Page: 791

77. A nuclear power plant cannot undergo a nuclear explosion because
    a) the amount of ^{235}U present is supercritical.
    b) there is no detonator present.
    c) the ^{235}U content is only 3% of the total uranium present.
    d) the fuel rods prevent the fission reaction from going critical.

    Answer: c Page: 791

78. Who is credited with first achieving fission of uranium-235?
    a) Fermi
    b) Rutherford
    c) Curie
    d) Dalton
    e) Faraday

    Answer: a Page: 794

ESSAY

79. What was the purpose of the Manhattan project?

    Answer: to build a bomb based on nuclear fission Page: 794

MULTIPLE CHOICE

80. What type of reaction is known as a thermonuclear reaction?
a) fission
b) fusion
c) transmutation
d) beta emission
e) neutron emission

Answer: b Page: 797

81. When ionizing radiation enters the body, what is the predominant free radical produced?
a) H
b) H_3O
c) protein
d) OH
e) H_2O

Answer: d Page: 797

82. What is the source of radon-222 in soil? The nuclear disintegration series of
a) ^{235}U
b) ^{238}U
c) ^{236}Pb
d) ^{235}Th
e) ^{14}C

Answer: b Page: 797

83. What type of reaction is a thermonuclear reaction?
a) fission
b) fusion

Answer: b Page: 797

84. What is a tokamak?
a) a device that uses strong magnetic fields to contain and heat nuclei with the goal of inducing sustained fusion
b) a linear particle accelerator
c) a variation on a cyclotron
d) a laser heating device

Answer: a Page: 797

85. The main scientific difficulty in achieving a controlled fusion process is the
    a) enormous repulsion between nuclei being fused
    b) enormous repulsion between the electrons of atoms being fused
    c) very large number of positrons emitted
    d) very large number of x-rays emitted
    e) very large number of gamma rays emitted

    Answer: a Page: 797

ESSAY

86. What are the clinical effects of acute exposure to radiation?

    Answer: decrease in white blood cell count, nausea, fatigue, diarrhea

    Page: 797

MULTIPLE CHOICE

87. Of the following, which is the most damaging when ingested?
    a) alpha emitters
    b) beta emitters
    c) gamma emitters

    Answer: a Page: 797

ESSAY

88. The relative biological effectiveness (RBE) values of beta rays, gamma rays, and alpha rays are, respectively

    Answer: 1, 1, 10 Page: 797

MULTIPLE CHOICE

89. What exposure level to radiation is fatal to most humans?
    a) 100 rem
    b) 200 rem
    c) 600 rem
    d) 300 rem

    Answer: c Page: 797

90. Which one of the following is not true concerning radon?
    a) it decays by alpha emission
    b) it decays to polonium-218, an alpha emitter
    c) it is chemically active in human lungs
    d) it has been implicated in lung cancer

    Answer: c Page: 797

91. The noble gas thought to be significantly carcinogenic due to its radioactive decay and that of its decay products is
    a) helium
    b) xenon
    c) argon
    d) radon
    e) neon

    Answer: d Page: 797

92. The curie is a measure of the
    a) number of disintegrations per second of a radioactive substance.
    b) total energy absorbed by an object exposed to a radioactive source.
    c) lethal threshold for radiation exposure.
    d) number of alpha particles emitted by exactly one gram of a radioactive substance.

    Answer: a Page: 797

93. Which one of the following forms of radiation can penetrate the deepest into body tissue?
    a) alpha
    b) beta
    c) gamma
    d) positron

    Answer: c Page: 797

Chapter 22: Chemistry of the Nonmetal

MULTIPLE CHOICE

1. An element with a very low electronegativity is most likely a
   a) metal
   b) nonmetal
   c) metalloid

   Answer: a Page: 807

2. In a group of nonmetals, which element(s) is(are) most likely to be able to form stable π-bonds?
   a) the bottom element
   b) the top element
   c) the middle element
   d) the second element
   e) none of them, nonmetals do not do this

   Answer: b Page: 807

ESSAY

3. What are the three crystalline allotropes of carbon?

   Answer: diamond, graphite, and buckminsterfullerene Page: 807

4. Explain why silicon does not form any allotropes with structures analagous to that of graphite or buckminsterfullerenes, even though it is in the same group as carbon.

   Answer:
   silicon is large enough to prevent efficient sideways overlap of p orbitals for π bond formation
   Page: 807

MULTIPLE CHOICE

5. How many oxygen atoms are bonded to each silicon atom in SiO_2?
   a) 1
   b) 2
   c) 3
   d) 4

   Answer: b Page: 807

6. Which atom below is most effective in forming pi bonds?
   a) As
   b) P
   c) N
   d) Si
   e) Ge

   Answer: c Page: 807

ESSAY

7. Complete and balance the following reaction.
   $Na_3P + H_2O \rightarrow$

   Answer: $Na_3P + 3H_2O \rightarrow 3NaOH + PH_3$ Page: 807

8. Complete and balance the following reaction.
   $C_5H_5N + O_2 \rightarrow$

   Answer: $4C_5H_5N + 25O_2 \rightarrow 20CO_2 + 10H_2O + 2N_2$ Page: 807

MULTIPLE CHOICE

9. The principal combustion products of compounds containing carbon and hydrogen in the presence of excess O_2 are
   a) CO_2 and H_2O
   b) CO_2 and H_2O_2
   c) CO_2 and H
   d) C(graphite) and H_2

   Answer: a Page: 807

10. Mg_3N_2 reacts with H_2O to produce which nitrogen-containing species?
    a) N_2
    b) N_2O
    c) NO
    d) NO_2
    e) NH_3

    Answer: e Page: 807

11. The most common isotope of hydrogen is called
    a) deuterium
    b) protium
    c) tritium
    d) heavy hydrogen

    Answer: b Page: 810

12. Which one of the following is false concerning tritium?
    a) it is radioactive, undergoing alpha decay with a half-life of 12.3 years
    b) it can be produced by neutron bombardment of lithium-6
    c) it is formed continuously in the upper atmosphere
    d) it has the same chemical properties as protium but reacts more slowly

    Answer: a Page: 810

13. Of the following, which has the smallest electron affinity?
    a) I
    b) Cl
    c) H
    d) F
    e) Br

    Answer: c Page: 810

14. What method is used to produce the most hydrogen gas in the United States?
    a) electrolysis of water
    b) reaction of zinc with acid
    c) reaction of methane with steam
    d) reaction of coke (carbon) with steam

    Answer: c Page: 810

15. What is the primary use of hydrogen?
    a) as a rocket fuel, especially on the space shuttle
    b) hydrogenation of vegetable oils
    c) manufacture of methanol
    d) manufacture of ammonia

    Answer: d Page: 810

16. Of the following, which is a metallic hydride?
    a) $TiH_{1.8}$
    b) LiH
    c) CaH_2
    d) PH_3

    Answer: a Page: 810

17. In metallic hydrides the oxidation number of hydrogen is considered to be
    a) -2
    b) -1
    c) 0
    d) +1
    e) +2

    Answer: b Page: 810

18. The main industrial use of H_2 in the U.S. is the
    a) manufacture of NH_3 by the Haber process
    b) manufacture of HCl
    c) manufacture of CH_3OH
    d) hydrogenation of C=C in vegetable oil in the food industry
    e) manufacture of metal hydrides

    Answer: a Page: 810

19. In its ability to form hydride ions, hydrogen resembles the elements of group _____ of the periodic table.
    a) 1A
    b) 2A
    c) 6A
    d) 7A

    Answer: d Page: 810

20. Which compound would produce an acidic aqueous solution?
    a) KH
    b) CaH_2
    c) H_2S
    d) NH_3

    Answer: c Page: 810

21. Which compound would produce a basic aqueous solution?
    a) MgH_2
    b) H_2S
    c) HCl
    d) HI

    Answer: a Page: 810

ESSAY

22. The most abundant element in the universe is ___ and in the crust of the earth is ___.

    Answer: hydrogen, oxygen Page: 810

23. Which noble gas is the most abundant?
    a) Ne
    b) He
    c) Ar
    d) Kr
    e) Rn
    f) Xe

    Answer: c Page: 815

ESSAY

24. ____ has the lowest boiling point of any substance known.
   a) Ne
   b) He
   c) Ar
   d) Kr
   e) Rn
   f) Xe

   Answer: b Page: 815

25. How are the oxygen-containing compounds of xenon made?
   a) by direct combination of the elements
   b) by reaction of xenon with peroxide
   c) by thermal decompostion of the hydroxide
   d) by reaction of the fluoride with water

   Answer: d Page: 815

26. Of the following compounds, which is the most stable?
   a) XeF_6
   b) $XeOF_4$
   c) XeO_3
   d) none of these is stable

   Answer: a Page: 815

27. The respective electron-pair geometry, molecular geometry, and central Kr atom hybridization in KrF_2 are
   a) trigonal bipyramidal; bent; sp^3d^2
   b) trigonal bipyramidal; linear; sp^3d
   c) trigonal bipyramidal; bent; sp^3d
   d) octahedral; linear; sp^3d^2
   e) octahedral; bent; sp^3d^2

   Answer: b Page: 815

28. The number of electrons in the valence shell of Xe in XeF_6 is
   a) 10
   b) 12
   c) 14
   d) 16
   e) 18

   Answer: c Page: 815

29. Which one of the following noble gases forms more than one fluoride?
   a) Ne
   b) Kr
   c) Ar
   d) Xe

   Answer: d Page: 815

30. What is the F-Xe-F bond angle in XeF_2?
    a) 90°
    b) 109°
    c) 180°
    d) 120°

    Answer: c Page: 815

31. Which one of the following is the least abundant in nature?
    a) iodine
    b) bromine
    c) chlorine
    d) fluorine

    Answer: a Page: 818

32. Which one of the following has the lowest ionization energy?
    a) iodine
    b) bromine
    c) chlorine
    d) fluorine

    Answer: a Page: 818

ESSAY

33. Write the correctly balanced equation for the reaction between elemental fluorine and sodium iodide.

    Answer: $F_2 + 2\ NaI \rightarrow I_2 + 2\ NaF$ Page: 818

34. Write the correctly balanced equation for the reaction between elemental iodine and sodium bromide.

    Answer: $I_2 + NaBr \rightarrow$ no reaction Page: 818

35. How is elemental fluorine produced industrially? What other free element is also produced in the process?

    Answer:
    by electrolysis of a solution of KF in anhydrous HF, elemental hydrogen is also produced
    Page: 818

MULTIPLE CHOICE

36. The silver salt of ___ is used extensively in production of photographic film.
    a) fluorine
    b) chlorine
    c) bromine
    d) iodine

    Answer: c Page: 818

ESSAY

37. HF and HCl are prepared by reaction of the appropriate salt with sulfuric acid. HBr and HI are not prepared this way. Why?

    Answer:
    Bromide and iodide are readily oxidized to the elemental form by sulfuric acid and so Br_2 and I_2 are formed in this reaction instead of the hydrogen halide.

    Page: 818

MULTIPLE CHOICE

38. Which hydrohalic acid cannot be stored in glass containers for extended periods of time?
    a) HI
    b) HBr
    c) HCl
    d) HF

    Answer: d Page: 818

ESSAY

39. Which hydrogen halide is a weak acid in aqueous solution?

    Answer: HF Page: 818

40. The acid and salts of which halogen-oxyanion are the most stable?

    Answer: perchlorate Page: 818

MULTIPLE CHOICE

41. Which halogen can react with fluorine to form the compound XF_7?
    a) bromine
    b) fluorine
    c) chlorine
    d) iodine

    Answer: d Page: 818

42. Interhalogen compounds
    a) are exceedingly reactive
    b) contain halogens in a positive oxidation state
    c) are powerful oxidizing agents
    d) are very active fluorinating agents
    e) all of these

    Answer: e Page: 818

43. Which halogen forms an oxyacid with the formula HXO_2?
    a) bromine
    b) fluorine
    c) chlorine
    d) iodine

    Answer: c Page: 818

44. Which elemental halogen(s) can be used to prepare I_2 from NaI?
    a) F_2 only
    b) Cl_2 only
    c) Br_2 only
    d) both Cl_2 and Br_2, but not F_2
    e) F_2, Cl_2, and Br_2

    Answer: e Page: 818

45. The most basic of the following oxyanions is
    a) ClO^-
    b) ClO_2^-
    c) BrO^-
    d) BrO_2^-
    e) IO^-

    Answer: e Page: 818

46. Which one of the following is the strongest acid in aqueous solution?
    a) HIO_4
    b) $HClO_3$
    c) HIO_3
    d) $HClO_4$

    Answer: d Page: 818

47. Br_2 can be prepared by reacting NaBr with
    a) Cl_2
    b) HBr
    c) HCl
    d) NaCl

    Answer: a Page: 818

ESSAY

48. What is a disproportionation reaction?

    Answer: A reaction in which the same element is both oxidized and reduced

    Page: 825

MULTIPLE CHOICE

49. The most stable allotrope of oxygen is
    a) H_2O
    b) O_3
    c) O_2
    d) HClO

    Answer: c Page: 825

50. What is the coefficient on $KClO_3$ when the following equation is completed and balanced?

$$KClO_3 \xrightarrow{\Delta} KCl + O_2$$

    a) 1
    b) 2
    c) 3
    d) 5

    Answer: b Page: 825

51. Most commercial oxygen is obtained
    a) by fractional distillation of liquefied air
    b) by electrolysis of water
    c) by thermal decomposition of potassium chlorate
    d) by thermal cracking of petroleum
    e) as a byproduct of the preparation of aluminum in the Hall process

    Answer: a Page: 825

52. The primary use of oxygen is
    a) medical, for treatment of respiratory distress
    b) in welding
    c) as a bleach
    d) as an oxidizing agent

    Answer: d Page: 825

53. Which one of the following is false concerning ozone?
    a) it is a better reducing agent than O_2
    b) it is produced by passing electricity through dry O_2
    c) it oxidizes all of the common metals except gold and platinum
    d) it rapidly decomposes to O_2 and O

    Answer: a Page: 825

ESSAY

54. With what element will carbon react to form compounds in which oxygen has a positive oxidation number?

    Answer: fluorine Page: 825

MULTIPLE CHOICE

55. Which one of the following will not react with water?
    a) SO_2
    b) N_2O
    c) CO_2
    d) P_2O_5

    Answer: b Page: 825

ESSAY

56. If a metal forms more than one oxide, the acid character of the oxide increases as the oxidation state of the metal

    Answer: increases Page: 825

MULTIPLE CHOICE

57. The most active metals react with oxygen to form
    a) oxides
    b) superoxides
    c) peroxides
    d) ozonides

    Answer: b Page: 825

ESSAY

58. Write the correctly balanced equation for the reaction of rubidium superoxide with water.

    Answer: $2\ RbO_2 + 2\ H_2O \rightarrow 2\ RbOH + O_2 + H_2O_2$ Page: 825

MULTIPLE CHOICE

59. Hydrogen peroxide
    a) is a colorless, odorless, gas at room temperature
    b) can act as either an oxidizing or reducing agent
    c) is sold as a 30% solution for use as an antiseptic
    d) contains oxygen in the - 1/2 oxidation state

    Answer: b Page: 825

60. Which of the following should be the most basic oxide?
    a) CO
    b) CO_2
    c) SO_2
    d) N_2O
    e) BaO

    Answer: e Page: 825

61. Which of the following should be the most acidic oxide?
    a) SO_3
    b) CO_2
    c) CO
    d) MgO
    e) CaO

    Answer: a Page: 825

62. Which one of the following compounds is peroxide?
    a) Li_2O
    b) H_2O
    c) Na_2O_2
    d) CsO_2

    Answer: c Page: 825

63. Which one of the following compounds is a superoxide?
    a) H_2O_2
    b) CaO
    c) CaO_2
    d) RbO_2

    Answer: d Page: 825

64. Which compound would produce a basic aqueous solution?
   a) CaO
   b) CO_2
   c) SO_2
   d) NO_2

   Answer: a Page: 825

65. Which compound would produce an acidic aqueous solution?
   a) Na_2O
   b) CO_2
   c) MgO
   d) Li_2O

   Answer: b Page: 825

66. Which element in group 6A is not found in compounds with an expanded valence shell?
   a) oxygen
   b) selenium
   c) tellurium
   d) polonium
   e) sulfur

   Answer: a Page: 830

67. Which one of the following is the strongest acid in aqueous solution?
   a) H_2Se
   b) H_2S
   c) H_2Te

   Answer: c Page: 830

68. Which group 6A element is not commonly found in a positive oxidation state?
   a) sulfur
   b) selenium
   c) oxygen
   d) tellurium

   Answer: c Page: 830

69. What is the trend in metallic character in group 6A?
   a) there is none, these are all nonmetals
   b) it increases going down the group
   c) it increases going up the group

   Answer: b Page: 830

70. What is the major source of elemental sulfur?
    a) sulfides
    b) sulfates
    c) underground deposits of elemental sulfur
    d) seawater

    Answer: c Page: 830

71. Which form of sulfur is the most stable at room temperature?
    a) rhombic
    b) monoclinic
    c) hexagonal
    d) triclinic

    Answer: a Page: 830

72. Which one of the following is used on the photosensitive drum in a photocopier?
    a) sulfur
    b) selenium
    c) oxygen
    d) tellurium

    Answer: b Page: 830

73. Which one of the following does not produce sulfur dioxide?
    a) $S_8 + O_2$
    b) $Hg + H_2SO_4$
    c) $CuS + O_2$
    d) $K_2SO_3 + HCl$
    e) all of these produce sulfur dioxide

    Answer: e Page: 830

ESSAY

74. State the three steps in sulfuric acid production.

    Answer:
    1. burning of sulfur in oxygen to produce sulfur dioxide, 2. oxidation of sulfur dioxide to sulfur trioxide, 3. dissolving sulfur trioxide in sulfuric acid and diluting with water

    Page: 830

MULTIPLE CHOICE

75. What is the most heavily produced chemical in industry?
   a) H_2SO_4
   b) NH_3
   c) NaCl
   d) asphalt
   e) Cl_2

   Answer: a Page: 830

76. Thiosulfate ion
   a) is used in developing black and white photographic film
   b) is made by boiling an alkaline solution of sulfite ion with elemental sulfur
   c) decomposes to sulfur and sulfurous acid when acidified
   d) is a reducing agent used for reducing iodine to iodide
   e) all of these

   Answer: e Page: 830

77. Which one of the following is insoluble in water?
   a) SeO_2
   b) TeO_2
   c) SO_2
   d) all of these are soluble in water

   Answer: b Page: 830

78. Which one of the following does not contain sulfur?
   a) iron pyrite
   b) dolomite
   c) galena
   d) cinnabar

   Answer: b Page: 830

79. Which oxide below is most acidic?
   a) SO_3
   b) SO_2
   c) SeO_2
   d) SeO_3
   e) TeO_3

   Answer: a Page: 830

80. Thiosulfate ion, provided as $Na_2S_2O_3 \cdot 5H_2O$, is used in photographic developing to convert
 a) insoluble AgBr to insoluble $Na_3[Ag(S_2O_3)_2]$
 b) insoluble AgBr to soluble $Na_3[Ag(S_2O_3)_2]$
 c) insoluble AgBr to insoluble $Ag_2S_2O_3$
 d) insoluble AgBr to soluble $Ag_2S_2O_3$
 e) soluble AgBr to insoluble $Ag_2S_2O_3$

 Answer: b Page: 830

81. Which one of the following is sodium thiosulfate?
 a) Na_2SO_4
 b) Na_2SO_3
 c) $Na_2S_2O_3$
 d) $Na_2S_4O_6$

 Answer: c Page: 830

82. Which one of the following is the strongest acid?
 a) H_2SO_3
 b) H_2SO_4
 c) H_2SeO_3
 d) H_2SeO_4

 Answer: b Page: 830

83. What is the coefficient of SO_2 when the following equation is completed and balanced?
 $MnO_4^- + SO_2 \rightarrow SO_4^{2-} + Mn^{2+}$ (acidic solution)

 a) 1
 b) 3
 c) 2
 d) 5

 Answer: d Page: 830

84. What is the shape of the SF_6 molecule?
 a) tetrahedral
 b) trigonal bipyramidal
 c) octahedral
 d) trigonal pyramidal

 Answer: c Page: 830

ESSAY

85. Write the correctly balanced equation for the reaction of lithium nitride with water.

 Answer: $Li_3N + 3\ H_2O \rightarrow NH_3 + 3\ LiOH$ Page: 836

MULTIPLE CHOICE

86. Nitrogen exhibits positive oxidation states in combination with all of the following except
    a) H
    b) F
    c) O
    d) Cl

    Answer: a Page: 836

ESSAY

87. What is the primary commercial source of elemental nitrogen?

    Answer: fractional distillation of liquefied air Page: 836

MULTIPLE CHOICE

88. The primary use of nitrogen is the manufacture of
    a) plastics
    b) explosives
    c) fertilizers
    d) rubber

    Answer: c Page: 836

89. Which one of the following is false concerning hydrazine?
    a) it is an oily, colorless liquid
    b) it can be made by reaction of hypochlorite and ammonia
    c) it is used as a rocket fuel
    d) it is non-toxic but will not support life

    Answer: d Page: 836

90. Which oxide of nitrogen is produced by thermal decomposition of ammonium nitrate?
    a) N_2O
    b) NO
    c) NO_2
    d) N_2O_3
    e) N_2O_5

    Answer: a Page: 836

ESSAY

91. What are the 3 steps in the Ostwald process of nitric acid synthesis?

    Answer:
    1. oxidation of ammonia to NO and water, 2. oxidation of NO to NO_2, 3. reaction of NO_3 with water
    Page: 836

92. Why are nitric acid solutions sometimes yellowish?

Answer:
due to the presence of some NO_2 resulting from photochemical decomposition of the HNO_3

Page: 836

MULTIPLE CHOICE

93. The primary use of nitric acid is
a) manufacture of plastics
b) manufacture of explosives
c) pool water maintenance
d) manufacture of fertilizers

Answer: d Page: 836

94. The poisonous gas evolved when household ammonia and chlorine bleach are mixed is
a) NO
b) NO_2
c) N_2O
d) NH_2Cl
e) NCl_3

Answer: d Page: 836

95. Urea, $H_2NC(=O)NH_2$, is usually prepared by reaction of NH_3 with
a) CO_2
b) CO
c) CH_4
d) C_2H_4
e) C_2H_6

Answer: a Page: 836

96. Which one of the following diatomic molecules has the largest bond dissociation energy?
a) N_2
b) F_2
c) O_2
d) H_2

Answer: a Page: 836

97. When compounds such as NH_3 and CH_3NH_2 are oxidized with molecular oxygen, the most likely nitrogen containing product is
a) NO_2
b) N_2O_3
c) N_2
d) N_2O

Answer: c Page: 836

98. What is the coefficient of NO_2 when the following disproportionation reaction is balanced?

$$NO_2 + H_2O \rightarrow HNO_3 + NO$$

a) 1
b) 2
c) 3
d) 5

Answer: c Page: 836

99. Which one of the following substances is both a strong acid and a strong oxidizing agent?
a) HNO_3
b) H_2SO_4
c) HCl
d) H_3PO_4

Answer: a Page: 836

100. The Haber process is used to make _____ from _____.
a) HNO_3, N_2
b) O_2, $KClO_3$
c) NH_3, N_2
d) NO_2, O_2

Answer: c Page: 836

ESSAY

101. What group 5A element is the most metallic?

Answer: bismuth Page: 841

102. Which allotrope of phosphorous is formed when phosphate rock is reacted with coke in the presence of silicon dioxide?

Answer: white Page: 841

MULTIPLE CHOICE

103. The end use of mined phosphate rock is predominantly
 a) as a strong acid
 b) as a reducing agent
 c) detergents
 d) fertilizer

 Answer: d Page: 841

104. The plugs in fire sprinkler systems are made of an alloy of lead, tin, and which group 5A element?
 a) nitrogen
 b) arsenic
 c) antimony
 d) bismuth
 e) phosphorous

 Answer: d Page: 841

105. The most electronegative element in Group 5A is
 a) N
 b) P
 c) As
 d) Sb
 e) Bi

 Answer: a Page: 841

106. Which of the oxides E_2O_3 of Group 5A is most basic?
 a) N_2O_3
 b) P_2O_3
 c) As_2O_3
 d) Sb_2O_3
 e) Bi_2O_3

 Answer: e Page: 841

107. Which of the following is a diprotic acid?
 a) H_3PO_4
 b) H_3PO_3
 c) H_3PO_2
 d) both H_3PO_4 and H_3PO_3

 Answer: b Page: 841

108. What is the hybridization of phosphorus in PCl_5?
 a) sp^2
 b) sp^3
 c) dsp^3
 d) d^2sp^3

 Answer: c Page: 841

109. The white allotropic form of which element bursts into flame when exposed to air?
 a) phosphorus
 b) carbon
 c) sulfur
 d) selenium

 Answer: a Page: 841

110. Which one of the following is false concerning buckminsterfullerene?
 a) it is the most recently discovered crystalline allotrope of carbon
 b) it was discovered in the mid-1980s
 c) it is a molecular form of carbon
 d) it is made up of C_{12} molecules
 e) it is made up of molecules that resemble soccer balls

 Answer: d Page: 848

111. What is produced when coal is heated strongly in the absence of air?
 a) buckminsterfullerene
 b) carbon black
 c) sulfur dioxide
 d) coke
 e) charcoal

 Answer: d Page: 848

112. Which one of the following cannot be isolated as a pure compound?
 a) $CaHCO_3$
 b) CaO
 c) H_2CO_3
 d) Na_2CO_3
 e) $CaCO_3$

 Answer: c Page: 848

113. Carbon black is produced by
 a) exposure of diamond to extremely high pressures and temperatures
 b) strongly heating wood in the absence of oxygen
 c) strongly heating coal in the absence of oxygen
 d) burning hydrocarbons in a very limited supply of oxygen

 Answer: d Page: 848

ESSAY

114. Why is carbon monoxide a better Lewis base than is N_2?

Answer:
due to the smaller nuclear charge on carbon, its lone pair is more readily donated to formation of a coordinate covalent bond

Page: 848

MULTIPLE CHOICE

115. The major use of carbon dioxide is
   a) manufacture of washing soda
   b) manufacture of baking soda
   c) refrigeration
   d) production of carbonated beverages

   Answer: d Page: 848

ESSAY

116. Why does calcium carbonate dissolve in water containing carbon dioxide?

   Answer: because the dissolved carbon dioxide makes the water slightly acidic

   Page: 848

117. What is an acetylide?

   Answer: a carbide containing the C_2^{2-} ion Page: 848

MULTIPLE CHOICE

118. Of the following, which is most likely to form interstitial carbides?
   a) active metals
   b) transition metals
   c) boron and silicon
   d) none of these

   Answer: b Page: 848

119. Carbon monoxide, CO, is toxic to mammals due to its
   a) strong Arrhenius acidity
   b) strong Arrhenius basicity
   c) reaction with H_2O to form highly toxic H_2CO_3
   d) reaction with NH_3 to form highly toxic urea
   e) ability to bind strongly to hemoglobin to interfere with oxygen transport

   Answer: e Page: 848

120. $CaCO_3$, although essentially insoluble in pure water, dissolves slowly in acidic ground water due to formation of
a) insoluble $Ca(OH)_2$
b) soluble $Ca(OH)_2$
c) insoluble $Ca(HCO_3)_2$
d) soluble $Ca(HCO_3)_2$
e) soluble CaO

Answer: d Page: 848

121. Calcium carbide is
a) CaC_2
b) CaC
c) $CaCO_3$
d) Ca_2C

Answer: a Page: 848

122. The addition of potassium cyanide to hydrochloric acid will produce
a) H_2O
b) HCN
c) NH_3
d) K_2CO_3

Answer: b Page: 848

123. Which one of the following forms of carbon contains only sp^3 hybridized carbon atoms?
a) diamond
b) charcoal
c) graphite
d) carbon black

Answer: a Page: 848

ESSAY

124. What is meant by the term, composite?

Answer: a combination of two or more materials Page: 849

125. What is meant by the statement that graphite is anisotropic?

Answer: its properties are different in different directions through the solid

Page: 849

MULTIPLE CHOICE

126. What is the limitation to the use of epoxy/graphite composites?
   a) they are very vibration sensitive
   b) they are very soft
   c) they are limited to use below 150°C
   d) they are very brittle at high temperatures
   e) they are highly toxic

   Answer: c Page: 849

127. What is the function of the carbon fibers in a composite?
   a) to provide a structure to help the epoxy resin solidify in the desired shape
   b) to transmit loads evenly in all directions
   c) to provide resistance to oxidation
   d) to provide ultraviolet protection
   e) to "spread out" the epoxy so that it remains more flexible

   Answer: b Page: 849

128. What is the formula of borax?
   a) H_3BO_3
   b) $H_2B_4O_7$
   c) P_5O_8
   d) B_2O_3
   e) $Na_2B_4O_0 \cdot 10H_2O$

   Answer: e Page: 854

129. Which group 4A element most readily forms multiple bonds?
   a) silicon
   b) lead
   c) tin
   d) germanium
   e) carbon

   Answer: d Page: 854

ESSAY

130. How is elemental silicon obtained?

   Answer: reaction of molten silicon dioxide with coke Page: 854

131. What is the purpose of converting silicon to silicon tetrachloride?

   Answer: purification of silicon Page: 854

MULTIPLE CHOICE

132. The most common oxidation state of silicon is
a) -4
b) +2
c) +6
d) -2

Answer: b Page: 854

ESSAY

133. Why is mica harder than talc?

Answer:
because mica is an aluminosilicate and the layers in an aluminosilicate have greater charge than those in a silicate such as talc, and the higher charge makes it more difficult for the sheets to slip past each other in mica than in talc

Page: 854

134. What are the principal components used in making soda lime glass?

Answer: calcium oxide, sodium oxide, and silicon dioxide Page: 854

135. What effect does substitution of K_2O for Na_2O in making soda lime glass have in its properties?

Answer: increases hardness and melting point Page: 854

MULTIPLE CHOICE

136. Which element in Group 4A most frequently exhibits catenation?
a) C
b) Si
c) Ge
d) Sn
e) Pb

Answer: a Page: 854

137. The gem zircon, regarded as formed by replacement of one-half of the silicons in SiO_2 by Zr^{4+}, has the formula
a) $ZrSiO_4^{4+}$
b) $ZrSiO_4^{2-}$
c) $ZrSiO_4$
d) $ZrSiO_4^{2+}$
e) $ZrSiO_4^{4-}$

Answer: c Page: 854

138. Feldspar minerals are formed by replacing up to half of the silicon in SiO_2 with
    a) oxygen
    b) boron
    c) germanium
    d) aluminum

    Answer: d Page: 854

139. Which group 3A element is a nonmetal?
    a) B
    b) Al
    c) Ga
    d) In
    e) Tl

    Answer: a Page: 859

ESSAY

140. Compounds containing only boron and hydrogen are called

    Answer: boranes Page: 859

MULTIPLE CHOICE

141. Which one of the following is the strongest reducing agent?
    a) CH_4
    b) NH_4Cl
    c) $NaBH_4$
    d) F_2

    Answer: c Page: 859

142. Which one of the following is not true concerning borax?
    a) it is the hydrated sodium salt of tetraboric acid
    b) it is found in dry lake deposits in California
    c) its aqueous solutions are alkaline
    d) it is commonly used in cleaning products
    e) it is also readily prepared from other minerals such as galena

    Answer: e Page: 859

143. The high melting point (2300°C) and low electrical conductivity of elemental boron are consistent with its structure as
    a) a molecular solid
    b) an ionic solid
    c) a metallic solid
    d) a network covalent solid
    e) either a metallic solid or a molecular solid

    Answer: d Page: 859

144. Tetraboric acid, $H_2B_4O_7$, is prepared by heating boric acid, H_3BO_3 (a condensation reaction involving water loss). If 400 mmol H_3BO_3 are used, what mass of H_2O in g is formed, assuming quantitative stoichiometric conversion?
a) 5.77
b) 0.500
c) 0.320
d) 7.21
e) 9.01

Answer: e Page: 859

145. Pyrex glass is formed by adding an oxide of _____ to soda-lime glass.
a) lead
b) cobalt
c) boron
d) silver

Answer: c Page: 859

Chapter 23: Metals and Metallurgy

MULTIPLE CHOICE

1. A deposit that contains a metal in economically exploitable quantities is called a(n)
   a) mineral
   b) ore
   c) vein
   d) comstock

   Answer: b Page: 869

2. Why are silicate minerals not commonly used as sources of metals?
   a) they are rare
   b) they usually do not contain important metals
   c) they are difficult to reduce and concentrate
   d) they are only found at excessive depths in the oceans

   Answer: c Page: 869

ESSAY

3. What is gangue?

   Answer: the unwanted material that accompanies an ore when it is mined

   Page: 869

MULTIPLE CHOICE

4. Which statement below is true?
   a) New mining techniques and relatively untapped ore fields mean that the environmental impacts of mineral extraction will decrease significantly in the future.
   b) There exists little correlation between the abundance of an element in the lithosphere and its commercial extraction and use.
   c) Most metallic elements are found in the lithosphere in oxidation state zero.
   d) The most important commercial class of minerals is the silicates.
   e) The United States has plentiful ore fields of all strategic metals.

   Answer: b Page: 869

5. The most common element by mass in the lithosphere is
   a) oxygen
   b) aluminum
   c) iron
   d) gold
   e) calcium

   Answer: a Page: 869

6. Which one of the following metallic elements is most likely to be found as the free metal in nature?
   a) Ca
   b) Au
   c) Al
   d) Fe

   Answer: b Page: 869

7. Metallurgical processes that utilize high temperatures are collectively called
   a) hydrometallurgy
   b) pyrometallurgy
   c) electrometallurgy
   d) alloying

   Answer: b Page: 873

ESSAY

8. Define calcining.

   Answer:
   heating an ore to bring about its decomposition and the elimination of a volatile product
   Page: 873

MULTIPLE CHOICE

9. Melting an ore and causing the melt to separate into two or more layers is called
   a) calcining
   b) roasting
   c) smelting
   d) slag
   e) alloying

   Answer: c Page: 873

10. A thermal process that causes reactions between an ore and the atmosphere of the furnace is called
    a) calcining
    b) roasting
    c) smelting
    d) slag
    e) refining

    Answer: b Page: 873

11. A slag is formed when a basic metal oxide reacts with molten _____ at high temperatures.
a) Fe_2O_3
b) CaO
c) $CaSiO_3$
d) SiO_2
e) CO

Answer: d Page: 873

ESSAY

12. Write the two reactions that are used to control the temperature in a blast furnace and indicate which provides heat and which cools.

Answer:
$2C(s) + O_2(g) \rightarrow 2CO(g)$, provides heat; $C(s) + H_2O(g) \rightarrow CO(g) + H_2(g)$, cools

Page: 873

MULTIPLE CHOICE

13. What is the purpose of a converter in steel production?
a) to reduce the iron in the ore to elemental
b) to remove impurity elements by oxidation
c) to allow the formation of phosphides within the metal for added corrosion resistance
d) to allow the addition of nitrogen for increased strength
e) to allow slow solidification of the molten metal so it will purify as it crystalizes

Answer: b Page: 873

14. What is produced when a carbonate is calcined?
a) the free metal and sodium carbonate
b) the free metal and sulfur dioxide
c) the metal oxide and carbon dioxide
d) water and the metal hydride

Answer: c Page: 873

15. During roasting, the metal reacts with
a) oxygen
b) carbon monoxide
c) sulfur
d) the furnace atmosphere

Answer: d Page: 873

ESSAY

16. Give the name and formula of the most important ores of iron.

Answer: hematite, Fe_2O_3, and magnetite, Fe_3O_4 Page: 873

17. What is the purpose of the limestone used in a blast furnace?

Answer: to form slag Page: 873

18. What is the purpose of coke in a blast furnace?

Answer:
to provide the needed heat and to provide carbon monoxide to act as a reducing agent
Page: 873

MULTIPLE CHOICE

19. Why is either pure oxygen or oxygen diluted with argon used in a converter instead of air?
a) the carbon dioxide in air will cause the iron to oxidize and form rust
b) the oxygen concentration is too low to function efficiently at removing impurities
c) the carbon monoxide in air reacts with the iron to form a volatile, and toxic, iron carbonyl
d) the nitrogen in air will react with iron to form iron nitride that will make the iron brittle

Answer: d Page: 873

20. What happens to the silicon that is a contaminant in crude iron in a converter?
a) it is converted to the tetrafluoride that bubbles out as a gas
b) it is precipitated as sodium silicate
c) it is converted to silicon dioxide and becomes part of the slag
d) it is precipitated as the carbide

Answer: c Page: 873

21. Roasting of the monosulfide of zinc (an active metal) in O_2 produces which products?
a) $Zn(s)$ and $SO_2(g)$
b) $Zn(s)$ and $SO_3(g)$
c) $ZnO(s)$ and $SO_2(g)$
d) $ZnO_2(s)$ and $SO_2(g)$
e) $ZnO(s)$ and $SO_3(g)$

Answer: c Page: 873

22. A basic slag is needed in steelmaking to
    a) remove SiO_2 as silicates
    b) reduce any nitrogen-containing compounds to N_2
    c) react with any Bronsted-Lowry acids present
    d) provide CaO to remove phosphorus oxides as $Ca_3(PO_4)_2$
    e) oxidize any carbon-containing compounds to CO_2

    Answer: d Page: 873

23. The products of calcining limestone, $CaCO_3$, are
    a) Ca(s) and CO_3(g)
    b) Ca(s) and CO_2(g)
    c) Ca(s) and CO(g)
    d) CaO(s) and CO_3(g)
    e) CaO(s) and CO_2(g)

    Answer: e Page: 873

24. What is the coefficient on $PbCO_3$ when the following equation is completed and balanced?

    $$PbCO_3 \xrightarrow{\Delta}$$

    a) 1
    b) 2
    c) 3
    d) 5

    Answer: a Page: 873

25. Roasting HgS in the presence of oxygen produces the free metal and SO_2. What is the coefficient of HgS when the equation for this reaction is completed and balanced?
    a) 1
    b) 2
    c) 3
    d) 5

    Answer: a Page: 873

26. Carbon monoxide is commonly used to produce free metals from their oxides. What is the coefficient of carbon monoxide in the balanced equation for the production of cobalt from Co_2O_3?
    a) 1
    b) 2
    c) 3
    d) 5

    Answer: c Page: 873

27. Roasting ZnS in the presence of oxygen produces the metal oxide and SO_2. What is the coefficient of ZnS when the equation for this reaction is completed and balanced?
a) 1
b) 2
c) 3
d) 5

Answer: b Page: 873

28. At high temperatures, carbon can be used as a reducing agent for metal oxides. What is the coefficient of carbon in the balanced equation for the production of manganese and CO_2 from manganese(II) oxide?
a) 1
b) 2
c) 3
d) 5

Answer: a Page: 873

29. Selectively dissolving a metal-containing compound from an ore is called
a) converting
b) sol formation
c) refining
d) oxidation
e) leaching

Answer: e Page: 876

ESSAY

30. What is the name and the formula of the most useful ore of aluminum?

Answer: bauxite, $Al_2O_3 \cdot xH_2O$ Page: 876

31. The anode sludges from copper refining are important sources of what two metals?

Answer: gold and silver Page: 876

MULTIPLE CHOICE

32. The transition metals in group ___ have the highest melting points.
a) 4B
b) 3B
c) 6B
d) 8B
e) 2B

Answer: c Page: 876

ESSAY

33. Gold can be obtained from a low grade ore by treatment of the crushed ore with aqueous sodium cyanide solution followed by reaction with zinc. What is the purpose of each of these treatments?

    Answer:
    the sodium cyanide converts the gold to a soluble complex ion so it can be separated from the ore and the zinc reduces the gold in the complex ion to its elemental form

    Page: 876

MULTIPLE CHOICE

34. Which one of the following is false concerning the Bayer Process?
    a) it is a hydrometallurgical process
    b) it involves treatment of bauxite with cold, dilute sodium hydroxide solution
    c) in the process, aluminum is converted to a soluble aluminate ion
    d) it results in the separation of aluminum from iron and silicon

    Answer: b Page: 876

35. The flotation process is used to separate
    a) magnetic minerals from nonmagnetic gangue
    b) cyanide-complexing elements from gangue
    c) hydroxide-soluble minerals from gangue
    d) high-melting and low-melting metal oxides
    e) minerals whose surfaces are hydrophobic from hydrophilic gangue

    Answer: e Page: 876

36. The undesirable material that is separated from an ore during the concentration process is called
    a) gangue
    b) leachate
    c) slag
    d) flocculent

    Answer: a Page: 876

37. The hydrometallurgical process used in refining gold ore entails converting metallic gold to water-soluble $Au(CN)_2^-$. What must happen to the metallic gold to allow it to complex with CN^- to form $Au(CN)_2^-$ removable in liquid form from the gangue?
a) It is reduced with a metal hydride.
b) It forms the complex $Au(H_2O)_3$.
c) It is oxidized in the presence of O_2 to Au(I).
d) It is reduced with CO(g) to form $Au(CO)_4^{2-}$.
e) It is oxidized with CO(g) to form $Au(CO)_4^+$.

Answer: c Page: 876

38. The Bayer process for purifying bauxite relies upon the
a) amphoteric nature of Al^{3+}
b) amphoteric nature of Fe^{3+}
c) amphoteric nature of SiO_2
d) selective complexation of Al^{3+} by CN^-
e) selective complexation of Fe^{3+} by CN^-

Answer: a Page: 876

39. Gold is frequently recovered from its ore by forming a water soluble complex with
a) NO_3^-
b) CO_3^{2-}
c) SO_4^{2-}
d) CN^-

Answer: d Page: 876

ESSAY

40. Why is an elaborate apparatus such as a Down cell used to obtain elemental sodium instead of a simple cell in which aqueous sodium chloride is electrolyzed?

Answer:
electrolysis of aqueous NaCl does not produce sodium because water is more easily reduced than sodium, thus a Down cell is required to electrolyze molten NaCl and to immediately separate the elemental sodium and chlorine produced

Page: 877

MULTIPLE CHOICE

41. What is the purpose of the cryolite that is used in the Hall process?
    a) to both lower the temperatures required and to make the mixture conductive
    b) to react with any silicon and iron present to form a slag
    c) to prevent interference by iron by forming FeF^{3-}_6
    d) to extend electrode life
    e) to prevent formation of sulfur dioxide

    Answer: a Page: 877

ESSAY

42. What are the anode and cathode materials used in the cells that purify copper?

    Answer: the anodes are impure copper and the cathodes are pure copper

    Page: 877

MULTIPLE CHOICE

43. A major byproduct in the Hall electrometallurgical process for refining aluminum is
    a) $O_2(g)$ from oxidation of H_2O at the anode
    b) $H_2(g)$ from reduction of H_2O at the cathode
    c) $CO(g)$ from oxidation of the graphite anode
    d) $CO_2(g)$ from oxidation of the graphite anode
    e) $Fe(s)$ from impurities present in bauxite ore

    Answer: d Page: 877

44. The respective standard oxidation potentials for Cu -> Cu^{2+}, Ni -> Ni^{2+}, and Ag -> Ag^{+} are (in V) -0.34, +0.28, and -0.80. Impure copper slabs at the anode are refined electrochemically, affording much purer metallic copper at the cathode. Which statement below is true?
    a) Cu is oxidized preferentially over both Ni and Ag, so both Ni and Ag metals are separated as sludges below the anode.
    b) Ni is oxidized preferentially over Cu, and Ni^{2+} is reduced much less readily than Cu^{2+}, so Ni is separated as Ni^{2+} in the electrolyte solution.
    c) Ag is oxidized preferentially over Cu, and Ag^{+} is reduced much less readily than Cu^{2+}, so Ag is separated as Ag^{+} in the electrolyte solution.
    d) Ag is oxidized preferentially over Cu, and Ag^{+} is reduced much more readily than Cu^{2+}, so Ag plates out with Cu at the cathode and cannot readily be removed from impure copper.
    e) Both Ni and Ag are oxidized preferentially over Cu and Ni^{2+}, and Ag^{+} is reduced much less readily than Cu^{2+}, so Ni and Ag are separated as Ni^{2+} and Ag^{+} in the electrolyte solution.

    Answer: b Page: 877

45. The molecular-orbital model for Ge shows it to be
    a) a conductor, because all the lower energy band orbitals are filled and the gap between the lower and higher bands is large
    b) an insulator, because all the lower energy band orbitals are filled and the gap between the lower and higher bands is large
    c) a semiconductor, because the gap between the filled lower and empty higher energy bands is relatively small
    d) a semiconductor, because the gap between the filled lower and empty higher energy bands is large
    e) a conductor, because its lower energy band orbitals are only partially filled

    Answer: c Page: 881

46. Which one of the following is <u>not</u> a property of metals?
    a) malleability
    b) ductility
    c) high electronegativity
    d) thermal conductivity

    Answer: c Page: 881

47. If the electronic structure of a solid substance consists of a valence band that is completely filled with electrons and there is a large energy gap to the next set of orbitals, then this substance will be a(n)
    a) alloy
    b) insulator
    c) conductor
    d) semiconductor

    Answer: b Page: 881

48. Silicon, doped with a group 5A element forms a(n) ___-type semiconductor. Silicon doped with a group 3A element forms a(n) ___-type semiconductor.
   a) p, n
   b) n, p
   c) n, n
   d) p, p

   Answer: b Page: 884

49. Substitutional and interstitial alloys are examples of a _______ alloy.
   a) solution
   b) heterogeneous
   c) covalent

   Answer: a Page: 886

50. For a substitutional alloy to form, the two metals combined must have similar
   a) ionization potential and electron affinity
   b) number of valance electrons and electronegativity
   c) reduction potential and size
   d) atomic radii and chemical bonding properties
   e) band gap and reactivity

   Answer: d Page: 886

51. What is the typical effect of the addition of an interstitial element on the properties of a metal?
   a) increase in malleability and corrosion resistance
   b) increase in hardness and strength, decrease in ductility
   c) decrease in melting point and increase in ductility
   d) decrease in conductivity and increase in brittleness
   e) increased surface luster

   Answer: b Page: 886

ESSAY

52. What two metals are alloyed to produce sterling silver?

   Answer: silver and copper Page: 886

MULTIPLE CHOICE

53. 18 karat gold contains ___ % gold.
   a) 18
   b) 25
   c) 89
   d) 75

   Answer: d Page: 886

54. For an interstitial alloy to form, the atoms added to the metal must
    a) be of the same size as the metal atoms
    b) have the same electronegativity as the metal atoms
    c) have the same number of valence electrons as the metal atoms
    d) be much smaller than the metal atoms

    Answer: d Page: 886

55. Heterogeneous alloys
    a) do not have uniform composition throughout
    b) have properties that depend on composition
    c) have properties that depend on the manner in which the melt is solidified
    d) all of these

    Answer: d Page: 886

56. Intermetallic compounds are examples of
    a) homogeneous alloys
    b) heterogeneous alloys
    c) interstitial alloys
    d) solution alloys

    Answer: a Page: 886

57. Alloys generally differ from compounds in that
    a) the former always contain some carbon
    b) the former always contain some iron
    c) the former always have semiconductor properties
    d) the atomic ratios of the constituent elements in the former are not fixed and may vary over a wide range
    e) the former never contain a transition element

    Answer: d Page: 886

58. The maximum oxidation state in the first transition series is ___.
    a) 2+
    b) 4+
    c) 5+
    d) 7+
    e) 8+

    Answer: d Page: 888

59. In the second and third transition series, the maximum oxidation state is ____.
    a) 2+
    b) 4+
    c) 5+
    d) 7+
    e) 8+

    Answer: e Page: 888

60. A substance that exhibits ________ can become a permanent magnet.
    a) paramagnetism
    b) ferromagnetism
    c) diamagnetism

    Answer: b Page: 888

61. Of the following, which is a bulk property?
    a) electron configuration
    b) ionization energy
    c) melting point
    d) atomic radius

    Answer: c Page: 888

ESSAY

62. Most of the metals in the third transition series have about the same atomic radius as the elements above them in second transition series. This is a result of

    Answer: the lanthanide contraction Page: 888

MULTIPLE CHOICE

63. What two oxidation states are more frequently observed in the first transition series than in the third?
    a) +3 and +7
    b) +2 and +3
    c) +2 and +7
    d) +5 and +6

    Answer: b Page: 888

64. In the second and third transition series, the maximum oxidation state observed is
   a) +8
   b) +7
   c) +5
   d) +4
   e) +2

   Answer: a Page: 888

65. A substance with all of its electrons paired will be
   a) slightly attracted to a magnet
   b) slightly repelled by a magnet
   c) strongly attracted to a magnet
   d) strongly repelled by a magnet
   e) a permanent magnet
   f) ferromagnetic

   Answer: b Page: 888

66. The electron configuration of Mn is $[Ar]4s^2 3d^5$, so that of Mn^{2+} is
   a) $[Ar]4s^2 3d^7$
   b) $[Ar]4s^2 3d^3$
   c) $[Ar]3d^5$
   d) $[Ar]3d^9$
   e) [Ar]

   Answer: c Page: 888

67. In the d transition elements
   a) each metal exhibits only one stable oxidation state
   b) almost all of their compounds are colorless
   c) all their compounds are diamagnetic
   d) higher oxidation states are more stable relative to the lower going down a group of transition metals
   e) higher oxidation states are generally more common at the left of each row of transition metals

   Answer: d Page: 888

68. The lanthanide contraction is responsible for the fact that
   a) Zr and Y have about the same radius.
   b) Zr and Nb have similar oxidation states.
   c) Zr and Hf have about the same radius.
   d) Zr and Zn have similar oxidation states.

   Answer: c Page: 888

69. Which one of the following is <u>not</u> true about transition metals?
    a) They frequently have more than one common oxidation state.
    b) Their compounds are frequently colored.
    c) Their compounds frequently exhibit magnetic properties.
    d) They are frequently found as the free metals in nature.

    Answer: d Page: 888

ESSAY

70. What substance, in addition to water, is produced by the condensation of two hydrogen chromate ions?

    Answer: dichromate ion Page: 892

MULTIPLE CHOICE

71. Reaction of iron with which one of the following acids will result in the direct production of Fe^{3+}?
    a) HNO_3
    b) HCl
    c) HI
    d) CH_3COOH
    e) dilute H_2SO_4

    Answer: a Page: 892

72. Which one of the following is black?
    a) CuI
    b) $CuSO_4$
    c) $Cu(H_2O)_4^{2+}$
    d) $CuCl_2$
    e) CuO

    Answer: e Page: 892

73. Most of the compounds of copper in the ___ oxidation state are insoluble in water.
    a) +1
    b) +2
    c) +3
    d) +7

    Answer: a Page: 892

74. Why do aqueous solutions of Cr^{2+} usually appear violet instead of blue?
    a) the intensity of the color is so low it appears violet instead of blue
    b) chromium(II) rapidly forms a complex ion with water and that ion is violet-colored
    c) water usually contains enough chloride ion to form a complex ion containing chloride and that substance is violet-colored
    d) chromium(II) reacts with water to form a hydroxide-containing complex ion that is violet-colored
    e) chromium(II) is rapidly oxidized to chromium(III) by atmospheric oxygen

    Answer: e Page: 892

75. Which one of the following is most likely to react with iron to form Fe^{2+}?
    a) dilute HCl
    b) dilute HNO_3

    Answer: a Page: 892

76. In its compounds, nickel is most commonly found in oxidation state
    a) -2
    b) 0
    c) +1
    d) +2
    e) +3

    Answer: d Page: 892

77. A small amount of barium chloride solution is added to a blue solution. A white precipitate forms. The blue solution contains
    a) $NiSO_4$
    b) $CuCl_2$
    c) $CuSO_4$
    d) $Co(NO_3)_3$

    Answer: c Page: 892

78. When metallic copper is dissolved in concentrated nitric acid it forms
    a) a colorless solution and a colorless gas
    b) a colorless solution and a brown gas
    c) a colored solution and a colorless gas
    d) a colored solution and a brown gas

    Answer: d Page: 892

79. Which one of the following compounds is yellow?
    a) $Cr(NO_3)_3$
    b) $CrCl_3$
    c) K_2CrO_4
    d) $(NH_4)_2Cr_2O_7$

    Answer: c Page: 892

80. What is the coefficient of Cl_2 when the following equation is completed and balanced?
    $Cr_2O_7^{2-}(aq) + Cl^-(aq) \rightarrow Cr^{3+}(aq) + Cl_2(g)$
    (acidic solution)
    a) 1
    b) 3
    c) 5
    d) 6

    Answer: b Page: 892

81. How many d electrons are present in the metal ion of $FeCO_3$?
    a) 3
    b) 5
    c) 4
    d) 6

    Answer: d Page: 892

82. What is the coefficient of Fe^{2+} when the following equation is completed and balanced?

    $Fe^{2+} + H_2O_2 \rightarrow Fe^{3+} + H_2O$ (acidic solution)

    a) 1
    b) 2
    c) 3
    d) 5

    Answer: b Page: 892

83. An aqueous solution of $Fe(NO_3)_3$ will slowly form a red-brown precipitate due to the formation of
    a) $Fe(OH)_3$
    b) Fe_3O_4
    c) FeO
    d) $Fe(OH)_2$

    Answer: a Page: 892

84. The first step in the production of nickel from its ore, NiS, is to roast it in the presence of oxygen to form the metal oxide and SO_2. What is the coefficient of oxygen when the equation for this reaction is completed and balanced?
    a) 1
    b) 2
    c) 3
    d) 5

    Answer: c Page: 892

85. The hydrated nickel(II) ion is
    a) orange
    b) blue
    c) yellow
    d) green

    Answer: d Page: 892

86. The hydrated copper(II) ion is
    a) orange
    b) blue
    c) yellow
    d) violet

    Answer: b Page: 892

87. CuS has a very low solubility in water. However, it will dissolve in nitric acid due to the following reaction.

    $CuS(s) + NO_3^-(aq) \rightarrow Cu^{2+}(aq) + S(s) + NO(g)$
    (acidic solution)

    What is the coefficient of CuS when this equation is balanced?
    a) 1
    b) 2
    c) 3
    d) 5

    Answer: c Page: 892

Chapter 24: Chemistry of Coordination Compounds

MULTIPLE CHOICE

1. The assembly consisting of a central metal atom bonded to a group of surrounding molecules or ions is called a
   a) ligand
   b) complex
   c) coordination compound
   d) Lewis acid
   e) Lewis base

   Answer: b Page: 901

2. The coordination numbers of cobalt(III) and of chromium(III) in their complexes is always
   a) 4
   b) 5
   c) 2
   d) 3
   e) 6

   Answer: e Page: 901

3. The coordination number of platinum in complexes is always
   a) 4
   b) 5
   c) 2
   d) 3
   e) 6

   Answer: a Page: 901

4. What is the most common geometry found in four-coordinate complexes?
   a) square planar
   b) octahedral
   c) tetrahedral
   d) icosahedral
   e) trigonal bipyramidal

   Answer: c Page: 901

5. During the formation of a coordination compound, the metal acts as a Lewis
   a) acid
   b) base

   Answer: a Page: 901

6. In the compound, $CaNa[Fe(CN)_6]$, what ligands are in the coordination sphere?
   a) Ca^{2+}
   b) Na^{+}
   c) CN^{-}
   d) none of these

   Answer: c Page: 901

ESSAY

7. What is the oxidation state of the iron atom in $CaNa[Fe(CN)_6]$?

   Answer: 3+ Page: 901

8. The most common coordination numbers are

   Answer: 4 and 6 Page: 901

9. Why is iron(III) able to coordinate six fluoride ions but only four chloride ions?

   Answer:
   the chloride ions are too big for six to get close enough to an iron(III) ion to bond
   Page: 901

10. What is the coordination number of the iron atom in $CaNa[Fe(CN)_6]$?

    Answer: 6 Page: 901

MULTIPLE CHOICE

11. Tetrahedral, four-coordinate complexes are most commonly formed by
    a) non-transition metals
    b) d^8 transition metals

    Answer: a Page: 901

ESSAY

12. Six-coordinate complexes generally have ___ geometry.

    Answer: octahedral Page: 901

MULTIPLE CHOICE

13. What is the respective central-metal oxidation state, coordination number, and the overall charge on the complex ion in

$NH_4[Cr(NH_3)_2(NCS)_4]$?
a) +3; 6; -1
b) +3; 6; +1
c) -3; 4; -1
d) -3; 2; -1
e) +1; 4; +1

Answer: a Page: 901

14. In the following reaction, Ni^{2+} is acting as a(n)

$$Ni^{2+}(g) + 6H_2O(l) \rightarrow Ni(H_2O)_6^{2+}(aq)$$

a) oxidizing agent
b) Lewis acid
c) precipitating agent
d) solvent

Answer: b Page: 901

15. Which one of the following species is paramagnetic?
a) Cu^+
b) Ni^{2+}
c) Zn
d) Ca

Answer: b Page: 901

16. How many d electrons are in the cobalt ion of $K_3[Co(CN)_6]$?
a) 3
b) 5
c) 6
d) 7

Answer: c Page: 901

17. What is the charge on the complex ion in $Mg_3[FeCl_6]_2$?
a) -2
b) +2
c) -3
d) +3

Answer: c Page: 901

18. What is the oxidation number of chromium in $[Cr(NH_3)_4Cl_2]Cl$?
    a) -3
    b) +3
    c) +2
    d) -2

    Answer: b Page: 901

19. Which one of the following complexes has a coordination number of 6?
    a) $[Pt(NH_3)_2Cl_2]$
    b) $[Zn(NH_3)_2Cl_2]$
    c) $[Cu(NH_3)_4]^{2+}$
    d) $[Co(NH_3)_5Cl]^{2+}$

    Answer: d Page: 901

20. What is the ligand in $Ca_3[Fe(CN)_6]_2$?
    a) Ca^{2+}
    b) Fe^{3+}
    c) CN^-
    d) $Fe(CN)_6{}^{3-}$

    Answer: c Page: 901

21. What is the charge of the central metal ion in $Ca_3[Fe(CN)_6]_2$?
    a) 0
    b) +1
    c) +2
    d) +3

    Answer: d Page: 901

22. What is the charge on the complex ion in $Ca_3[Fe(CN)_6]_2$?
    a) -3
    b) +2
    c) -2
    d) -1

    Answer: a Page: 901

23. What is the oxidation number of cobalt in $[Co(NH_3)_4F_2]$?
    a) -3
    b) +2
    c) +1
    d) +3

    Answer: b Page: 901

24. The charge of the complex ion in $[Zn(H_2O)_3Cl]Cl$ is
    a) 0
    b) -1
    c) +2
    d) +1

    Answer: d Page: 901

25. An analogous simple salt which would have similar conductivity to $[Zn(H_2O)_3Cl]Cl$ is
    a) $ZnCl_2$
    b) NaCl
    c) Na_2SO_4
    d) $MgSO_4$

    Answer: b Page: 901

26. The coordination number for $[Zn(H_2O)_3Cl]Cl$ is
    a) 5
    b) 4
    c) 2
    d) 1

    Answer: b Page: 901

27. A ligand with a single donor atom is called
    a) a chelon
    b) a chelate
    c) polydentate
    d) monodentate
    e) bidentate

    Answer: d Page: 904

ESSAY

28. What is the chelate effect?

    Answer:
    The larger formation constants for polydentate ligands as compared with corresponding monodentate ligands
    Page: 904

MULTIPLE CHOICE

29. What is the purpose of adding EDTA to prepared foods?
    a) to keep ions such as Ca^{2+} in solution so the foods look good
    b) to complex trace metal ions that catalyze decomposition reactions
    c) to complex iron(III) ions so they can catalyze protein decompositon on cooking
    d) to aid in browning of the surface during cooking
    e) to prevent dissolution of the container in the food when stored for long periods of time

    Answer: b Page: 904

30. What purpose would sodium tripolyphosphate serve in a detergent formulation?
    a) to aid in removal of rust stains from surfaces and from clothes
    b) to aid in keeping the inside of washing machines clean and free from corrosion
    c) to improve the flow characteristics of the detergent in the box
    d) to complex and hence sequester metal ions in hard water
    e) to reduce bacterial growth in the detergent upon storage

    Answer: d Page: 904

ESSAY

31. List three of the seven transition metals required for human life.

    Answer: Any three of : Co, Cu, Cr, Fe, Mn, V, Zn Page: 904

MULTIPLE CHOICE

32. What are the donor atoms in a porphine molecule?
    a) N
    b) O
    c) S
    d) Br
    e) F

    Answer: a Page: 904

ESSAY

33. Complexes derived from porphine are called

    Answer: porphyrins Page: 904

MULTIPLE CHOICE

34. What metal is complexed in chlorophyll?
    a) iron
    b) chromium
    c) manganese
    d) vanadium
    e) magnesium

    Answer: e Page: 904

35. What form of hemoglobin is purplish-red?
    a) oxyhemoglobin
    b) deoxyhemoglobin

    Answer: b Page: 904

36. How many bonds can ethylenediamine form to a metal ion?
    a) 1
    b) 2
    c) 3
    d) 4

    Answer: b Page: 904

ESSAY

37. What is the chelate effect?

    Answer:
    the generally larger formation constants for polydentate ligands compared to the corresponding monodentate ligands

    Page: 904

38. What is the purpose of adding sodium tripolyphosphate to a detergent?

    Answer:
    to sequester the metal ions in hard water to prevent their interference with the action of the detergent

    Page: 904

MULTIPLE CHOICE

39. What are the donor atoms in porphine?
    a) oxygen
    b) nitrogen
    c) sulfur
    d) oxygen and nitrogen

    Answer: b Page: 904

40. What is the metal ion in the porphyrin of chlorophyll?
    a) iron
    b) calcium
    c) molybdenum
    d) magnesium

    Answer: d Page: 904

41. What is the metal ion in the porphyrin of heme?
    a) iron
    b) calcium
    c) molybdenum
    d) magnesium

    Answer: a Page: 904

42. How many iron atoms are coordinated in a hemoglobin molecule?
    a) 1
    b) 2
    c) 3
    d) 4

    Answer: d Page: 904

ESSAY

43. What colors of light does chlorophyll-a absorb?

    Answer: red and blue Page: 904

MULTIPLE CHOICE

44. A porphyrin is a complex containing
    a) the ethylenediaminetetraacetate ligand
    b) the ethylenediamine ligand
    c) only monodentate ligands
    d) only hexadentate ligands
    e) the porphine group, which contains a set of four planar nitrogen electron-pair donors

    Answer: e Page: 904

45. Based on entropy considerations alone, which homogeneous aqueous equilibrium would be expected to lie to the right?
a) $AgI_2^- + 2Br^- \rightleftharpoons AgBr_2^- + 2I^-$
b) $Ni(H_2NC_2H_4NH_2)_3^{2+} + 6NH_3 \rightleftharpoons Ni(NH_3)_6^{2+} + 3H_2NC_2H_4NH_2$
c) $CoCl_4^{2-} + 6H_2O \rightleftharpoons Co(H_2O)_6^{2+} + 4Cl^-$
d) $Fe(NH_3)_6^{2+} + C_{20}H_{10}N_4^{2-} \rightleftharpoons Fe(NH_3)_2(C_{20}H_{10}N_4) + 4NH_3$
e) $Cu(NH_3)_4^{2+} + 6H_2O \rightleftharpoons Cu(H_2O)_6^{2+} + 4NH_3$

Answer: d Page: 904

46. The chelate effect is best attributed to considerations of which type?
a) hydration
b) enthalpy
c) entropy
d) hydrogen bonding
e) resonance

Answer: c Page: 904

47. Which one of the following species is a potential polydentate ligand (chelating agent)?
a) NH_3
b) Cl^-
c) CO_3^{2-}
d) H_2O

Answer: c Page: 904

ESSAY

48. When is the metal named first in the name of a complex ion?

Answer: never, this is not done Page: 908

49. What is meant by the prefix, tetrakis-, and when is it used?

Answer:
it means 4 and is used when there are 4 of a ligand whose name includes a Greek prefix
Page: 908

MULTIPLE CHOICE

50. The names of complex anions end in
a) -o
b) -ium
c) -ate
d) -ous
e) -ic

Answer: c Page: 908

ESSAY

51. Name the compound, $Ca[AlH_4]_2$.

Answer: calcium tetrahydroaluminate Page: 908

52. Name the compound, $[Os(en)_3]_2[NiCl_2Br_2]_3$.

Answer: tris(ethylenediamine)osmium(III) dibromodichloronickelate(II)

Page: 908

53. Name the compound, $Cu(H_2O)_4{}^{2+}$

Answer: tetraaquacopper(II) Page: 908

MULTIPLE CHOICE

54. The formula for potassium dibromodicarbonylrhodate(I) is
a) $K_2[Rh(CO)_2Br_2]$
b) $K[Rh(CO)_2Br_2]$
c) $K_3[Rh(CO)_2Br_2]$
d) $K[Rh(CO)_2Br_2]_2$
e) $K_3[Rh(CO)_2Br_2]_2$

Answer: b Page: 908

55. The correct name for $Na_3[CoF_6]$ is
a) trisodium hexakisfluorocobalt(III)
b) trisodium hexakisfluorocobalt(II)
c) trisodium hexakisfluorocobalt(IV)
d) sodium hexafluorocobaltate(III)
e) sodium hexafluorocobaltate(IV)

Answer: d Page: 908

56. The formula for lithium iodotris(trifluorophosphine)nickelate(0) is
    a) $Li_3[Ni(PF_3)I_3]$
    b) $Li[Ni(PF_3)_3I_3]$
    c) $Li[Ni(PF_3)_3I]$
    d) $Li_2[Ni(PF_3)I_3]$
    e) $Li_2[Ni(PF_3)_3I]$

    Answer: c Page: 908

57. The name for $W(CO)_5^{2-}$ is pentacarbonyltungstate _____.
    a) (II)
    b) (I)
    c) (0)
    d) (-I)
    e) (-II)

    Answer: e Page: 908

58. Triphenylphosphine is often given the abbreviated formula PPh_3. The correct name for $Rh(PPh_3)_3Cl$ is
    a) chlorotriphenylphosphinerhodium
    b) chlorotriphenylphosphinerhodium(I)
    c) tris(triphenylphosphine)chlororhodium(I)
    d) chlorotris(triphenylphosphine)rhodium(I)
    e) chlorotris(triphenylphosphine)rhodate(-I)

    Answer: d Page: 908

59. A complex of correctly written formula $[Pt(NH_3)_3Br]Br \cdot H_2O$ has which set of ligands in its inner coordination sphere?
    a) 3 NH_3
    b) 3 NH_3 and 2 Br^-
    c) 3 NH_3 and 1 Br^-
    d) 3 NH_3, 1 Br^-, and 1 H_2O
    e) 3 NH_3, 2 Br^-, and 1 H_2O

    Answer: c Page: 908

60. Which one of the following is the correct formula for potassium diaquatetrachloromolybdate(III)?
    a) $K_2[Mo(H_2O)_2Cl_4]$
    b) $K[Mo(H_2O)Cl_2]Cl_2$
    c) $K[Mo(H_2O)_2Cl_4]$
    d) $Mo[K(H_2O)_2]Cl_4$

    Answer: c Page: 908

61. The correct name for $[Ni(NH_3)_6](NO_3)_2$ is
    a) dinitrohexaamminenickel(II)
    b) hexaamminenickel(III) dinitrate
    c) dinitrohexaamminenickelate(III)
    d) hexaamminenickel(II) nitrate

    Answer: d Page: 908

ESSAY

62. What is a siderophore?

    Answer:
    a ligand that forms an extremely stable water-soluble complex, called ferrichrome, with iron

    Page: 911

MULTIPLE CHOICE

63. What are the donor atoms in ferrichrome and how many of them are in one molecule?
    a) Cr, 5
    b) N, 4
    c) O, 6
    d) Fe, 4
    e) S, 6

    Answer: c Page: 911

ESSAY

64. How does an elevated body temperature deprive some bacteria in the body of iron?

    Answer:
    in some bacteria, siderophore production decreases as temperature increases

    Page: 911

MULTIPLE CHOICE

65. In ___ isomers the bonds are the same but the spatial arrangement of the atoms is different.
    a) structural
    b) linkage
    c) coordination-sphere
    d) stereo

    Answer: d Page: 913

ESSAY

66. Two compounds have the same formula and contain an SCN^- ligand. In one compound the SCN^- ligand is bonded to the metal atom via the N atom and in the other it is bonded via the S atom. These two compounds are examples of ___ isomers.

    Answer: linkage Page: 913

MULTIPLE CHOICE

67. A geometrical isomer with like groups located on opposite sides of the metal atom is denoted with the prefix
    a) cis-
    b) trans-

    Answer: b Page: 913

68. Which one of the following geometries does not exhibit geometrical isomerism?
    a) square planar
    b) octahedral
    c) trigonal bipyramidal
    d) tetrahedral

    Answer: d Page: 913

69. Does either or both cis- or trans-$[Mn(en)_2Br_2]$ have optical isomers?
    a) cis only
    b) trans only
    c) both cis and trans
    d) neither cis nor trans

    Answer: a Page: 913

70. Linkage isomerism would most likely occur when which of the following ligands is present?
   a) H_2O
   b) NH_3
   c) Cl^-
   d) PF_3
   e) NCS^-

   Answer: e Page: 913

71. The anti-cancer drug cis-platin has the formula $Pt(NH_3)_2Cl_2$. One other isomer (medically inactive) exists, so the structure of cis-platin must be
   a) tetrahedral
   b) trigonal bipyramidal
   c) octahedral
   d) square planar
   e) either tetrahedral or square planar

   Answer: d Page: 913

72. Which of the following will display optical isomerism?
   a) square-planar $Rh(CO)_2Cl_2^-$
   b) square-planar $Pt(H_2NC_2H_4NH_2)_2^{2+}$
   c) octahedral $Co(NH_3)_6^{3+}$
   d) octahedral $Co(NH_3)_5Cl^{2+}$
   e) octahedral $Co(H_2NC_2H_4NH_2)_3^{3+}$

   Answer: e Page: 913

73. Which one of the following complex ions would most likely have tetrahedral geometry?
   a) $[NiCl_4]^{2-}$
   b) $[Co(H_2O)_6]^{2+}$
   c) $[Cr(NH_3)_6]^{3+}$
   d) $[Fe(CN)_6]^3$

   Answer: a Page: 913

74. Which one of the following complexes can exhibit geometrical isomerism?
   a) $[Pt(NH_3)_2Cl_2]$ (square planar)
   b) $[Zn(NH_3)_2Cl_2]$ (tetrahedral)
   c) $[Cu(NH_3)_4]^{2+}$ (square planar)
   d) $[Co(NH_3)_5Cl]^{2+}$ (octahedral)

   Answer: a Page: 913

75. How many isomers exist for the octahedral complex ion $[Co(NH_3)_4F_2]^+$?

    a) 1
    b) 2
    c) 3
    d) 4

    Answer: b Page: 913

76. Only one geometric form is known for $[Zn(NH_3)_2Br_2]$. Its shape must therefore be
    a) tetrahedral
    b) square planar
    c) octahedral
    d) trigonal bipyramidal

    Answer: a Page: 913

77. Trans-$[Fe(H_2O)_2Cl_4]^{2-}$ must be
    a) tetrahedral
    b) octahedral
    c) square planar
    d) trigonal bipyramidal

    Answer: b Page: 913

78. Complexes containing metals with which one of the following electron configurations are usually colorless?
    a) d^0
    b) d^1
    c) d^5
    d) d^8

    Answer: a Page: 916

ESSAY

79. In what two ways can an object appear blue?

    Answer:
    absorb all wavelengths except blue and reflect or transmit only blue, or absorb the complementary color of blue and reflect or transmit all others

    Page: 916

MULTIPLE CHOICE

80. Based on electron configuration, which is most likely colorless?
a) $Cu(NH_3)_4{}^{2+}$
b) $Cd(NH_3)_4{}^{2+}$
c) $Ni(NH_3)_6{}^{2+}$
d) $Cr(NH_3)_5Cl^{2+}$
e) $Co(NH_3)_6{}^{2+}$

Answer: b Page: 916

81. Which one of the following substances has three unpaired d electrons?
a) $[Zn(NH_3)_4]^{2+}$
b) $[V(H_2O)_6]^{2+}$
c) $[Ag(NH_3)_2]^{+}$
d) $[Cu(NH_3)_4]^{2+}$

Answer: b Page: 916

82. Which one of the following is a strong-field ligand?
a) Cl^-
b) NH_3
c) H_2O
d) F^-
e) CN^-

Answer: e Page: 916

83. Consider a complex in which manganese(III) is bonded to six identical ligands. Which one of the following ligands will result in the smallest value of Δ?
a) Cl^-
b) NH_3
c) H_2O
d) F^-
e) CN^-

Answer: a Page: 919

84. All ___ complexes are high spin.
a) square planar
b) octahedral
c) tetrahedral

Answer: c Page: 919

85. Metals with ___ electron configurations characteristically form diamagnetic, square planar complexes.
a) d^0
b) d^9
c) d^6
d) d^8

Answer: d Page: 919

86. Based on the crystal-field strengths $F^- < CH_2CN < NH_3 < NO_2^- < CN^-$ which Co(III) complex is most likely high-spin?
a) $Co(NH_3)_6^{3+}$
b) $Co(NO_2)_6^{3-}$
c) $Co(CN)_6^{3-}$
d) CoF_6^{3-}
e) $Co(CH_3CN)_6^{3+}$

Answer: d Page: 919

87. Which complex is most likely to be high-spin?
a) square-planar $Ni(CN)_4^{2-}$
b) octahedral $Fe(CN)_6^{3-}$
c) square-planar $Pt(NH_3)_4^{2+}$
d) octahedral $Fe(CN)_6^{4-}$
e) tetrahedral $FeCl_4^{2-}$

Answer: e Page: 919

88. Which complex below has 2 unpaired electrons?
a) square-planar $Ni(CN)_4^{2-}$
b) low-spin octahedral $Fe(CN)_6^{3-}$
c) tetrahedral $CoCl_4^{2-}$
d) octahedral $Ni(NH_3)_6^{2+}$
e) tetrahedral FeI_4^{2-}

Answer: d Page: 919

89. Based on the crystal-field strengths $Cl^- < F^- < H_2O < NH_3 < H_2NC_2H_4NH_2$, which octahedral Ti(III) complex below has its d-d electronic transition at shortest wavelength?
a) $Ti(NH_3)_6^{3+}$
b) $Ti(H_2NC_2H_4NH_2)_3^{3+}$
c) $Ti(H_2O)_6^{3+}$
d) $TiCl_6^{3-}$
e) TiF_6^{3-}

Answer: b Page: 919

90. Which one of the following complex ions will be paramagnetic?
   a) $[Fe(H_2O)_6]^{2+}$ (low spin)
   b) $[Fe(H_2O)_6]^{3+}$ (low spin)
   c) $[Co(H_2O)_6]^{3+}$ (low spin)
   d) $[Zn(H_2O)_4]^{2+}$

   Answer: b Page: 919

91. Which one of the following ions cannot form both a high spin and a low spin octahedral complex ion?
   a) Fe^{3+}
   b) Co^{2+}
   c) Cr^{3+}
   d) Mn^{3+}

   Answer: c Page: 919

92. Using the following abbreviated spectrochemical series, determine which complex ion is most likely to absorb light in the red region of the visible spectrum.

   small splitting $Cl^- < H_2O < NH_3 < CN^-$ large splitting

   a) $[CuCl_4]^{2-}$
   b) $[Cu(H_2O)_4]^{2+}$
   c) $[Cu(NH_3)_4]^{2+}$
   d) $[Cu(CN)_4]^{2-}$

   Answer: a Page: 919

93. Which one of the following coordination compounds would be paramagnetic?
   a) $[Zn(NH_3)_4]Cl_2$
   b) $K_2[FeCl_4]$ (low spin)
   c) $[Cu(H_2O)_4]Br$
   d) $[Mn(H_2O)_6]Cl_2$ (low spin)

   Answer: d Page: 919

94. What transition metal is responsible for the color of ruby?
   a) manganese
   b) cobalt
   c) titanium
   d) gold
   e) chromium

   Answer: e Page: 920

95. What transition metal is responsible for the color of amethyst?
    a) manganese
    b) cobalt
    c) titanium
    d) gold
    e) chromium

    Answer: a Page: 920

96. What transition metal is responsible for the color of topaz?
    a) manganese
    b) cobalt
    c) iron
    d) gold
    e) chromium

    Answer: c Page: 920

Chapter 25: The Chemistry of Life: Organic and Biologal Chemistry

MULTIPLE CHOICE

1. Hydrocarbons containing only single bonds between the carbon atoms are called
   a) alkenes
   b) alkynes
   c) aromatics
   d) alkanes
   e) ketones

   Answer: d Page: 933

2. What general class of compounds is also known as olefins?
   a) alkenes
   b) alkynes
   c) aromatics
   d) alkanes
   e) ketones

   Answer: a Page: 933

3. The simplest alkyne is
   a) ethylene
   b) ethane
   c) acetylene
   d) propyne
   e) benzene

   Answer: c Page: 933

4. The melting and boiling points of hydrocarbons are determined by
   a) ion-dipole attraction
   b) dipole-dipole attraction
   c) London forces
   d) hydrogen bonding
   e) ionic bonding

   Answer: c Page: 933

5. As the molecular weights of hydrocarbons increase, boiling and melting points
   a) remain constant
   b) increase
   c) decrease

   Answer: b Page: 933

6. Hydrocarbons containing carbon-carbon triple bonds are called
   a) alkanes
   b) aromatic hydrocarbons
   c) alkynes
   d) alkenes

   Answer: c Page: 933

7. Which one of the following is a saturated hydrocarbon?
   a) alkanes
   b) aromatic hydrocarbons
   c) alkynes
   d) alkenes

   Answer: a Page: 933

8. Alkanes with ___ carbons are found in gasoline.
   a) 2 to 3
   b) 5 to 12
   c) 1 to 5
   d) 9 to 15
   e) 20 to 60

   Answer: b Page: 935

9. The geometry of each carbon atom in an alkane is
   a) octahedral
   b) square planar
   c) trigonal planar
   d) tetrahedral
   e) trigonal pyramidal

   Answer: d Page: 935

10. The minimum number of carbons necessary for a hydrocarbon to form a branched structure is
    a) 4
    b) 6
    c) 3
    d) 9
    e) 12

    Answer: a Page: 935

11. Which one of the following could be a cyclic alkane?
    a) C_5H_5
    b) C_3H_6
    c) C_4H_6
    d) C_2H_6
    e) C_9H_{20}

    Answer: b Page: 935

ESSAY

12. Why is cyclopropane more reactive than propane?

Answer:
the small ring forces the C-C-C bond angle to be significantly less than 109.5°

Page: 935

MULTIPLE CHOICE

13. How many possible structural isomers are there of octane?
a) 1
b) 4
c) 75
d) 18
e) 24

Answer: d Page: 935

ESSAY

14. What is the name of $CH_3CH_2CH_2CH(CH_2CH_2CH_2CH_3)CH_2CH_2CH_3$?

Answer: 4-n-propyloctane Page: 935

15. Write the formula for 2-methyl-4-propylnonane.

Answer: $CH_3CH(CH_3)CH_2CH(CH_2CH_2CH_3)CH_2CH_2CH_2CH_2CH_3$ Page: 935

MULTIPLE CHOICE

16. If each of the following is an alkane, which one must be cyclic?
a) C_3H_8
b) $C_{12}H_{26}$
c) $C_{22}H_{46}$
d) C_7H_{14}
e) none of these is cyclic
f) all of these are cyclic

Answer: d Page: 935

17. If each of the following represents an alkane and a carbon atom is located at each vertex with the proper number of hydrogen atoms also bonded to it, which one is the most reactive?

a) 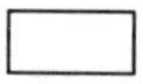 ▭ b)  ⬠ c) 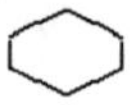 ⬡ d)  △

Answer: d Page: 935

18. Cyclohexane has how many fewer hydrogens than n-hexane?
    a) 0
    b) 1
    c) 2
    d) 3
    e) 4

    Answer: c Page: 935

19. How many structural isomers of heptane exist?
    a) 2
    b) 4
    c) 6
    d) 8
    e) 10

    Answer: d Page: 935

20. Alkanes have the general formula
    a) $C_{2n}H_{2n+2}$
    b) C_nH_{2n}
    c) C_nH_{2n+2}
    d) C_nH_{2n-2}

    Answer: c Page: 935

21. How many isomers are possible for C_4H_{10}?
    a) 1
    b) 2
    c) 3
    d) 4

    Answer: b Page: 935

22. How many isomers are possible for C_5H_{10}?
    a) 1
    b) 2
    c) 3
    d) 4

    Answer: c Page: 935

23. Which one of the following structures is 3,3,4-trimethylhexane?

a) 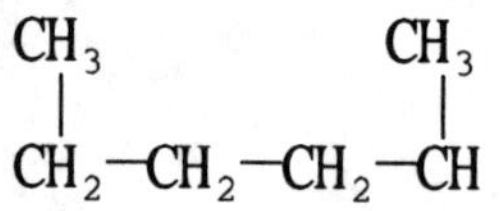
```
CH3            CH3
|              |
CH2—CH2—CH2—CH
```

b) 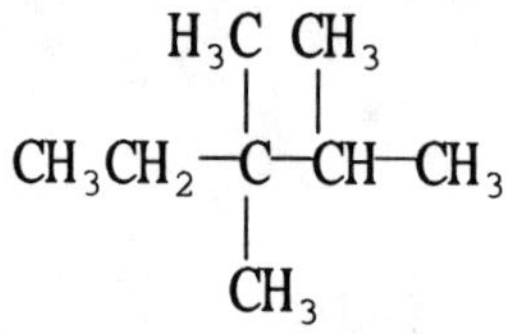
```
          H3C CH3
           |   |
CH3CH2—C—CH—CH3
           |
          CH3
```

c)
```
H3C    CH3  CH3
 |      |    |
CH2—C—CH—CH2
      |   |
     H3C CH3
```

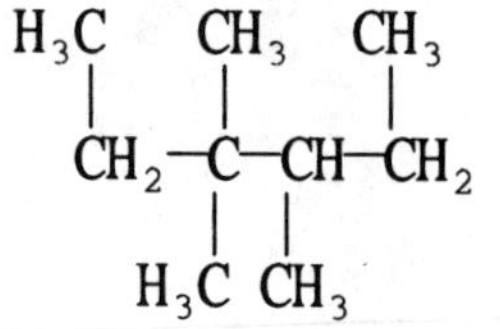

d) 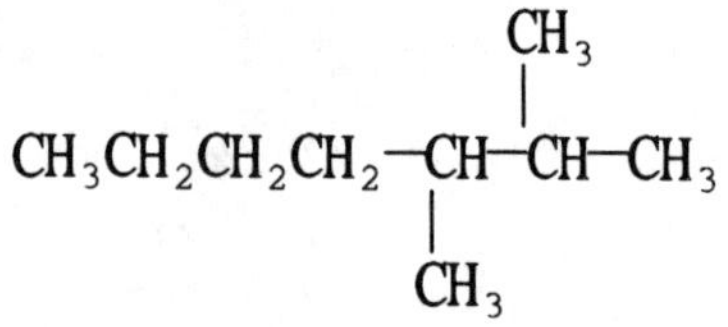
```
                         CH3
                          |
CH3CH2CH2CH2—CH—CH—CH3
                   |
                  CH3
```

Answer: c Page: 935

24. Which of the following is 2-methylbutane?

a) 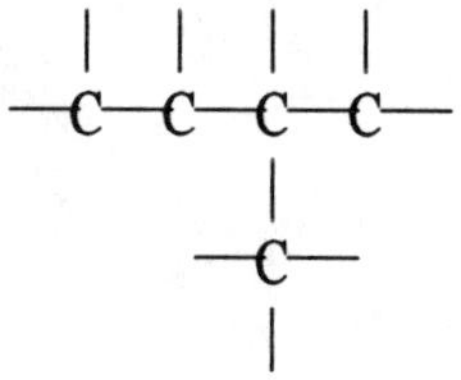
```
 |  |  |  |
—C—C—C—C—
       |
      —C—
       |
```

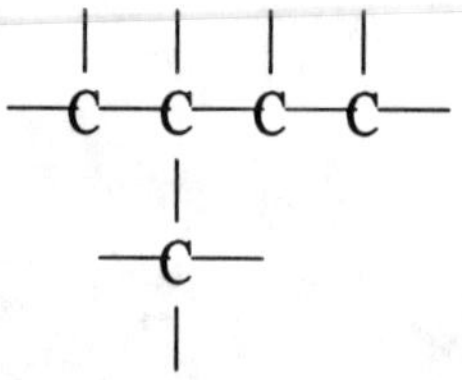

b) 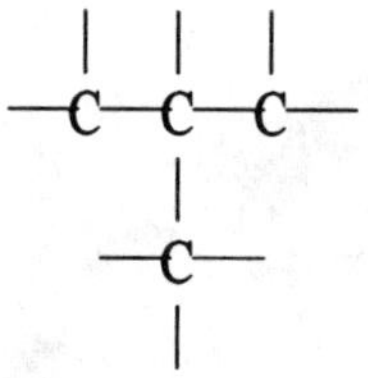
```
 |  |  |
—C—C—C—
    |
   —C—
    |
```

c)
```
 |  |  |  |
—C—C—C—C—
    |
   —C—
    |
```

d) both of the following:

```
 |  |  |  |            |  |  |  |
—C—C—C—C—          —C—C—C—C—
       |                  |
      —C—                —C—
       |                  |
```

Answer: d Page: 935

25. Gasoline and water do not mix because gasoline is
    a) less dense than water
    b) less viscous than water
    c) nonpolar
    d) volatile

    Answer: c Page: 935

26. Which substance would be the most soluble in gasoline?
    a) water
    b) $NaNO_3$
    c) HCl
    d) hexane

    Answer: d Page: 935

ESSAY

27. What is the correct name for the compound, $CH_3CH_2CH{=}CHCH_2CH{=}CHCH$?

    Answer: 2,5-octadiene Page: 942

MULTIPLE CHOICE

28. Which one of the following could be an alkene with one double bond?
    a) C_3H_8
    b) C_3H_6
    c) C_6H_6
    d) $C_{17}H_{36}$

    Answer: b Page: 942

ESSAY

29. What is the name of the compound, $CH_3CH(CH_3)CH(CH_3)CH_2CH_2C{\equiv}CH_2$?

    Answer: 5,6-dimethyl-1-heptyne Page: 942

MULTIPLE CHOICE

30. Of the following, which is the most reactive?
    a) alkenes
    b) alkynes
    c) alkanes
    d) cycloalkanes

    Answer: b Page: 942

ESSAY

31. Hydrogenation of an alkene requires high temperatures and a catalyst such as nickel. Why?

    Answer: due to the large bond energy of H_2 Page: 942

32. Predict the product of hydrogenation of 6-ethyl-3-decene.

    Answer: 6-ethyldecane Page: 942

33. Hydrogenation of what alkyne produces propane?

    Answer: propyne Page: 942

MULTIPLE CHOICE

34. While alkenes and alkynes readily undergo ___ reactions, aromatic hydrocarbons do not. Instead, they undergo ___ reactions.
    a) addition, substitution
    b) elimination, addition
    c) substitution, elimination
    d) substitution, addition
    e) addition, elimination

    Answer: a Page: 942

ESSAY

35. What are the names given to the three possible isomers resulting from the substitution of two hydrogens on a benzene ring for other groups?

    Answer: ortho, meta, and para Page: 942

MULTIPLE CHOICE

36. Alkynes always contain a
    a) C=C bond
    b) C≡C bond
    c) C-C bond
    d) C=H bond
    e) C≡H bond

    Answer: b Page: 942

37. Alkenes always contain a
    a) C=C bond
    b) C≡C bond
    c) C-C bond
    d) C=H bond
    e) C≡H bond

Answer: a Page: 942

38. Alkenes have the general formula
    a) C_nH_{2n}
    b) C_nH_{2n-2}
    c) C_nH_{2n+2}
    d) C_nH_n

Answer: a Page: 942

39. To which class of compounds does this molecule belong?

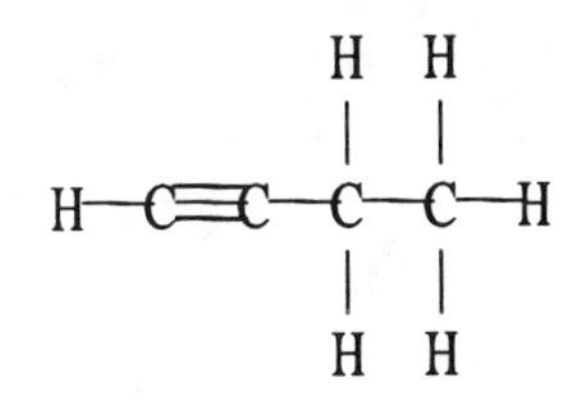

a) alkynes
b) alkenes
c) alkanes
d) aromatics

Answer: a Page: 942

40. What is the IUPAC name for the following compound?

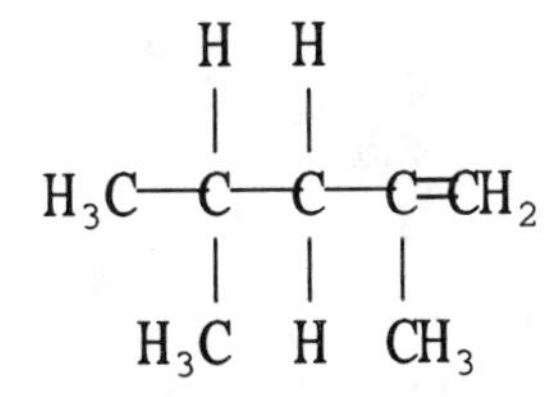

a) 2,4-methylbutene
b) 2,5-dimethylpentane
c) 2,4-ethylbutene
d) 2,4-dimethyl-1-pentene

Answer: d Page: 942

41. Which of the following may be an unsaturated hydrocarbon?
    a) C_4H_8
    b) C_6H_{14}
    c) C_3H_8
    d) all of the above

    Answer: a Page: 942

42. The addition of HBr to 2-butene produces
    a) 1-bromobutane
    b) 2-bromobutane
    c) 1,2-dibromobutane
    d) 2,3-dibromobutane

    Answer: b Page: 942

43. What is the product of the following reaction?

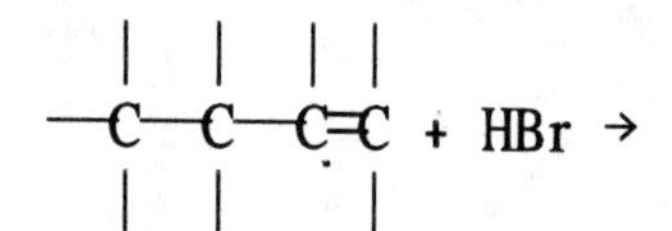

a)
```
 |  |  |  |
—C—C—C—C—
 |  |  |  |
    Br
```

b)
```
 |  |  |  |
—C—C—C—C—
 |  |  |  |
          Br
```

c)
```
 |  |  |  |
—C—C—C—C—
 |  |  |  |
       Br Br
```

d)
```
 |  |  |  |
—C—C—C—C—
 |  |  |  |
    Br Br
```

Answer: a Page: 942

44. What is the product of the following reaction?

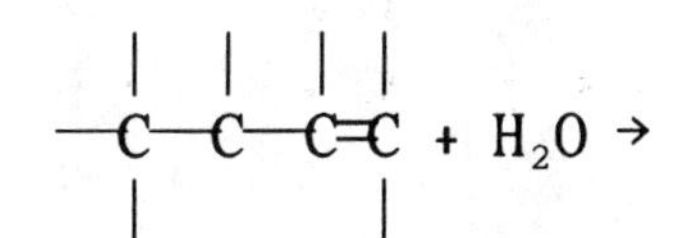

a)
```
 |  |  |  |
—C—C—C—C—
 |  |  |  |
          OH
```

b)
```
 |  |  |  |
—C—C—C—C—
 |  |  |  |
       OH OH
```

c)
```
 |  |  |  |
—C—C—C—C—
 |  |  |  |
    OH OH
```

d)
```
 |  |  |  |
—C—C—C—C—
 |  |  |  |
       OH
```

Answer: d Page: 942

45. Benzene behaves differently from a hydrocarbon which simply contains three C=C bonds in that the latter would be expected to react much more readily with
a) H_2
b) Cl_2
c) Br_2
d) HCl
e) all of the above

Answer: e Page: 942

46. When petroleum is distilled to separate the components by boiling point, the component with the highest boiling point is called
a) gas
b) gasoline
c) kerosene
d) paraffin
e) asphalt

Answer: e Page: 940

47. The more highly branched octanes have ____ octane numbers than straight chain hydrocarbons.
   a) higher
   b) lower

   Answer: a Page: 940

48. Isooctane is assigned an octane number of 100, ____ is assigned an octane number of 0.
   a) methane
   b) propane
   c) benzene
   d) heptane
   e) nitrous oxide

   Answer: d Page: 940

49. The octane number of straight-run gasoline is about
   a) 0
   b) 25
   c) 50
   d) 75
   e) 93

   Answer: c Page: 940

50. What type of compound has been used to replace tetraethyl lead as an antiknock agent in gasoline?
   a) aromatic compounds
   b) olefins
   c) fluorochlorocarbons
   d) paraffins
   e) oxygenated hydrocarbons

   Answer: e Page: 940

51. How was teflon used in the development of the first atomic bomb?
   a) it was used as gasket material in the gaseous diffusion plant for separation of uranium isotopes
   b) it was used to form the tube to keep the separate parts of the critical mass apart until time for detonation of the bomb
   c) its characteristic color change upon exposure to radiation made it an excellent indicator of radiation leaks
   d) it was used as a liner inside the bomb to protect the guidance system from radiation
   e) it was used to package the shrapnel incorporated into the bomb

   Answer: a Page: 945

52. What is the general formula for an alcohol?
    a) R-O-R
    b) R-CO-R
    c) R-CO-OH
    d) R-OH
    e) R-CO-H

    Answer: d Page: 947

ESSAY

53. What is the name of the compound, $CH_3CH_2CH(OH)CH_2CH_2CH_3$?

    Answer: 3-hexanol Page: 947

MULTIPLE CHOICE

54. How many hydroxyl groups are on a glycerol molecule?
    a) 0
    b) 1
    c) 2
    d) 3
    e) 4

    Answer: d Page: 947

55. Which one of the following is not an alcohol?
    a) acetone
    b) glycerol
    c) ethanol
    d) isopropanol
    e) cholesterol
    f) ethylene glycol

    Answer: a Page: 947

56. What is the general formula for an ether?
    a) R-O-R
    b) R-CO-R
    c) R-CO-OH
    d) R-OH
    e) R-CO-H

    Answer: a Page: 947

57. Ethers can be made by condensation of
    a) alkynes
    b) alcohols
    c) ketones
    d) aldehydes

    Answer: b Page: 947

58. Which one of the following compounds is an isomer of $CH_3CH_2CH_2CH_2OH$?
   a) $CH_3CH_2CH_2OH$
   b) 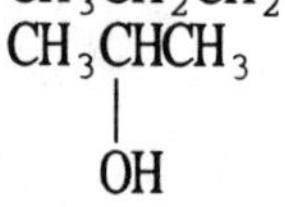 CH_3CHCH_3 with OH on the central carbon
   c) 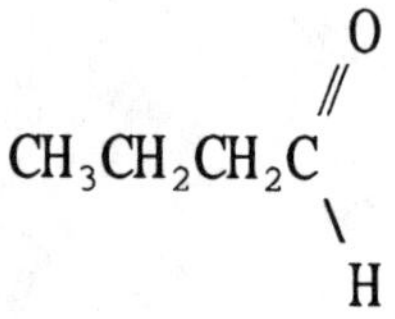 $CH_3CH_2CH_2C(=O)H$
   d) 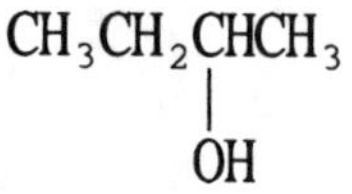 $CH_3CH_2CHCH_3$ with OH on the third carbon

   Answer: d Page: 947

59. The functional groups in $N{\equiv}C\text{-}CH_2{=}CH\text{-}CH_2\text{-}O\text{-}CH_2\text{-}CH_2OH$ are
   a) nitrile, ketone, ether, and aldehyde
   b) nitro, alkene, ester, and aldehyde
   c) nitro, alkyne, ester, and aldehyde
   d) nitrile, alkene, ether, and alcohol
   e) nitro, alkyne, ketone, and alcohol

   Answer: d Page: 949

ESSAY

60. What functional group is characteristic of carboxylic acids?

   Answer: -COOH Page: 951

MULTIPLE CHOICE

61. What is the general formula for a ketone?
   a) R-O-R
   b) R-CO-R
   c) R-CO-OH
   d) R-OH
   e) R-CO-H
   f) R-CO-OR

   Answer: b Page: 951

62. What is the general formula for an aldehyde?
    a) R-O-R
    b) R-CO-R
    c) R-CO-OH
    d) R-OH
    e) R-CO-H
    f) R-CO-OR

    Answer: e Page: 951

63. What is the general formula for a carboxylic acid?
    a) R-O-R
    b) R-CO-R
    c) R-CO-OH
    d) R-OH
    e) R-CO-H
    f) R-CO-OR

    Answer: c Page: 951

64. Carboxylic acids can be formed by oxidation of
    a) alkenes
    b) aldehydes
    c) ketones
    d) alcohols

    Answer: d Page: 951

65. The general formula of an ester is
    a) R-O-R
    b) R-CO-R
    c) R-CO-OH
    d) R-OH
    e) R-CO-H
    f) R-CO-OR

    Answer: f Page: 951

66. $CH_3CH_2C(=O)NH_2$ is called a(n)
    a) amine
    b) amide
    c) ketone
    d) aldehyde
    e) ester

    Answer: b Page: 951

67. Select the compound below which is an isomer of

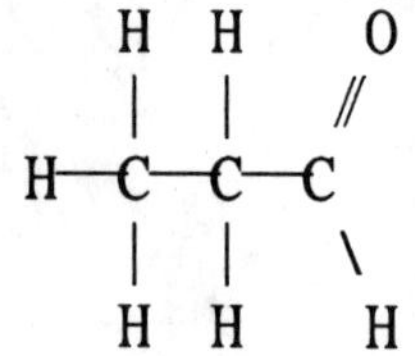

a)
```
 H  O  H
 |  ||  |
H—C—C—C—H
 |     |
 H     H
```

b)
```
 H    O
 |   //
H—C—C
 |    \
 H     H
```

c)
```
 H  H    O
 |  |   //
H—C—C—C
 |  |   \
 H  H    O—H
```

d)
```
 H  H  H
 |  |  |
H—C—C—C—O—H
 |  |  |
 H  H  H
```

Answer: a Page: 951

68. To which class of compounds might this molecule belong?
C_3H_6O
a) alcohol
b) ester
c) ketone
d) carboxylic acid

Answer: c Page: 951

69. To which class of compounds does this molecule belong?

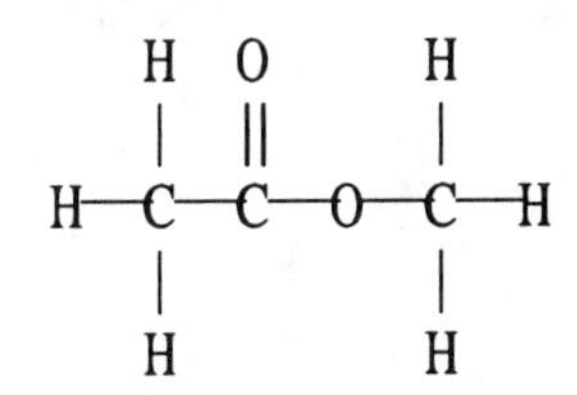

a) carboxylic acid
b) ketone
c) aldehyde
d) ester

Answer: d Page: 951

70. Which structure represents a ketone?

a) CH_3CH_2—O—CH_2CH_3

b) C_6H_5—C(=O)—OH

c) CH_3CH_2C(=O)H

d) C_6H_5—C(=O)—CH_3

Answer: d Page: 951

71. Which structure represents an aldehyde?

Answer: c Page: 951

72. Which structure represents an ether?

Answer: a Page: 951

73. What is the hybridization of the oxygen atom in an aldehyde?
a) sp
b) sp^3
c) sp^2
d) d^2sp^3

Answer: c Page: 951

74. The portion of the earth in which living organisms are formed and live is called the
    a) lithosphere
    b) troposphere
    c) mesosphere
    d) biosphere

    Answer: d Page: 955

75. Which one of the following is false concerning proteins?
    a) they are present in most living cells
    b) they are major structural components in animal tissues
    c) they act as biological catalysts
    d) they are made up of amino acids

    Answer: a Page: 956

ESSAY

76. Of the 20 amino acids found in our bodies, ___ of them must be ingested because our bodies cannot synthesize them.

    Answer: 10 Page: 956

77. Mirror-image isomers of a substance are called

    Answer: enantiomers Page: 956

MULTIPLE CHOICE

78. Which amino acid is non-chiral?
    a) leucine
    b) histidine
    c) arginine
    d) glycine

    Answer: d Page: 956

ESSAY

79. What isomer of amino acids is found in nature?

    Answer: S- or L- Page: 956

MULTIPLE CHOICE

80. What kind or reaction results in formation of a peptide bond?
    a) addition
    b) substitution
    c) condensation
    d) none of these

    Answer: c Page: 956

81. The arrangement of amino acids along a protein chain is called the ___ structure of the protein.
    a) primary
    b) secondary
    c) tertiary

    Answer: a Page: 956

82. An α-helix is an example of a protein's ___ structure.
    a) primary
    b) secondary
    c) tertiary

    Answer: b Page: 956

83. Which one of the following types of proteins is generally water soluble and mobile within cells?
    a) fibrous
    b) globular

    Answer: b Page: 956

ESSAY

84. Large protein molecules that serve as catalysts are called

    Answer: enzymes Page: 956

MULTIPLE CHOICE

85. Proteins are biopolymers formed via multiple condensation coupling of which two functional groups?
    a) ester and amine
    b) amine and carboxylic acid
    c) alcohol and carboxylic acid
    d) alcohol and amine
    e) ester and carboxylic acid

    Answer: b Page: 956

86. Which amino acid below is one whose structure is inconsistent with incorporation into a conventional protein?

a)
```
       H
       |
 CH3—C—CO2H
       |
       NH2
```

b)
```
    H
    |
  H—C—CO2H
    |
    NH2
```

c)
```
H3C   H
   \  |
   CH—C—CO2H
   /  |
H3C   NH2
```

d)
```
H3C   H
   \  |
   HC—C—CO2H
   /  |
H2N   CH3
```

e)
```
              H
              |
  HOH2C—C—CO2H
              |
              NH2
```

Answer: d Page: 956

87. The structures of four amino acids are shown below.

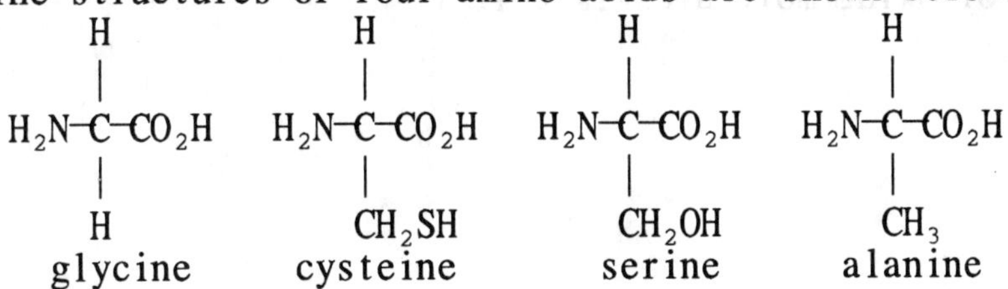

the dipeptide of structure $H_2N{-}CH(CH_2OH){-}C(=O){-}NH{-}CH(CH_2SH){-}CO_2H$ is named

a) serylcysteine
b) cysteylalanine
c) glycylalanine
d) serylalanine
e) alanylcysteine

Answer: a Page: 956

88. Which of the following is a peptide linkage?

a) 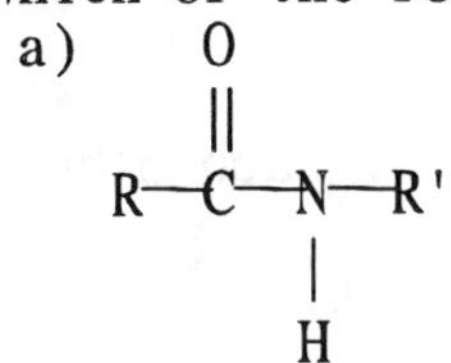

b) 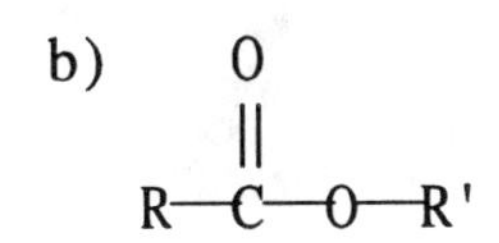

c) 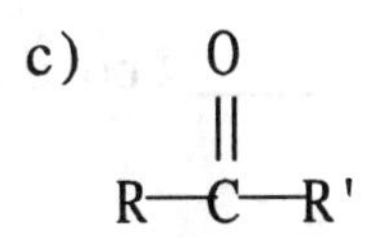

d) $R{-}N(H){-}R'$

Answer: a Page: 956

89. Which one of the following molecules is chiral?

a)
```
  H
  |
H—C=O
```

b)
```
  O
  |
H—C—OH
```

c)
```
  H
  |
H—C—NH2
  |
  CH3
```

d)
```
   H
   |
HO—C—NH2
   |
   CH3
```

Answer: d Page: 956

90. Two optically active molecules that are mirror images of each other are called
a) allotropes
b) geometrical isomers
c) enantiomers
d) cofactors

Answer: c Page: 956

91. The secondary structure of a protein is the result of _______ bonding.
a) covalent
b) peptide
c) ionic
d) hydrogen

Answer: d Page: 956

92. Starch, glycogen, and cellulose are made of repeating units of
a) lactose
b) glucose
c) fructose
d) sucrose
e) amino acids

Answer: b Page: 962

93. Sugars are examples of what type of molecule?
    a) proteins
    b) carbohydrates
    c) nucleic acids
    d) amino acids

    Answer: b Page: 962

94. Which one of the following is a monosaccharide?
    a) sucrose
    b) maltose
    c) glucose
    d) lactose

    Answer: c Page: 962

95. Which one of the following is a polysaccharide that is used to store energy in the human body?
    a) fructose
    b) cellulose
    c) starch
    d) glycogen

    Answer: d Page: 962

96. The principal difference between fructose and glucose is that
    a) fructose is a disaccharide and glucose is a monosaccharide
    b) fructose is a monosaccharide and glucose is a disaccharide
    c) fructose is chiral and glucose is not
    d) glucose is chiral and fructose is not
    e) fructose is a ketone sugar and glucose is an aldehyde sugar

    Answer: e Page: 962

97. Which one of the following is a monosaccharide?
    a) fructose
    b) lactose
    c) sucrose
    d) maltose

    Answer: a Page: 962

98. A polysaccharide stored in animal muscles is
    a) lactose
    b) starch
    c) cellulose
    d) glycogen

    Answer: d Page: 962

99. Which one of the following is the largest?
    a) nucleotide
    b) RNA
    c) DNA
    d) glucose
    e) sucrose

    Answer: c Page: 966

100. What forces hold the strands of DNA together?
    a) covalent bonds
    b) hydrogen bonding
    c) ion-dipole attraction
    d) coordinate covalent bonds
    e) London forces

    Answer: b Page: 966

ESSAY

101. What are the three parts of a nucleic acid?

    Answer:
    phosphoric acid, a five-carbon sugar, and a nitrogen-containing organic base

    Page: 966

MULTIPLE CHOICE

102. The nucleic acid based on ___ is found in the nucleus of animal cells.
    a) ribose
    b) deoxyribose

    Answer: b Page: 966

103. Which one of the following base pairs is not found in DNA?
    a) A-G
    b) C-G
    c) A-T

    Answer: a Page: 966

104. The double helix of DNA is based upon hydrogen bonding between ________ on the opposing strands.
    a) deoxyribose and guanine or adenine
    b) deoxyribose and thymine or cytosine
    c) adenine and thymine, and cytosine and guanine
    d) phosphoric acid linkages and deoxyribose
    e) phosphoric acid linkages and guanine or adenine

    Answer: c Page: 966

105. A nucleotide consists of all of the following except a(n)
    a) amino acid
    b) nitrogen-containing organic base
    c) phosphoric acid molecule
    d) sugar

    Answer: a Page: 966

106. The base sequence of a portion of a single strand of DNA is C-T-A-A-G. The base sequence of the complementary strand is
    a) T-G-C-C-A
    b) G-A-T-T-C
    c) G-A-C-C-T
    d) T-C-G-G-A

    Answer: b Page: 966